Barnacle Parp's

new CHAIN SAW GUIDE

BY WALTER HALL

Published 1985

Printed in the United States of America

THE MOTHER EARTH NEWS, Inc.
105 Stoney Mountain Road
Hendersonville, North Carolina 28791

Library of Congress Catalog Card Number 84-61591

ISBN 0-938-43224-9
Canadian ISBN 0-938-43225-7

FROM:

MOTHER EARTH NEWS PROD
1901 BELL AVE/DEPT CDS
DES MOINES IA 50340

217531

ACCOUNT NO.
11/12/92

SHIP TO:

KENT ATWELL
PO BOX 7905
BONNEY LAKE   WA   98390

Barnacle Parp says
this book is for
Fifty Horses,
Amigo,
and Muskrat—
still and always.

CONTENTS

PREFACE

Looking back at the original edition of *Barnacle Parp's Chain Saw Guide* in preparation for doing this new version, I was pleased to find that, for the most part, the book has held up quite well, and indeed few changes were absolutely required—other than to remove some obviously dated quirks. Nevertheless, this is a *new* book with *new* information, covering *new* procedures and *new* products. Much of the detailed material relating to chain saw selection, use, and maintenance has not changed significantly. And, of course, nothing has changed my concern for safety.

That is the real subject of this preface: safety.

Since the original *Chain Saw Guide* appeared in 1978, I have seen far too many avoidable accidents and injuries related to chain saws. These are not accidents I've read about or that I am quoting statistically; these are accidents I've *witnessed*, including a pretty bad one seen from the receiving end. All of the several bad chain saw accidents that I've personally witnessed in the past few years have happened to experienced cutters who were ignoring some basic chain saw safety rule.

Just a couple of seasons ago, for example, Parp was out cutting some very dead pine branches on the floor of an ancient mysterious forest some miles from home. It was a warm day, unusual at that altitude in October, so Parp took off his jacket. That was fine, except that he failed to replace his hard hat and safety glasses afterward. A few minutes later, a small but especially heavy chunk of wood caught on a friend's chain and flew through the air like a cannon shot, striking Parp's skull, which is admittedly thick, but not *that* thick. Unconscious on his feet, Parp staggered across a clearing and fell face first into the iron twigs of the forest's edge.

Fortunately, the eye injury that resulted has almost completely healed. But I have only to squint a little for plenty of motivation to make sure that I will always follow *all* of the safety rules *all* of the time from now on, no matter how inconvenient it may seem. There is enough danger in using a chain saw when you do it right.

So that's the message of this preface. Don't just be careful. Obey all the safety rules. And then be *extra* careful, extra watchful at all times. Do not rush your work and do not take any shortcuts. Remember that a chain saw is dangerous, no matter how carefully you use it.

INTRODUCTION

WHAT IS A CHAIN SAW?

A chain saw, according to the *American Heritage Dictionary*, is "a power saw with teeth linked in an endless chain." There's nothing like a definition that doesn't tell you what the key word means. In this case, it's because a chain saw, in itself, has no meaning. The only good definition of a machine is a description of its *function*. The word "function" is defined in the same dictionary as "the natural or proper action for which a person, office, mechanism, or organ is fitted or employed."

So, according to Parp, the only way to define a chain saw meaningfully is to describe the proper or natural action for which it is fitted. That's what this book is about, and we're not going to ignore the implications of the words "proper" and "natural." Can we describe a "natural" or "proper" action for something as unnatural as a complex piece of noisy and foul-smelling machinery? We can try. For now, we will simply say that the best definition of a chain saw is a brief description of what it does. It cuts wood.

WHO NEEDS A CHAIN SAW?

Anyone who cuts wood or uses cut wood needs a chain saw. If you have, or are going to have, a wood-burning stove or a fireplace, you certainly need a chain saw. A good saw can pay for itself in one season— or less—of cutting your own wood. If your wood-burning heater is efficient, you can significantly lower your utility bills and your consumption of such nonrenewable and disappearing energy sources as natural gas, oil, and coal. Several excellent chain saw models cost less than three cords of split wood, and practically everyone lives near some source of seasoned logs.

If you have a fireplace, you know the deep satisfaction that comes from sitting by the fire. Another satisfaction, a stranger and older one, comes from simply bringing in that split wood from the porch. Yet another comes from simply living with a woodpile. (How many of us have stood in a small yard in the middle of the city at night, staring at a stack of firewood, and have found ourselves transported far from the buildings and the noise to a place of trees and stars?)

The shapes and colors and smells of your own wood supply can fill your mind with a primitive wonder at your ingenuity and your magical ability to keep the wolves away. The experience is deepened immeasurably when you know you cut the wood yourself. Almost anyone can do it, and should. All forms of life crave the wilderness for health, survival, and sanity. There is a wilderness within you that you must preserve.

Whoever you are and wherever you live, you can escape to the peace and strangeness of the wild spirit within you by finding, cutting, splitting, and contemplating your own wood supply—your store against the winter. By doing so you will also help, just a little, to fight the giant fuel conspiracies of governments, conglomerates, and friendly neighborhood utility companies. It really doesn't matter whether you do it with a chain saw or not. A chain saw just makes it easier.

If you build things out of wood, a chain saw will greatly increase the number and variety of things you can build, the places where you can build them, and the materials you can use. With a chain saw you can easily and quickly learn to make your own lumber—any kind of lumber—and the lumber you make will quite likely be more attractive, durable, and natural than anything you could buy at a lumberyard.

If you are a professional builder or carpenter, you doubtless already use chain saws in your work because they are accurate, portable, dependable, versatile . . . and loud. If you're a logger, you've always cursed chain saws and always will—but you use them to help supply the wood that provides the rest of us with housing, furniture, toilet paper, and the zillion little frills that our culture thrives upon.

Working a small- or medium-sized farm, or an independent farm of *any* size, is difficult enough without spending Sunday mornings clearing brush, pruning trees, and building fences by hand. A good chain saw speeds these operations and hundreds of other farm chores.

Then there's another group of people, many of whom are completely unfamiliar with chain saws, who need these tools as much as anyone. They are the new homesteaders, the back-to-the-landers, the folks who are heading for the woods, the mountains, or the country.

Out there where you're going you'll need firewood every day, and you'll need buildings, fences, tree houses, and all the other things a chain saw can provide. It doesn't matter if you've never seen a chain saw, and it doesn't matter whether you've been in the woods for five years or are just getting ready to go. You need a chain saw, and you can take Parp's word for it. It doesn't even matter if you're no good with machines and you're scared to death of anything that makes noise, cuts stuff, and might blow up. It won't be long until your saw is *your* saw and you have your own way with it. It won't be long before you're the expert who can fell dead trees safely, cut your own firewood, make your own lumber, and keep your own chain saw sharpened correctly and running perfectly.

Finally, if you're a woman who went back to the land with someone who finds it difficult to lace his shoes in the morning, you certainly need a chain saw. After you use it to cut the first decent wood supply you've had since you arrived, you can use it to wake him up and chase him out (and that's the only violence in this book).

HOW DOES A CHAIN SAW AFFECT THE ENVIRONMENT?

What impact does a chain saw have on the environment? Now that's a tough question. Nobody really knows, because the answer is all bound up with contemporary forestry methods, the zillion frills, the corporations, and the governments—not to mention thoughtless individuals.

Here's an interesting fact: The total timber harvest for the year 1900, before the advent of the chain saw, was 12.1 billion cubic feet; the total timber harvest for 1983 was 13.6 billion cubic feet, with extensive use of tractors, cranes, and chain saws. The figures are almost the same.

The amount of waste involved is impossible for an outsider to determine because the government and the lumber companies always lump fuel and waste figures together. (Apparently they feel that if we use wood to heat a cabin, that's a waste of wood, but if *they* use living trees to make cigarette cartons, toothpaste, or plastic, that's efficient.)

Weyerhaeuser Lumber Company says that 21 percent of each acre of the timber harvested in 1950 went into lumber. They say that 79 percent was "fuel and waste." In 1973, however, 28 percent went for lumber, 10 percent for plywood, 9 percent for particleboard, 32 percent for linerboard, and 21 percent for fuel for the company's own boiler plants. Apparently there was no waste.

A chain saw used in any way that is not fitting, proper, or natural is dangerous to the environment. If you do not use your chain saw to cut living trees for firewood or for senseless fun, you'll do little harm to the environment. There are still millions of unused cords of dead wood left in the forests every year, and that's not likely to change suddenly.

As for the exhaust emissions from a chain saw, they are relatively slight. A chain saw sounds and smells awful, but it really puts out far less poison than an automobile and is far more efficient in fuel consumption. If you use fuel in any other way, you use more fuel for each minute of work than you use with a chain saw.

The Central Institute for Industrial Medicine at Hamburg, West Germany, and the Dolmar chain saw people recently cooperated in extensive tests of the effect of chain saw emissions on operators. These tests were scientific and tough, Parp says. The results show that using a chain saw is much less harmful than being around a cigarette smoker.

WHO INVENTED THE CHAIN SAW?

Andreas Stihl invented the chain saw in 1926 or 1927, depending upon how you look at it. Stihl invented the first two machines that resembled the modern chain saw, and he was the first person to envision the ultimate development of the chain saw. The whole story is considerably more complex and ironic, in a way, because it obscures itself. That healthy force known as young capitalism made the refinement of the chain saw possible through incentive, individualism, and competition. That same force, in its uglier and more decadent form as corporate consciousness, also deprived us of the true history of the chain saw's development by obscuring it with dozens of conflicting claims. War, pride, and prejudice added their confusions, too.

The real beginning of the chain saw is tied to the beginning of woodcutting, and that, of course, is beyond the scope of history. Even the specific idea of using chains moved by machines to tear down trees goes back to at least 1770. From the time of the first controlled fire to the present, people all over the world have tried to find easier, faster, and safer ways of obtaining wood from the forest. All of this is a major part of the history of the chain saw. How, then, can we separate this single invention from all the rest of those efforts? Let's follow the trail of some of the most recent events, pieced together by Parp, and see who really "invented" the chain saw, and how.

In 1896, the Allis Chalmers Manufacturing Company first used electricity to help power a sawmill. In 1904, Jacob Smith of Des Moines, Iowa, invented a crank-operated, semiportable woodcutting machine. A year later, the Ashland Iron Works in Oregon developed a similar saw that was powered by compressed air. All this was part of the beginning of a worldwide effort to mechanize the forest products industry. At the turn of the century, inventors and engineers in Canada, Sweden, Germany, and other countries were making the first Industrial Age attempts to speed lumber production. Most of the inventions and developments were unsuccessful in themselves and never went into production. Most, in fact, were completely unknown to all but the people who worked with them. None of these inventions was portable, none was intended for use in the forest itself, and not one was a chain saw.

In 1910, R.L. Muir of California invented a saw that cut wood with a moving chain—or sort of a chain. The cutting attachment was a chain of cutting edges that traveled around a steel bar. That part bore a notable resemblance to the modern chain saw, but it was driven by a huge machine mounted on a giant cart. A crane was used to lift and lower the cutting bar. Although intended for mill-yard use, this machine pointed the way—or *would* have if the right people had been looking. Muir's invention, like most of the others, was unsuccessful in industrial terms because it never went into production.

About the same time, a great American named Charles Wolf was gaining national recognition as an inventor and engineer. He was one of the inventors and developers of the submarine. He also built electric tramways and railroads and things of that sort. He installed the first fully electric sawmill for the Blackwell Lumber Company in Coeur d'Alene, Idaho. In the process, he encountered a smaller electric saw built by the Potlatch Lumber Company for its own use. It gave him ideas. Wolf developed a refined model that became the first crew-operated, chain-equipped woodcutting machine produced and sold in quantity. It was still electric, and it was intended primarily for mill use, not for carting about in the woods.

Somewhat later, a brilliant and meticulous Swedish engineer named von Westfelt became the first person to operate a chain-equipped wood-cutting machine in the woods. The chain rode on a giant U-shaped bow guide and was driven by a flexible shaft that was rotated by a separate gasoline engine. Many other engineers experimented with flexible shaft machinery through the years, including the American Arthur Mall. But this was not the answer to bringing the saw and the engine together.

Von Westfelt's chain was a beautiful handmade masterpiece. Each link was shaped by hand and was connected by springs formed through old-world metalsmithing. Von Westfelt worked very hard on his futuristic machine and continually improved it through the years. It was produced in limited quantity and sold in Sweden, Germany, Russia, and other countries. Today, the Swedish chain saws made by Husqvarna, Jonsereds, and Partner are among the world's finest machines.

In 1921, back in the United States, another brilliant inventor named Charles H. Ferguson was designing a new lightweight, gasoline-powered generator. This had no immediate effect on the development of the chain saw, but Ferguson is certainly a major part of chain saw history. Electricity was not yet available in most rural areas. Ferguson's invention was designed to supply the power for lighting homes in these areas. That's why he called it the "Homelite." Homelite didn't produce chain saws until 1949, but it sure has since then.

Andreas Stihl was a young inventor, repairman, and putterer in Stuttgart, Germany, in the 1920's. Those were pleasant years in the old towns near the Black Forest, and most folks lived at a slower pace than did the frantic Americans across the ocean. Andreas Stihl earned his modest living by repairing all sorts of things, as well as by building some innovative but rather mundane machinery for the folks thereabouts.

An early German two-man saw

Andreas Stihl loved nature, and he loved the forest; so quite naturally, he frequently loafed in the woods. Why not? His business was not a pressing burden. He loved to rest on the warm grass and listen to the many birds singing in the trees. None of the birds or small animals seemed frightened of Stihl. He would lie there motionless with his eyes closed as dozens of forest residents scampered and chirped and chattered.

One day Stihl was loafing in the woods and watching a logging crew work near the skid road down the hill. The workers were using hand-powered whipsaws to fell giant trees. Stihl thought about how awful it would be to have to work like that. His heart went out to the loggers.

Time went on, and almost every day Stihl loafed in the forest, watching the loggers work. After a while, he began to notice some changes in the way they worked. They were starting to get machines. Unfortunately, the machines didn't work very well and didn't seem to help the poor loggers very much. Their labors continued to look unbearably difficult to the young Stihl. He contemplated this every day, relaxing under the trees. The subject began to occupy his mind as he strolled back to his little shop, and even while he listened to classical music on his radio and fixed small appliances for his neighbors.

Although Stihl's mind was in the woods, he was not idle. In 1923, he invented the world's first gasoline-powered washing machine. Parp says Stihl wanted to use gasoline because the tank would run dry and stop the machine automatically. That way, he could put in a load of clothes, add a little gasoline, and forget about it as he headed for the woods.

All this time, don't forget, Charles H. Ferguson was out in the woods, too; however, he was going door-to-door selling Homelite generators to all the progressive country dwellers across the United States.

One sunny afternoon in Stuttgart, Stihl was enjoying a beer in his favorite garden when he recognized two of the loggers sitting at the next table. He overheard enough of their conversation to understand that they were in town to buy some materials with which they hoped to repair their newest logging machine. Stihl attempted to introduce himself, but the loggers were anxious to return to their work site before their foreman came looking for them.

Back in the woods the next day, Stihl struck up a friendship with some of the loggers. They liked the affable young fellow and enjoyed his amusing questions about cutting trees and using machines. They showed him their brand-new von Westfelt woodcutter, which was not working. Stihl managed to get it running, a little, but he realized then how inefficient and unreliable the thing was. From that day forward, Andreas Stihl never stopped thinking of ways to improve woodcutting methods and make the load a little lighter for his logger friends.

Stihl devoted himself to the study of existing power saws and found that they were not good machines. For one thing, they kept getting bigger and heavier. Stihl realized that manufacturers were going in the wrong direction. He envisioned, right then, the future of the chain saw: He would take the basic idea of a power saw and make it smaller rather than larger. It seems obvious now, but such is the stuff of genius. Stihl made up his mind, as he always said, to develop a motor-driven chain saw that could be carried and that would work reliably from morning to night—a light, portable chain saw that would be easy to handle.

Stihl had the idea now, and he worked hard and long. He carefully studied American, Swedish, Czech, and German crew-operated logging machines. He studied how the power saws worked and why they didn't. His research was thorough, but it was that original brainstorm that really did the trick. "Make it little" was his inspiration. He sank all of his savings and all of his strength into his research. Word got around about Stihl's goals, and he soon found himself in hot water with logging crew foremen and with forestry officials. Certain of them opposed—for personal financial reasons—mechanizing the logging industry. Oh well, Stihl thought, every good inventor must face reactionary forces.

Charles H. Ferguson, meanwhile, was selling Homelite generators like hotcakes. Every rural American wanted to be ready for television.

In 1926, Andreas Stihl finally finished his invention. He had worked on his "Cutoff Chain Saw for Electric Power" for more than two years, but he still couldn't pick it up by himself. It was a chain saw, though. It looked like a chain saw, ran like a chain saw, cut wood like a chain saw, and sounded like *several* chain saws. All chain saws since then have been quite a lot like it. Stihl sold a lot of them, too. It was the first portable chain saw.

The only trouble was that it had an electric motor. When his logger friends finally broke the news that there were no electrical outlets in the Black Forest, Stihl almost felt like giving up. He didn't, though. Who knows? Maybe he read a magazine story about Ferguson's gasoline-engine generator. Maybe he just remembered his own washing machine.

In any case, it was 1927 when Stihl finally hooked the gasoline engine and the chain saw together. He had to take them apart again in order to transport them, but the job was done. He had invented and produced the world's first gasoline-engine chain saw that could be carried into the woods and operated by a gorilla.

Stihl manufactured and sold his new invention for the next two years. Then, in 1929, he developed a new friction-reducing guide bar that greatly improved the machine. This design alone was critical to the development of the modern chain saw.

By 1930, Stihl was advertising his chain saw as "The Midget." When he exhibited his new machine at the Leipzig European Trade Fair in 1930, it weighed "just" 127 pounds and gained far-reaching recognition for Stihl and his young company whose sales offices were becoming established in both Europe and North America.

A year later, Stihl had pared the saw's weight down to 104 pounds, and the crowds were cheering. He was clearly established as the leader of the race he had started, the race for a lightweight, powerful, dependable, portable chain saw. He started selling in Russia and opened a new factory that employed 200 of Germany's finest skilled craftspersons. By this time, lots of loggers and forestry officials feared for their jobs, but his old friends never turned against him.

In 1931, one of his older logger friends arranged for Stihl to meet and speak with forestry officials and other chain saw opponents at a logging camp in the Black Forest. At that meeting, Andreas Stihl described the chain saw of the future with uncanny accuracy. All chain saw developments for years to come were sketched out for his skeptical audience. He described the light, powerful engines of the future and the metal alloys with which he was experimenting. He described the one-person operation that would someday be possible. He described the modern cutting chain, guide bar, and fuel system. He even specified and described the centrifugal clutch. He explained how this dreamy new tool would make life a pleasure for the beleaguered loggers and how they would have time to loaf and drink. When he finished that talk, Stihl had their full support. They carried him back past his newest factory to his quaint little cottage. They even helped him hang out his clothes to dry.

Things were less cheerful back in the United States. The Great Depression had just about halted the lumber industry, as well as everything else. Stihl sold chain saws in North America all through the Thirties, and he had very little effective competition. This was partly because of the Depression itself and partly because most of the crucial aspects of chain saw design were protected by Stihl's patents.

Demonstrations of Stihl chain saws were held at logging congresses, lumber mills, and forest logging camps everywhere. The Depression and the Forest Service worked together, and soon the government-employed loggers of the United States were all using Stihl chain saws and liking it. At last, the chain saw was fully accepted in the woods by the people who counted.

By that time, Stihl almost never loafed in the woods. Before the end of the Thirties, he had invented, developed, and incorporated most of the essential features of the modern chain saw. These included his light-weight alloys, the modern guide bar, an efficient cutting chain, an automatic oiling system for the chain and bar, and a decompression release. All of these features, together with critical aspects of Stihl's exclusive engine design, were protected by German, U.S., and international patents. Stihl chain saws weighed 47 pounds by 1936. The competition was baffled and frustrated. The only important thing Stihl hadn't invented yet was direct drive, and no one else had thought of it either.

This is where the war comes in. The market was pretty depressed everywhere. Stihl, of course, could no longer sell his chain saws in the United States, and because of the war, his designs were no longer protected by U.S. patents. As a result, companies like the Mill and Mine Supply Company of Seattle, Washington, began making their own chain saws instead of selling Stihl's. By the time of Pearl Harbor, at least six U.S. companies were mass-producing gasoline-powered chain saws that were direct copies of Stihl models. Stihl paid the price of war, and while that is thoroughly understandable, we cannot and should not ignore Stihl's contributions. His factories were completely destroyed, his markets cut off, and his patents released by the United States government. If it hadn't been for that, the rest of the history of the chain saw would be very different and much clearer.

Charles H. Ferguson was also affected by the war. He supplied 200,000 Homelite generators that helped power the war toward its end.

Sometime around in here, maybe 1942, a new company named Pioneer produced what it still claims was "the world's first one-person chain saw." It wasn't. Pioneer has done a lot since then, and they make fine chain saws, but they didn't do it *first*. They, uh, "adapted" Stihl's designs. Again, that's acceptable under the conditions, but claiming the saw was a first, and continuing to do so, is less understandable. Stihl's 1936–37 chain saw weighed only 47 pounds, and that definitely put it in the one-person class. Many other companies have made similar claims for the same period, but not one company advanced beyond Stihl's 1936–37 models.

In 1947, a man named Joe Cox, from Portland, Oregon, became interested in the logging industry, much as Stihl had been. It is not known whether Cox loafed in the woods, but it *is* known that he watched bugs. He watched bugs while he was trying to develop a new saw chain design. He wanted to make a chain that would cut wood even more efficiently than Stihl's chain, which everyone had copied along with Stihl's saws. Joe tells about watching bugs.

"My first [saw chain] designs weren't working the way I thought they should. Knowing that nature usually figures things out better than man, I spent several months looking for nature's answer to the problem. I found it in the larva of the timber beetle.

"The larva has two cutters, but it alternates them. While one is cutting, the other acts as a depth gauge. Actually, I'd already figured out the alternating part and the depth gauge principle. It was the curvature of the cutters that the larva taught me. That's what made my chain cut better, last longer, file easier, and require less maintenance."

Isn't that interesting? Actually, the alternating cutters and the depth gauge principle were present in Stihl's original chain, but that really doesn't take away from Cox's discovery of the larva's rounded cutters. Joe Cox of Portland, Oregon, invented the first "chipper" saw chain, a chain that has been the standard ever since.

Joe showed his new chain to his old friend, Jack Jamieson, a professional logger from Lebanon, Oregon. Jack quickly found out that one chain saw equipped with Joe's chain "could do the job of two hand sawyers in a quarter of the time." And he still says so. Within a year, Jack had seven chain saws equipped with Joe's chains, and with those seven saws, he and his hired persons were doing the work of 16 fallers and 40 buckers.

Both Jack and Joe did very well. In his first year of operation, Joe sold $300,000 worth of his new chain right out of his basement shop in Portland (better than fixing toasters). Today, Joe's outfit is called Oregon Saw Chain and is the world's largest manufacturer of saw chain.

On to 1948: The war had been over for three years, and lots of folks wanted to make chain saws. Why not? It was so easy with all those unpatented designs floating around. Dozens of companies converged on the old competitive battlefield. Among the newcomers was the McCulloch Chain Saw Company. They got off to a good start with some really tough machinery. McCulloch still proudly announces the fact that they produced the first 50-pound chain saw in 1948. As we have seen, Stihl's 1936–37 model weighed only 47 pounds, so 50 pounds seems more like a reasonably good try than a ground-breaking achievement. McCulloch's first die-cast magnesium chain saw, also introduced in 1948, was more significant.

Although Stihl jumped squarely back into the race in 1948, his position was no longer the strongest. He was, after all, coming from behind because of the war. Through 1947 and 1948, the U.S. manufacturers really got serious about chain saw development, and they had Stihl's designs to work from. Stihl's saws for 1948 were nevertheless the most advanced and, in fact, were dramatically close to today's saws in everything but size and weight.

One of the chief figures on the United States chain saw scene was Arthur Mall of the now legendary Mall Tool Company. Mall had been around for a long time, and his contribution to machine and tool design had been significant. In the 1930's, Mall made flexible-shaft machinery. In 1937, he created a flexible-shaft machine that drove a chain saw cutting attachment. Mall built chain saws from 1937 until 1956, when he sold his company to Remington Chain Saws. That company was swallowed by Desa Industries in 1969 and is now best known for inexpensive electric chain saws.

The following quote is from a letter Arthur Mall wrote to Andreas Stihl in 1948:

"Through the showing of your original machine in Canada and the United States, you taught the [logging] industry the possibilities of using gasoline engines for cutting down trees as well as bucking them into log lengths. Throughout the United States and Canada, you were the first one to demonstrate a practical, lightweight gasoline-engine [chain] saw for this application. Today, there are at least 100,000 chain saws being used in Canada and in the United States for this work, all of which are more or less copies of your original machine."

Stihl was in no position to complain, and he never did.

McCulloch's 1949 chain saw weighed just 25 pounds—half the weight of the company's 1948 model. Homelite entered the market and was suddenly producing a 30-pound chain saw. Pioneer and other companies also broke the 35-pound barrier, and no Stihl saw had yet done that. The year 1949 also saw the first all-position carburetor and fuel pump from McCulloch. These advances, predicted much earlier by Stihl but never developed, were essential to the modern chain saw.

The competition and the advancements continued all through the Fifties. Everyone came up with something good. In 1953, McCulloch introduced a 21-pound, gear-driven chain saw. In 1954, Stihl introduced (and patented) his Mahle Long Life Cylinder, still used today. In 1955, McCulloch put bearings in its pistons. Homelite kept making good, lightweight chain saws. In 1956, Stihl produced the Stihl "BLK," a professional 30-pound chain saw. (Stihl, Inc. now claims that was "the world's first really lightweight chain saw." Thirty pounds is heavier than 21 pounds, but Stihl, Inc. is taking a tip from the U.S. companies on how to achieve records—claim them.)

In 1955, Charles H. Ferguson's Homelite Company was absorbed by Textron, a giant U.S. conglomerate that does everything from import chinaware to sell generators to the country folk. The company still makes great chain saws, but somehow it doesn't seem the same.

In 1959, the Stihl "Contra" appeared. It weighed 26 pounds, had a 7-horsepower output, and was a direct-drive chain saw. The Contra was immediately accepted as the world's standard by loggers everywhere, and it put Stihl back on top. The Contra, which is still used today, is now known as the Stihl 070. It's one of the very best heavy-duty production saws.

The appearance of Stihl's efficient direct-drive system began to change the chain saw industry. In 1963, four years after the Contra and as a direct result of it, Homelite introduced the historic Homelite XL-12, another great saw that remains popular today. At 12 pounds (more or less), the XL-12 was 40 percent lighter than any other chain saw in existence. Consumer interest and extensive nonprofessional use of chain saws began with it. The pros continued to buy the Contra and other Stihl models, but everyone else grabbed up the XL-12's and a few McCullochs.

Later in the Sixties, Stihl finally entered the consumer market. (By that time, he had completely forgotten how to get to his old loafing place in the woods.) In 1967, he came out with the first chain saw antivibration system; in 1968, the first chain saw with an electronic ignition. In 1970, he designed a new cutting chain. By 1971, Stihl, Inc. was unquestionably the leader in both professional and consumer chain saw markets, and the comeback was complete. Stihl, the man, was 75.

When Andreas Stihl died in 1973, he held over 400 international patents and 200 registered designs, all related to chain saws. He never sold out to a conglomerate, and the company is still independent today. Parp hopes it stays that way.

Popular history has a way of cutting corners. If it didn't, we would never be able to name a single inventor. Nearly everyone really believes that Henry Ford invented the automobile. We like to pretend that inventions occur by miracle—a bolt of lightning from a brilliant brain. The truth is that inventions are created primarily by the need for them. No idea or machine ever appears without the need for it and without hundreds of contributions by people other than the inventor we remember and name.

The history of the chain saw goes back from all of the present manufacturers, through Stihl, von Westfelt, Wolf, Muir, Smith, and all the others, to prehistory. But we like to name our inventors, and when we have trouble doing it—because of war, pride, or prejudice—we behave badly. We start naming all the wrong people. Usually, Parp couldn't give two hoots, but in this case, there's a responsibility. Parp does care about credit where it's due. Everyone connected with chain saws has always known who "invented" the chain saw, and we should have named this ingenious man long ago instead of ducking the issue and confusing it with false claims.

Andreas Stihl invented the chain saw in Stuttgart, Germany, in 1926. Parp has told as much of the story as he could dig up, but there was considerable resistance to its being told at all. All the facts presented here are accurate. If Parp added a bird singing here and a man loafing there, it's only because every good inventor deserves a little myth. It doesn't change the facts.

WAS THE CHAIN SAW WORTH INVENTING?

Since the introduction of the Homelite XL-12 in 1963, the chain saw has become one of the most popular power tools. That's partly because of the lure of the woods, but it's mostly because a chain saw is a practical and versatile tool.

Every year there are attachments available to fit more saws: hedge trimmers, blowers, posthole diggers, drills, winches, cutoff saws, and so on. Every year there are more and more jobs that become easier and easier with a chain saw.

In his 1948 letter to Andreas Stihl, Arthur Mall noted that there were more than 100,000 chain saws in North America. In 1963 alone, 300,000 chain saws were sold, and 800,000 were sold in 1972. By 1975, manufacturers were selling more than 2,000,000 chain saws each year, and sales were increasing.

In the Sixties, the buying market for chain saws began shifting from professional users to home or "casual" users. Today, most "market" chain saws weigh less than 12 pounds and sell for less than $200. The manufacturers sell about 20,000 minisaws each month, and about a fifth of all chain saws are now purchased by women.

Retail sales of professional logging saws have increased greatly, also. Not counting sales to corporations and governments, at least three times as many professional saws are now purchased as were purchased in the early Seventies.

WHO NEEDS A CHAIN SAW GUIDE?

Anyone who owns or will ever own a chain saw needs to know how to use and care for it. If you know little or nothing about chain saws, but need one or want one, this book will serve as an introduction. It will then help you select one, start it, keep it running, and use it well.

If you've used chain saws quite a lot, it's still likely that you'll find some new and useful information in this book—especially if you keep losing your owner's manual, if you want to learn to do some repair work for yourself, if you want to know about different kinds of cutting chains and attachments, or if you want to start using your saw to earn some extra income.

If you're a logger who can tear apart a production saw in the middle of a rainy night, make the repair parts you need from a beer can and the gaskets from a cracker box, and be ready to cut wood again before dawn, you still need something to sit on. This book will do as well as anything.

QUICK TIPS FOR IMPULSIVE BUYERS

If you happen to be thumbing through this book in a chain saw dealer's showroom and you're about to buy your first chain saw, here are a few tips that may help.

First, try to match the saw to your needs. This is covered in greater detail in Chapter 2, but for the moment, you should at least consider the amount of cutting you are likely to do, as well as the size and toughness of the wood in your region.

Clearly, bigger is not always best in chain saws. For example, Parp bought two new chain saws in 1978. One was a top-of-the-line, but very trim and lightweight, professional-quality limbing saw. The other was a top-of-the-line *almost* heavy-duty logging saw. The limber still rides in Parp's pickup; the bucker has long since been recycled.

If you expect to use your new saw lightly—for trimming, pruning, and cutting modest amounts of firewood for your fireplace, auxiliary heater, or hideout—a well-built minisaw will suit your needs. It should have a 12″ or 14″ bar and a 1/4″-pitch chain. There are many such saws on the market and from a number of reputable manufacturers.

If you plan to use your saw to cut enough wood each fall to heat your entire home throughout the year, you should probably choose a mid-range saw of approximately 3.0 cubic-inch displacement, with a 16″ bar and a 3/8″-pitch chain.

Choose a saw that is not too heavy for you to handle safely. Avoid off brands and supercheap deals; they're usually a waste of money.

For bells and whistles, Parp recommends antivibration handles, a trigger interlock, a sprocket-nose bar, and a chain design that reduces kickback. If you think you'll enjoy doing your own tune-ups, get a standard ignition. Otherwise, go for the electronic option; an automatic chain-brake system may make you feel a little safer.

Parp does *not* recommend a built-in automatic sharpening system.

Be sure to get your owner's manual and warranty card. Also, buy the recommended two-cycle engine oil as well as a quality bar-and-chain lubricant. Reasons for this are covered elsewhere in this book.

Finally, before you start your new saw, read the safety precautions in your owner's manual and at the end of Parp's Chapter 1. And, of course, you wouldn't dream of cutting a live tree unless it was absolutely necessary, would you?

Happy woodcutting!

EDITOR'S NOTE: Products and procedures change rapidly in the chain saw industry. In the course of bringing out this revised edition of Barnacle Parp's Chain Saw Guide, *new developments occurred, of course, and these are reflected in various ways throughout the book—in photos, illustrations, and parts of the text. There will doubtless be other advancements after the book is in print. Like products and procedures, regulations change periodically. See the Appendix for addresses of the Consumer Product Safety Commission and the Portable Power Equipment Manufacturers Association, where you can obtain copies of recent industry regulations pertaining to chain saws.*

CHAPTER 1
THE BASIC
CHAIN SAW

A chain saw is one of those machines that you could see a dozen times and never recognize. I have only a foggy memory of seeing my first chain saw. I grew up visiting Goodwill stores, and that's where the saw was. I remember moving a box away from a table in the back room of the store. Behind the box was an ugly machine covered with dust and oil. It had a mean-looking arm with a dangerous chain of claws circling it. I shuddered and went to look at old radios. I know now that it was a chain saw.

If you look around a little, especially if you're shopping for a used chain saw, you might run into that monster from my foggy memory. If you do, let it rest in peace. It has done its share of work and undoubtedly carries a curse or two.

This old-fashioned saw is a clumsy, outmoded hunk of machinery in contrast to the light, simple, streamlined saws in use today.

THE BASIC COMPONENTS

The modern chain saw is a lightweight, well-designed, precision machine that can cut firewood or build cabins, as well as power a growing number of very useful attachments. The modern chain saw is one of the most efficient products of industrial society. Few other machines can match a good chain saw's power-to-weight proportion.

The chain saw has two major and obvious components. The cutting attachment is similar on all chain saws, and Parp will have lots to say about it in a minute, as well as throughout this book. For now, let's look at the other component: the power unit.

The power unit of a chain saw is the part that has the handles. Portable chain saws are powered by either an electric motor or a gasoline engine.

There's little to say by way of introduction about the power unit of an electric chain saw. You connect it to the cutting attachment and plug it in. (Be sure you have a dry place to stand!)

The second kind of power unit is a gasoline engine. This power unit doesn't plug in, so it won't kill you if your pole house isn't finished when the monsoons come—but it's louder than the electric version, and it smells worse. And you'd better learn how to feed and care for it, or it'll snore its last quicker than a pheasant in a logging camp.

A lightweight electric chain saw for trimming backyard trees and cutting firewood near a convenient power source

THE ENGINE: AN INTRODUCTION

In this first and basic chapter, we will limit our discussion to those aspects of the engine that will be of practical help to you in selecting and buying a *new* chain saw.

Most chain saws are powered by lightweight, portable, internal-combustion gasoline engines.

In order to be efficient tools for their specialized jobs, chain saws must be capable of operating in various positions. In fact, chain saw users occasionally operate their machines upside down, and anyone who is about to cut down a tree will realize that the chain saw frequently must operate on its side. Therefore, a chain saw engine must be able to operate in all positions as efficiently as it operates right side up.

If you could pick up the engine in your motor vehicle and carry it about, you would soon discover that it won't operate upside down or on its side. It doesn't operate that way because it's impossible for the engine to lubricate itself in any position except right side up.

As an engine operates, its pistons go up and down in their cylinders. In many engines, a "flipper" extends below the crankshaft. As the piston goes up and down, it causes the flipper to throw oil up onto the moving parts of the engine. Many small engines are lubricated in exactly this way. Your car's engine is somewhat more complicated than this, since it has an oil pressure system with an oil pump and oil passageways. But the pump has to reach into a pool of oil, so the principle is the same. When the engine is tilted, the flipper can't reach the oil. When the engine is upside-down, the situation is even worse.

Obviously, the oil-pool kind of engine can't be operated upside down or on its side. So how are we going to design an engine that we can carry around and run on its side or upside down? Why don't we mix the oil with the fuel—just enough so that little drops of oil will fly around with the vaporized gasoline when the engine is operated in any position?

Since we're going to mix the oil with the gasoline, we won't need a place to store the oil in the engine. There are lots of other things we won't need—that flipper, for one thing.

That's exactly what the engineers did when they realized the need for a portable engine that could be operated in any position. They combined the lubrication and fuel processes. An engine that uses fuel mixed with oil is called a *two-cycle* engine. Unlike most automobile engines, many two-cycle engines have only one cylinder and only one piston, but they're called two-cycle engines because the piston in each transmits power on every downward stroke and compresses fuel vapor, including the oil, on every upward stroke. Other engines are called *four-cycle* engines, but there is no particular reason for us to bother with explaining them here; they aren't used on chain saws. (For a more detailed discussion of two-cycle engines, see Chapter 12.)

COOLING

You will notice that, unlike most automobile engines, there is no radiator on a chain saw. That's because gasoline chain saw engines are air-cooled, for fairly obvious reasons. First, a radiator full of coolant is too heavy to add to a portable engine. Second, a radiator needs to be reasonably stationary in relationship to the engine in order to work properly. Like the oil-pool system of lubrication, a radiator won't work on its side or upside down. So chain saw engines are *air-cooled*. That means, for one thing, that all that shiny metal surrounding the engine isn't just streamlined decoration; it's essential to the operation of the engine because it deflects air into currents that move around the engine and help to cool it.

At this point, you may begin to appreciate how efficient and precise a chain saw engine is. There's no fat because there can't be. Loggers wouldn't tolerate it. Every bit of weight on a chain saw has to do at least one essential job, and often more than one.

DISPLACEMENT

We've already mentioned the function of a piston in a cylinder. Throughout your acquaintance with chain saws and other engines, you will encounter the term *displacement*. One of the reasons that this term is used in relation to chain saws is that displacement is a more accurate and informative measurement of a small engine's size and capability than is *horsepower*, the term often used in connection with automobiles.

As a piston travels upward in its cylinder, it compresses the vaporized fuel-oil-air mixture that is trapped above it. At exactly the right time, the spark plug fires, causing the trapped and compressed fuel vapor to burn rapidly (explode). The burning fuel produces gases that rapidly expand to force the piston back down, subsequently turning the *crankshaft* that transmits the power.

The power of the engine is largely determined by the amount of fuel-oil-air vapor that is trapped and compressed in the cylinder—which, in turn, is determined by a combination of the distance traveled by the piston and the size of the cylinder itself. The figure resulting from the correct combination of these factors is known as *displacement*. This refers, simply, to the volume of space that is displaced by the piston during its upward stroke.

Stroke is the distance traveled by the piston from its lowest position, called bottom dead center, to its uppermost position, called top dead center.. *Bore* is the term that refers to the diameter of the inside of the cylinder. Displacement is often incorrectly defined as the product of bore multiplied by stroke. It is sufficient for our purposes to understand that displacement refers to the total volume of vaporized fuel that is compressed by the piston on its upward stroke.

That's all there is to it. If you're curious, the formula for determining displacement is available, but it really isn't necessary to a working understanding of displacement. The important thing is to have an idea of what the displacement figure represents and to allow your understanding of the term to grow naturally. You'll probably never have occasion to determine displacement mathematically, but stated displacement will come to mean more and more to you in terms of an engine's practical ability. Your response to particular statements of displacement will become increasingly intuitive as you gain experience with chain saws.

The displacement of chain saw engines ranges from about 1.6 cubic inches to about 8.36 cubic inches. As you may suspect, either end of that range is quite extreme. A 1.6-cubic-inch engine is very small and has definite limitations when it comes to cutting up logs that are big enough to chop. An 8.36-cubic-inch engine comes only on a chain saw that most of us would rather not carry around. The practical range is roughly 2.0 cubic inches to 4.0 cubic inches.

BAR AND CHAIN

We're back to that mean-looking arm with its chain of claws.

The *guide bar*, around which the chain travels, is made of a very strong, hardened steel, often with an even harder steel around the tip. The bar is grooved all along its edge, with rails standing up to form the sides of the groove. Chain saw guide bars come in various lengths— from a useless eight inches to a very demanding five feet. The practical range of guide-bar lengths for most users is from one foot to about 20 inches.

The links of a saw chain are arranged in a specific pattern and in an endless loop. Each chain contains several different kinds of links. The bottom of the chain has tangs that fit into the groove in the guide bar. These pieces are called *drive links*. They receive the turning force from the engine and are the parts that move the chain around the bar. They also keep the chain from falling off the bar, and they help keep the guide bar groove clean so that dirt and sawdust don't completely clog it.

It's easy to see which of the chain parts cuts the wood as the chain speeds around the guide bar. It's the part that looks most like a claw and has a sharpened front edge. All the other parts are equally important, and the *cutters* couldn't actually cut if the other parts weren't there to do their specialized jobs.

The *depth gauge* is a part of the same link as the cutter, and sticks up right in front of the sharpened edge. Coming right before the cutting edge, the depth gauge helps keep the cutter from digging too far into the wood and jamming. The depth gauge feeds the wood to the cutter, leads the cutter into the wood, and determines how deeply the cutter will cut.

The *tie strap* or *side strap* has several important jobs. First of all, it's the link that holds the rest of the chain together and keeps the cutters properly spaced. It holds the chain together with rivets between itself and other parts of the chain. It also acts as a bearing that helps the chain be flexible enough to bend around the guide bar. Finally, it acts as a shoulder that rides on the rails of the guide bar to keep the tangs of the drive links from hitting the bottom of the guide bar groove.

Now we need to know how cutting chains are measured.

PITCH AND GAUGE

There are two measurements to consider when determining the size of a cutting chain. One is *pitch*. In order to make an intelligent choice of a chain saw for yourself and in order to repair or replace its chain, you will need to understand pitch.

Pitch is a measurement of a length of chain from one specific point to another. Amusingly, the experts disagree about exactly where these points are. A measurement commonly is taken between the centers of the rivets of one of the drive links; scientifically, and more precisely, pitch is one-half the distance from the center of the second rivet in one drive link to the center of the second rivet in the next drive link.

As we will see later, the most common saw chain size is 3/8″ pitch, though many popular minisaws (or small chain saws for occasional users) utilize chain that is 1/4″ pitch. Again, pitch will become a familiar term and will come to mean more as we go along.

Chain *gauge* is another measurement that you will need to know when you replace or repair the chain on your saw. The gauge of a chain is determined by the kind of chain saw; you will generally find the gauge of your chain listed in the owner's manual. If that fails, any saw-chain dealer, including mail-order companies, can usually tell you what gauge chain or chain parts you need—if you can tell him what kind of saw you have.

Gauge is a measurement of the thickness of a drive-link tang, where it rides inside the grooves of the bar. Of these two terms, pitch and gauge, pitch is the one that will be important when you determine your needs and go out to buy a chain saw.

CONNECTING THE ENGINE TO THE BAR AND CHAIN

On almost all modern chain saws, a toothed *sprocket* is connected directly, or almost directly, to the crankshaft. As the piston goes up and down, it turns the crankshaft. As the crankshaft turns, the sprocket turns, too. As the sprocket turns, it engages the drive links in the cutting chain and moves the chain forward around the bar, which is bolted to the body of the chain saw.

Some chain saws have a gear or set of gears between the crankshaft and the sprocket. This system allows the chain to turn more slowly than the crankshaft. Many early chain saws were gear-driven. Most contemporary gear-driven chain saws are very large felling saws used by professional loggers.

Guide bar assembly

Chain
Guide bar
Sprocket

Assembled and disassembled guide bar, chain, and sprocket

OIL FOR THE BAR AND CHAIN

We've already noted that a two-cycle engine is lubricated by mixing the oil with the fuel and that this kind of engine doesn't require an oil storage tank or an oil filler cap. A chain saw does have an oil tank and an oil filler cap, but the oil isn't for the engine.

As the cutting chain speeds around the bar, at 50 feet per second or so, it must endure several sources of resistance—with resulting friction, heat, and wear. The chain is in constant contact with the bar, of course, and then there are the moving parts of the chain wearing against each other and against the wood itself. If the chain and bar weren't well lubricated, they would quickly burn. Hence, all chain saws employ some method of lubricating the bar and chain.

Parp tells some scary stories of loggers with huge old saws, plunging the bar with its moving chain into a steel bucket full of dirty oil. You don't have to do that these days.

On many modern chain saws, bar and chain lubrication is automatic. As the throttle trigger is depressed, increasing the engine speed, a pump system shoots out increasing amounts of oil through a small opening in the side of the saw's body, next to the tail of the bar. The oil lands on the chain and in the groove of the bar through which the chain's drive-link tangs pass. When the saw slows down, the amount of pumped oil decreases.

A manual chain-oil system is similar, but a plunger or lever must be depressed in order to operate the pump that delivers the oil to the chain and bar. When you use a chain saw with a manual oiler, you have to learn how to control the oiler so as to deliver the proper amount of oil for the work you are doing. In any kind of cutting, you must pump the oiler often. When cutting dense, hard, frozen, or wet wood, you must pump more often. That is why more and more mass-produced chain saws have automatic oiling systems.

Some chain saws employ *both* systems. That is, a saw may have an automatic oiling system which is supplemented by a manual control. Many professionals prefer this combination. For several years, adjustable automatic chain lubrication systems have been standard equipment on most new chain saws for the consumer market.

FUEL MIXTURE

In order for a chain saw engine to operate properly, it must be supplied with fresh, regular-grade leaded gasoline that is premixed in the proper proportions with clean, new, two-cycle engine oil. The fuel can't be high-octane or unleaded gasoline, and the oil must be made especially for two-cycle engines. It can't be automobile engine oil; automobile engine oil is often as much as 50 percent additives—which may be good for automobile engines, but can be fatal to chain saw engines. We've already discovered that chain saw engines are air-cooled. As such, they operate at much higher temperatures than do automobile engines. Also, in a two-cycle engine, the fuel is mixed with the oil, so the oil is exposed to the high temperature of the inside of the combustion chamber. At these high temperatures, the "viscosity improvers" in automobile engine oil (or in additives such as STP) undergo a chemical change known as *polymerization*. They turn into something a lot like glue. A factory warranty is void if multiviscosity lubricants or automobile additives are used. The evidence is always obvious and conclusive.

High-octane fuels are blended to burn more completely than regular-grade fuels. In order to accomplish this, an unburned portion of the fuel in the compression chamber reaches a point of self-ignition. This causes a second expansion in the compression chamber that has the force of an explosion. Since the two ignitions do not occur at the same time, the second has a hammering effect on the piston. This, together with the much higher temperature caused by the double ignition, quickly causes engine damage.

Always use the fuel and oil recommended by the manufacturer (check your owner's manual) and mix the two according to the instructions.

WHO SELLS CHAIN SAWS?

Chain saws are available almost anywhere these days, including discount department stores, drugstores, gas stations, and automobile showrooms.

But Parp recommends two sources in particular, for very good reasons. Your local hardware store is probably run by experienced, friendly people who back up what they sell and who know how to contact the people who make and repair the chain saws they carry. It's good insurance.

Another good bet is the parts distributor or authorized factory service center for the chain saw you're most interested in. This will often be the local franchised dealer for that particular saw. If you're lucky enough to have one of these franchised dealers in your locality, give him your business on new saws and try him first for used ones. He will take good care of you in order to protect that valuable franchise.

Very often a farm machinery dealer will also be a franchised dealer for one or more brands of chain saws. If you're also in the market for a tractor, truck, or tiller, look around the showroom for a chain saw display and ask your salesperson for a package price. Getting a good deal is worth a try, and you have nothing to lose.

In this chapter, we've seen and discussed the basic chain saw. In many areas of the world, life on the farm or in the wilderness now includes a chain saw, even for people who don't have a motor vehicle or a tractor. A chain saw is not quite a basic tool, and it never will be unless we somehow develop a new fuel or power system less dangerous, cumbersome, foul, and expensive than using cans of gasoline or generating plants. But the chain saw is such a useful addition to a basic tool collection that it might be considered a basic convenience, like a cookstove in addition to your fireplace.

During pleasant and remote years without electricity, Parp has used his chain saw to supply both fire and ice; wood for the stoves, of course, and ice for the icebox (manageable blocks cut from a nearby frozen lake). And the chain saw made the boards that made the skids that got the ice home. It could have been done with basic hand tools—axes and saws—as has been done before, by Parp and by millions of others, but the chain saw saved a lot of time. And time, for himself, was what Parp was there to save.

BASIC CHAIN SAW SAFETY RULES

1. Wear protective gear, gloves, and close-fitting clothing.
2. Keep the chain sharp, the sprocket new, and the bar in good condition.
3. Keep the chain properly adjusted.
4. Keep the chain well oiled.
5. Keep the exterior of the saw clean.
6. Keep all screws, bolts, and nuts tightened.
7. Use the correct fuel-oil mix.
8. No smoking.
9. Start the saw at least ten feet from the fueling area.
10. Clean the air filter frequently.
11. Start the saw on the ground, braced safely with one foot.
12. Don't walk with a running saw.
13. Hold the saw firmly with both hands, keeping your thumbs curled around the handles. Keep your left arm as straight as possible.
14. Keep spectators well back out of your way and well out of danger.
15. Prevent the tip of the bar from touching anything, to avoid kickback.
16. Move only with the saw turned off and the guide bar pointing behind you, unless you are walking down a steep incline, in which case the guide bar should point forward.
17. Don't race the engine "in the air" or when not cutting.
18. Don't allow the chain near metal, stone, or ground.

19. Use accepted cutting techniques.
20. Keep your body to one side (left) of the plane of chain rotation.
21. Don't bore the end of the bar straight into the work. Use accepted boring techniques.
22. Don't raise the saw above chest height.
23. Stand uphill from the work.
24. Keep your eyes and your attention on the saw and the work.
25. Wear gloves when handling or sharpening the chain.
26. When felling, clear the area, watch for dead branches, and plan your escape route.
27. Don't operate a chain saw while up a tree.
28. Don't get too confident.
29. Foresee the unforeseeable.
30. Never loan your chain saw.
31. Don't consume alcoholic beverages until the work is done and your chain saw is put away.

CHAPTER 2
HOW TO BUY
A NEW CHAIN SAW

Many old-timers experience great anxiety when faced with the prospect of buying a new chain saw. That's understandable. People who've used chain saws for years believe that they are temperamental, unpredictable beasts and that each saw has an individual personality which will reveal itself only after the warranty has lapsed. Many old woodsmen hold this mystical view of their chain saws because the performance of their saws reflects the treatment they've received. You just can't take a working knowledge of truck mechanics from the 1940's and apply it to the high-performance, lightweight chain saws of the 1980's, either in selecting or in using these machines.

It is true, of course, that not all chain saws are created equal. Several manufacturers produce machines that are dependable, year after year, given proper care and maintenance; unfortunately, others produce saws that are poorly engineered or are made of components unable to stand up to hard use. But for the most part, today's gasoline chain saws are remarkable examples of the highest standards in manufacturing technology. The problems develop with improper use or inadequate maintenance, and much of this book is concerned with how to avoid those problems.

DETERMINE YOUR NEEDS

What you need in a chain saw is, of course, determined by how much you will use your saw and for what kind of cutting. If you do not heat or cook exclusively with wood fuel and if you don't plan to build a log cabin, you'll probably use your saw for occasional light cutting such as pruning, trimming, or harvesting a small firewood supply for your fireplace or auxiliary heater. This level of use is probably within the scope of a good minisaw.

If you plan to cut enough wood every year to supply all of the fuel needed to heat your home through the average North American winter, you will want to choose a good lightweight saw with an engine of about 3.0-cubic-inch displacement.

If you're going to cut wood for heating—and possibly for cooking—

and if you plan to do any building, you should probably opt for a saw in the medium-duty range. If you think you'll also be milling logs for lumber and cutting really tough or large trees, or if you're going into the firewood business in a big way, you'll need a professional heavy-duty saw. It might be smart to get a second saw, a lightweight model for limbing and for cutting up the smaller stuff.

Once you've determined what jobs you're most likely to do with your saw, you can start looking for exactly the right machine to fit your needs.

TYPES OF CHAIN SAWS

As indicated earlier, most chain saws on the market today fit into one of four general categories: minisaws, lightweight saws, medium-duty saws, and production or professional (heavy-duty) chain saws. In addition, there are various special-purpose saws, such as models for tree-trimming and hydraulic mining saws.

Once you've determined the general category of chain saw that best suits your needs, you should take some time to find out about the particular models available from the various manufacturers. New models appear every year, and somehow someone always manages to come up with at least one major improvement over last year's offerings.

Write to the major chain saw manufacturers (listed at the back of the book) and request product information. Some excellent chain saws are not easily accessible, and writing the manufacturers is the only satisfactory method of learning about them. While you're waiting for the responses, visit all the chain saw dealers in your area. Examine the saws and become as familiar with them as you can. Ask all the questions you want, both in the dealer's showroom and in the repair shop out back.

You should also consult your local library or bookstore for recent articles on chain saws in any of the consumer information publications, such as *Consumer Reports*.

The accessories and special features of a product are often emphasized both in the manufacturer's advertisements and in the publications that determine ratings. Remember that the presence of a chain-brake system, a heated handle, an automatic chain-sharpening system, or a trim design does not necessarily indicate a gutsier engine, a stronger bar and chain, or serviceability. Some of these features—such as automatic sharpening systems and electric starters—are disparaged by woodspersons in general and by Parp in particular. Remember also that no safety feature makes chain saw use entirely safe, and no manufacturer should hint otherwise.

Later we'll discuss some of these features in more detail. Right now you need to know more about the various types and sizes of chain saws that are available, the jobs they were designed to do, and the various features you can expect to find on certain models.

GUIDE BAR SIZE

Gasoline chain saws are commonly available in bar lengths from 10″ to 36″. There are some 8″ bars available, especially on electric chain saws, but they're not very practical, even for trimming the hedge. And there are professional saws that are available with 60″ bars. They're very practical *for the work they're intended to do*, but not for much else.

The common and most useful lengths for most of us are 12″, 14″, 16″, and 20″. Many people who cut a great deal of wood year-round keep two saws, one lightweight with a 14″ or 16″ bar, and one medium-duty or lightweight production machine with a 20″ or 25″ bar. For most users, anything longer than 25″ is too awkward and therefore unsafe.

Most people find that a 16″ bar is sufficient. In areas where you're likely to cut a lot of large wood, you may want a 20″ or 25″ bar. If you're cutting wood for your fireplace, however, you can do fine in almost any area with a smaller bar. All you have to do is find wood that your saw can cut. There's always plenty of that: dead brush, stands of small aspen or birch, and good-sized logs up to 32″ in diameter.

Whatever size bar you decide you need, be sure that your saw's engine is more than adequate in power. In other words, look up the specifications for any saw you're considering. Find the bar lengths available for that saw. If you're buying anything larger than a minisaw, get the bar length you want on a saw that can take a bar at least one size larger. In other words, if you want a 20″ bar, don't buy a saw that can only take up to a 20″ bar; get one with enough power for a 25″ or a 30″ bar. This is important for two reasons. First, if your engine's power is more than adequate for the bar and chain you're using, you have an extra margin against strain and wear. Second, if you later decide you need more reach, you simply go to the next size bar and chain. My own idea for heavy use is to get as large an engine as is practical and combine it with a medium-length cutting attachment. Parp uses a saw that can take a 25″ bar, but he equips it with a 16″ bar. He suggests that this configuration makes a useful and versatile all-around chain saw. On the other hand, if what you need is a minisaw, then what you need is a minisaw.

MINISAWS

If you're about to buy your first chain saw and expect to use it casually and infrequently—mostly around your home—and if you can obtain a supply of small logs or poles, such as birch or aspen, to cut up for your fireplace, you may well want to choose a minisaw.

STIHL 011 Top Handle, a "pro-mini"

The mini-sized gasoline chain saw has an engine displacement of about two cubic inches and is available with a 10″, 12″, or 14″ bar and chain. It weighs about seven pounds and has a fuel capacity of about two-thirds of a pint. In spite of their size, many of these saws are professionally dependable and are often used, as they were originally designed to be, by tree surgeons who must climb trees with chain saws clipped to their belts and then hold the saw in one hand to cut small limbs. (Don't you try that.) If you're going to buy a minisaw, it might be a good idea to find a friendly local tree surgeon for advice on which new saw might be best suited to your needs. They all disagree with one another, but the advice could be useful anyway.

Minisaws have some very real advantages over larger saws and often are the best choice for light-duty use around the home or in the orchard. Many of the advantages are obvious: They are light, easy to handle, and inexpensive. Surprisingly, they also hold their value very well and often bring more on resale or trade-in, dollar for dollar, than do medium-duty or production saws.

Minisaws utilize a special type of saw chain, commonly called minisaw chain or low-profile chain. Minisaws come equipped with a small, 1/4″-pitch chain.

Low-profile chain or 1/4″-pitch chain is not as strong as full-size 3/8″- or .404″-pitch chain, simply because the side straps holding the chain together are lighter and thinner. For the average homeowner or part-time woodsperson who uses a chain saw only occasionally, this chain is adequate, but the user must be extra careful of hazards such as stones or nails. A 1/4"-pitch chain may cut a thinner slice, but the slice can be just as deep and just as deadly. Be especially watchful of the small stones and other debris that often collect on top of logs or brush piles.

Most minisaws look radically different from larger saws. The handle, trigger mechanism, and other controls of a minisaw are often mounted on top of the engine housing. Many smaller models either have no bumper spikes for grabbing the wood or have so-called "integral bumper spikes" that are very small and are structurally a part of the saw's body, rather than separate parts that may be removed or replaced. This integral construction is a disadvantage when cleaning or repairing the saw.

At the upper end of the minisaw range are the professional models. As indicated earlier, these saws are designed for use by tree surgeons, nursery workers, orchard pruners, landscapers, park and road crews, and other professionals who use chain saws only occasionally and for special purposes and who require minisaw size and weight. The engines are the same size on these models, and other differences are few. Sometimes the fuel capacity is increased, and the handles on these professional models are often mounted behind the saw in the conventional manner. They may also be available with a chain-brake system, as well as with hand guards and larger bumper spikes. "Pro-minis" may also come with 16" bars.

Except for these professional models, all minisaws are designed for light, casual, and occasional use. Many people use minisaws to cut up to two cords of wood per year. All minisaws do best on light hardwoods and softwoods. They don't do very well when you're cutting down trees, unless the trees are small.

LIGHTWEIGHT CHAIN SAWS

Chain saws classified as lightweight or light-duty actually have much more in common with medium-duty or production saws than they do with minisaws. They are not just "big minisaws"—they are the beginning of the line of traditional chain saws. The lightweight chain saw is actually a smaller and lighter version of the logger's tool that most of us think of when we hear the term "chain saw."

If you'll be using your new chain saw to cut somewhat more than small, weekend fireplace wood—to cut, say, up to three cords of wood each year—or if you'll be cutting medium hardwoods or dense, wet, or frozen softwoods, and if you don't need a professional minisaw for a specific application, you'll do well with a quality lightweight.

Good, professional-quality lightweights are produced by most manufacturers. They usually weigh between 9 and 12.5 pounds and have a displacement of 2.5 to 3.0 cubic inches. You usually have a wide choice of bar lengths, from about 14″ to about 20″, though these saws do best when equipped with a 14″ or 16″ bar. Lightweights usually hold around one pint of fuel. That means, roughly, that the average user will need to refuel only once while cutting a pickup load of softwood. A saw classified as lightweight will run about one-third again as long as a minisaw on a tank of fuel. That can be a significant advantage if you work with your saw for an entire afternoon or more.

A quality lightweight has all the advantages of a minisaw, including high resale and trade-in value, with only a slight increase in weight. And the slight increase in weight is countered by the improved balance resulting from the rear-mounted handle and by a great increase in power and performance. The common minisaw displacement is less than 2.0 cubic inches; the common lightweight engine displacement is 3.0 cubic inches.

A lightweight chain saw is quick to start and easy to maneuver. Most lightweights are large enough to start in a safe position on the ground with one foot holding down the handle. A 3/8″-pitch cutting chain, pretty much the standard of the industry, is supplied on all models.

There are several optional features that may be available on a lightweight saw, including a chain-brake system, manual override for the automatic chain-lubrication system, and vibration control. Some lightweights will accept a few attachments, such as a hedge trimmer or a brush cutter.

In addition to good, solid home or farm use, these saws may be put to work on the construction site to cut boxing boards, moldings, or fence posts. You can do a great deal with a lightweight gasoline chain saw, and it doesn't take a great deal of getting used to.

MEDIUM-DUTY CHAIN SAWS

Chain saws are classified as medium-duty if they are built for medium-duty logging and heavy pulpwood cutting. They usually weigh between 12.5 and 16 pounds, and have an engine displacement of between 3.0 and 4.9 cubic inches.

Medium-duty saws offer the greatest versatility in model choice, attachments, and optional features. In addition to standard bar and chain cutting attachments from 16″ to 25″ or more, you can use the power head to run accessories such as a brush cutter, a hedge trimmer, an earth auger, an ice or wood drill, a bow bar for clearing or pulpwood cutting, or a cutoff attachment, which is a large circular-type saw for cutting stone, asphalt, and tile.

Medium-duty saws are used by such professionals as loggers, firewood suppliers, pulpwood cutters, construction workers, and road and rescue crews. They are widely used on large farms and in small private timber operations. Most people who earn part of their living by cutting and selling firewood use medium-duty saws exclusively. They are entirely satisfactory for any kind of chain saw work up to—and sometimes including—the heaviest professional logging application. And there is no reason at all that a homeowner or occasional user shouldn't have the best medium-duty saw that the budget and the muscles can accommodate, although it may take some getting used to.

If you anticipate cutting three or more cords of wood every year, especially hardwood, either for your own use or for selling by the truckload, a good-quality medium-duty saw will pay its way as a good investment and, with proper care and maintenance, will give years of dependable service. Such saws are better made and easier to service and repair than smaller saws.

Medium-duty saws are, of course, heavier and larger than minisaws or lightweights, but any healthy person with average coordination can get used to these saws, especially if you've chosen a quality machine with good balance. During use, a 16" or 20" bar will balance the heavier engine weight, and if the chain is sharp, the work will go much easier than with an inadequate saw. Also, these saws have the considerable advantage of a much larger fuel capacity. If you're selling firewood, that factor could make the difference between profit and loss.

PRODUCTION CHAIN SAWS

Professional heavy-duty or production chain saws are produced by several United States and Canadian companies and by every major European manufacturer.

They are just what their name says: heavy-duty. They are not for everybody, and they are not the only professional-quality saws you can buy. Most medium-duty saws, lots of lightweights, and several minisaws are also high-quality machines designed for professional use. The majority of us should get one of those.

Production saws are simply bigger, heavier, and louder. Of course, if you're going to do contract logging for the Forest Service, or if you're going to operate an outpost in the far North or in the tropics, or if you mill a lot of rough lumber, or if you fell giant trees every day for whatever reason, then maybe you do need a production saw.

But for almost all of us who use chain saws, even very extensively, production saws are much more than we need. And since they are heavier and have huge cutting attachments, they are considerably more dangerous than medium-duty saws. Nothing is so awesome as a giant production saw with a 40" bar running at high speed with its throttle-lock stuck, jumping all over the ground after being dropped. Even if you can afford it, be sure you really need a production saw before you decide to live with one.

STIHL 090. This heavy-duty production saw is one of the world's most powerful one-person chain saws.

A top-of-the-line production saw, like the Stihl 909, has a displacement of 8.36 cubic inches. Its power unit alone weighs nearly 30 pounds. The smallest bar available with that saw is 21″ with a .404″-pitch or 1/2″-pitch chain. A smaller bar and chain would probably not be properly balanced. That saw is the heavy-duty standard of the logging industry. (Got that?)

ELECTRIC CHAIN SAWS

Chain saws that are powered by electricity rather than by a lightweight, two-cycle internal combustion gasoline engine can be somewhat less expensive to manufacture. They can also be just plain cheap. The cheap ones are pretty obvious, and you should avoid them. They have plastic parts that wear and break quickly and that often cannot be repaired.

A quality electric chain saw, and there are several brands available, will cost roughly the same as a comparable saw with a gasoline engine.

Electric chain saws are light, easy to "start," quiet, and much less messy. The fact that they can also be used in a closed area without danger from fumes implies good construction possibilities if the saw's strength is adequate to the job.

But the greatest potential for the electric chain saw is seldom mentioned: the backyard woodpile. It's strange that this obvious application of the electric chain saw is so often ignored. Parp has greatly enjoyed the peace, convenience, and quiet of working close to the cabin on a still and snowless winter day, effortlessly and pleasantly cutting huge amounts of kindling and small wood, without disturbing the atmosphere or his communion with nature. If you're looking for a chain saw to use exclusively around the yard, house, or shop, a small, well-made electric chain saw may be a better investment than a cheap gasoline minisaw. And you can make things with it in the basement.

New models are equipped with a special centrifugal clutch to help prevent both motor damage and dangerous kickback should the chain catch in the wood. When the chain encounters extreme resistance, this clutch acts to disengage the motor. Because of the delicacy of electric motors, Parp advises against investing in a used electric chain saw unless you know the owner and know that the saw is almost brand-new and a recent model.

In general, electric chain saws are equipped with small bars. That is, almost all consumer-type electric saws are available with 8″, 10″, or 12″ bars and a minisaw-type 1/4″-pitch cutting chain. Don't buy an 8″ model. Unless you have a very specific need for such a saw (such as electric chain saw carving or crafts), you'll be better off with a good $20 hand-powered bow saw.

There are professional models, made by several companies, available with 16″ bars. Stihl produces an exceptional line of electric saws: the E-10, E-15, and E-30. The Stihl E-30 is a powerful electric chain saw that is available with a wide range of bar sizes from 17″ up to 48″. It weighs a hefty 31.3 pounds (and that's without the bar and chain), but the E-30 is great for construction where 220 volts and lots of muscle power are available.

Other quality electric chain saws are produced by Skil, Sears, Solo, and Wen. (See Chapter 7 for more information on electric chain saws.)

SPECIAL-PURPOSE CHAIN SAWS

As the chain saw industry moves forward through the 1980's, more and more manufacturers are adapting their basic machines for an increasing number of special applications. Although most of these new special-purpose saws are intended for use chiefly by professionals in the construction, timber, and mining industries, several are also of potential interest to consumers and homesteaders.

Hydraulic chain saws were developed for use by mining companies in situations where internal combustion engines must be limited to avoid excessive air supply problems. Some of the smaller models available from various manufacturers can be fitted for efficient use from the hydraulics of a tractor or other heavy equipment. Since these saws are extremely powerful, they can be used to cut very tough woods such as those that grow in the Southeast.

Other manufacturers have developed extremely heavy-duty electric chain saws for use on rural building sites. A saw such as the Stihl E-30 would be a useful tool for building a rural log home or cabin where electric power is available and the use of gasoline is inadvisable for one reason or another.

Ripping saws are not actually different from other chain saws, except that they must be gutsy enough (at least 5.0 cubic inches of displacement) to go against (in the direction of) the grain. The main difference in a saw used especially for ripping is the chain. Ripping chains are filed with very thin top plates to present as little resistance as posssible while slicing a log the long way.

Some ripping saws are equipped with an extra handle fitted onto the tip of the bar. This enables a helper to assist in the process of ripping boards from logs.

Clearing saws and bow saws with large, curved chain guides are specially designed to facilitate the thinning and cutting of thick stands of close-growing, small-diameter trees and brush, such as those that occur in the South and Northeast. Although these saws are potentially highly dangerous tools for the nonprofessional to use, they could serve an experienced cutter well in difficult situations; where a lot of thinning must be done, the same work could be even more dangerous if attempted with a standard-configuration saw. Both clearing and bow saws must be equipped with the safety guards specified by the U.S. Forest Service. Do not use a bow or clearing saw without the safety guards in place.

Tree surgeon saws are small, professional-quality chain saws designed for light weight and ease of use. They must be dependable starters since tree surgeons often carry them while climbing trees. (A saw that doesn't start after being carried to the top of a tree often comes down hard.)

Two excellent small saws designed especially for this kind of work are the Poulan S25 DA, an under-ten-pound model with a lot of desirable features and the endurance of a tank, and the Stihl 020 AV Professional. Both are of considerable interest to consumers looking for small, lightweight saws of professional dependability and great power-to-weight ratios.

In recent years, chain saw carving has become a popular craft among woods people all over the country. The popularity of this art form has resulted in the newest chain saw innovation, the carving saw. Saws designed especially for carving are usually based on one of the small professional saws such as the Poulan S25 DA or the Stihl 020 AVP just mentioned. Although none of the manufacturers are as yet offering specially configured factory-designed carving saws, the parts necessary to convert a small, professional mini into a good carving saw are available from third-party sources such as Bailey's, the big California and Tennessee mail-order house. Bailey's presently offers a thin, curved guide bar and specially filed chain for use on the Poulan S25 DA. This makes an excellent carving saw package at a modest cost. Parp cautions that carving with a standard chain saw is very dangerous, especially with a model larger than a minisaw.

THE FINAL CHOICE

From the preceding description of the general types and sizes of chain saws and from your own research and investigation, you should now have a pretty good idea what kind of chain saw will best suit your needs. Now you can shop in earnest.

Try to find chain saw dealers that have demonstration models or used saws that will give you some idea of the feel of working with particular saws. You might decide to invest a few dollars in renting a saw of the desired model from a rent-all shop; work with it for an entire afternoon. This is worthwhile for several reasons. If you've never used a chain saw before, you'll get some valuable practice without risking your own brand-new saw and chain. You'll also soon decide if the saw you're considering is capable of, or too much for, the work you're likely to be doing. And you might decide that you never again want anything to do with a chain saw.

"Feel" is an important consideration and will often be the determining factor in your final choice. If you can't actually start and use a chain saw, and if you can't rent the model you're considering, spend some time in the dealer's showroom. Pick up the saw and hold it awhile. Get the heft of it; try holding and moving it in all directions and from several angles. Simulate cutting stances and imagine working in the woods with your feet on the natural ground. After you consider reputation and everything else, the decision between two different saws comes down to the one that feels better.

There are many brand-name chain saws produced in the United States and in other countries. The United States is not the only country where trees grow, nor is it where the trees are largest or thickest. It is not the only country with an important forest products industry, and, as a matter of fact, it is not the country where chain saws first appeared.

There are huge forests in Germany, Sweden, Norway, and other European countries, and it is from these areas that the chain saw has come. There are many outstanding manufacturers whose names are unfamiliar to most Americans. Even if you have just started looking for a saw, you've probably already heard of Homelite, McCulloch, Pioneer, Poulan, and other U.S. and Canadian chain saw manufacturers. You may never have heard of Husqvarna, Jonsered, Solo, or even Stihl. That doesn't mean that you shouldn't choose one of these saws or another saw from an unfamiliar manufacturer. If you hang around chain saws awhile or read this book, you'll soon know which names have been around and which are newcomers.

As a matter of fact, Parp believes that for the vast majority of chain saw users, especially occasional users, a lightweight saw or a minisaw from *any* of the companies mentioned above will be entirely satisfactory and will hold up well with proper care and maintenance.

Parp also believes that the European manufacturers still produce the best and toughest professional-quality chain saws—in all sizes and all price ranges.

TOOLS AND ACCESSORIES

There are many tools and accessories that you will need in order to do chain saw work and in order to keep your saw in good condition. Several of these items should come with your saw, and you should make sure you have all of them when you leave the store. You should also purchase all the others, either before or just after you pick up your saw, so you won't be unnecessarily delayed in using your saw. If you get home without the tools to adjust the chain tension, for example, you could damage your new saw in your enthusiasm to start and use it.

Parp's Best Advice: DO NOT START your new saw until you have carefully read your owner's manual and Parp's "An Ersatz Owner's Manual" (Chapter 5), and "Using Your Chain Saw" (Chapter 9).

You can put off Parp for a while if you're in a real hurry to fire up that bright and powerful machine, but don't put off a thorough reading of your owner's manual. If you do, you may injure yourself, the garage, or the neighbor's tree. And, of course, you could easily damage your machine with an incorrect chain adjustment or fuel mix. All of this will seem elementary to many readers, but people ruin new saws every day and then expect the dealer to take them back. Of all chain saw tools and accessories, your owner's manual is certainly the most essential.

Here's a list:

Tools and Accessories

*	1.	Owner's manual and warranty information in writing.
*¶	2.	Spark plug wrench.
*¶	3.	Wrench to loosen nuts on sprocket cover.
*¶	4.	Screwdriver to fit chain-tensioning screw.
*	5.	Other special tools peculiar to your saw or recommended by the manufacturer. (Check owner's manual.)
*	6.	Grease gun and grease if required for roller nose.
?	7.	Chain-sharpening device or file holder.
*	8.	Round file to fit your chain (not tapered).
*	9.	Depth gauge or jointer.
	10.	Flat safety edge or triangular file for depth gauges.
?	11.	Chain repair kit (extra cutters, drive links, rivets, etc.).
	12.	Chain repair tool.
	13.	Extra chain.
?	14.	Spare air filter.
	15.	Plastic wedges for felling and bucking.
?	16.	Chain guard or chain saw carrying case.
	17.	Bar-and-chain lubricant.
	18.	Small funnel for bar lubricant.
	19.	Clean SAE 10-weight oil for chain bath.
	20.	Two-cycle engine oil.
	21.	Regular-grade leaded gasoline.
	22.	Safe gas can with filter nozzle.
	23.	Fuel funnel with screen filter.

24.   Kerosene or commercial cleaner for saw parts and body.
25.   Small tub or flat dish or pan for soaking chain.
26.   Small cleaning brush or old toothbrush.
27.   Safety gear: hard hat; ear-and-eye protection; good, well-fitting leather gloves; safety shoes for tough work.

----

*   You may expect these items to be supplied with your new saw.

¶   Most manufacturers supply a combination tool designed to perform all these functions. You may want to replace it with separate, higher-quality tools, but the combination can come in handy if you tromp off into the woods, away from your toolbox.

?   The question mark is used advisedly. You might be able to convince the salesman to "throw in" any of these items, especially with an expensive saw or a new "last year's" model.

Additional Notes

Needs for, details regarding, and proper uses of the above tools, fuels, and accessories are covered in other chapters, but a few essential hints now may save you some time and trouble. (Numbers refer to the previous list.)

1. If it doesn't have a warranty, it isn't a new saw.

5. Some manufacturers supply a crankshaft locking screw, or a special wrench for unlocking the clutch shoes or pulling the clutch. Check the owner's manual; there should be a list of included tools at the end of the manual. Check them off; they sometimes get lost in the store or repair shop.

6. Ask your salesman and check your owner's manual. If you've decided on a saw with a roller nose, you probably already know that it needs grease daily, when it's used daily.

7. Even if you receive a file guide with your saw, Parp advises that you further invest in a clamp-on-type sharpener such as the Granberg "File-n-Joint." These sharpeners are hard to find, so you may want to order one through your dealer or direct from Granberg or Zip Penn (addresses are in the Appendix). Many old woodspersons will snort at this advice, but they will also go on, year after year, getting less than maximum service from their cutting chains and saws. And it takes a lot of practice to be able to hand-sharpen as well as clamp-ons do. Get started with good habits, habits as modern as your new saw. You'll still have plenty of opportunity to field-sharpen or touch up your chain by hand, and then you

can correct any mistakes with your clamp-on sharpener before they get out of hand.

8., 9. If these items don't come with your saw, check your owner's manual for the manufacturer's recommendations.

12. For repairing chains and replacing rivets, Parp recommends Granberg's "Break-n-Mend," available from Granberg/Firmont Inc. or Zip Penn.

13. Get two chains and rotate them frequently to equalize wear on the sprocket and chain parts. Besides, everyone except the most casual user should have an extra chain on hand when cutting. It can save a lot of time.

17. Don't take that old mechanic's advice and use worn-out automobile crankcase oil as a bar-and-chain lubricant in your new chain saw. Oil wears out—it loses its slickness—and your bar and chain need maximum lubrication. The grime and grit in old crankcase oil will ruin your saw quickly, no matter what the old-timers say. Use good-quality bar-and-chain oil.

18. Any good two-cycle engine oil will do, provided it matches the requirements stated in your owner's manual. NOTE: Outboard motor oil is usually SAE 40. Check your manual.

20. Keep fuel in well-marked containers. One-gallon cans will do for casual and minisaw users and five-gallon cans for frequent users (or for anyone at the start of a heavy season). NOTE: Gasoline goes stale, especially when mixed with two-cycle engine oil.

27. Listen to ol' Parp. He wants you to have lots of fun with your new saw and many pleasant evenings in front of the fireplace instead of bad hours in the office of some sawbones, getting your fingers or scalp repaired. And if you're going to cut trees, you've got to be able to see them. At least wear a hard hat, eye protection, and snug-fitting leather gloves.

BE SURE TO GET THE BOOK

The importance of the owner's manual can't be overstated. If you buy a new chain saw, get the book. If the dealer doesn't have the book, don't close the deal until he does. It may take a long time; even though it "only takes two weeks," it may, in fact, take forever. Most saw manufacturers are good about supplying owner's manuals, *if* they have them, and *if* you can get the manufacturer's correct, up-to-date address. That is often amazingly difficult. One more thing: If you plan to keep your saw for a long time, take steps now to obtain the expensive and hard-to-get shop or technical manual from the manufacturer or distributor.

ANOTHER WORD ABOUT SAFETY

Again, read your owner's manual before you start your saw. And you should read the first part of this book, through Chapter 6, before you actually cut any wood. If you can't wait, get a large log—the bigger the safer—and practice cutting only one-third of the way through with the entire log well supported, preferably by the ground. Don't hit the ground with your saw. Stand uphill from the log. Good luck, have fun, and cut those utility bills—not yourself.

TYPES OF GASOLINE CHAIN SAWS

	Minisaws	Lightweight	Medium-Duty	Production
Dry weight	6–9 lbs.	9–13.5 lbs.	12.5–20 lbs.	18–28+ lbs.
Displacement	2–2.5 cu. in.	2.5–3.7 cu. in.	3.5–4.8 cu. in.	4.5–8.5 cu. in.
Fuel capacity	.7–.85 pints	.85–1.1 pints	1.2–2.0 pints	2.0–2.6+ pints
Bar lengths	8"–14", av. 12"	14"–18", av. 16"	15"–20", av. 18"	16"–60", av. 21"
Chain types & sizes	1/4" pitch or 3/8" pitch, low profile	3/8" pitch, standard	3/8" or .404" pitch, standard	.404" or 1/2" pitch, standard
Chain-oil capacity	.30–.50 pts.	.55–.65 pts.	.65–1.0 pts.	1.1+ pts.
Chain-brake system	uncommon	common	common option	some models
Automatic chain-oil system	common	common	common	some models
Manual chain-oil control/override	uncommon	uncommon	common w/automatic	common w/automatic; manual standard
Bumper spike	inadequate	adequate	good	professional
Vibration control	uncommon	some models	common	common
Heated handles	uncommon	some models	common	common
Hedge trimmer	uncommon	common	some models	no
Brush cutter	no	some models	common	some models
Bow bar	no	no	common	common
Cutoff attachment	no	no	common	some models
Earth auger	no	no	some models	common
Ice/wood drill	no	no	some models	some models
Automatic sharpening	no	too common	some models	no

CHAPTER 3 ACCESSORIES AND FEATURES

DESIGN

At first glance, most modern gasoline chain saws appear to be very much alike. It is interesting that they all share the same basic design. The modern chain saw demonstrates the modern idea of good design: Form follows function.

It was clear to the pioneers of the early chain saw that loggers needed a portable saw they could carry into the woods and work with all day. A few of the early developers of the chain saw could see that the possibilities were not limited to felling trees. Some inventors, especially Andreas Stihl, had an early vision of the ultimate development of the chain saw, and they could foresee a portable saw that would be light enough for one-person handling and capable of cutting at any angle—in other words, a saw that could be used for bucking and limbing, as well as for felling. That early vision of the chain saw resulted in its present form.

When you consider buying a chain saw, used or new, you can determine some important matters on the basis of appearance. You can often spot a flimsy chain saw just by the way it looks. If the finish is chipped, you know that the paint won't prevent corrosion. If there are sharp cor-

Homelite Super 2 with Safe-T-Tip

ners or exposed metal parts, they will catch on clothing and brush and will be a safety hazard. If the power head is large, awkward, or crude, you know that particular manufacturer has failed to progress from the chain saw designs of 1948. All of these considerations bear directly on the saw's balance and ability to perform. When you're limbing a fallen tree, you don't want a chain saw that hangs up in the work.

Finally, design reflects the manufacturer's concern and progress. A good chain saw is ergonomically designed. Working in the woods, you appreciate that a designer of chain saws must carefully consider the work that the *user* is to do. Chain saw design has come a long way since 1948, and it has come that far only because its inventors and designers have understood the work that has to be done by a chain saw. A chain saw's design is the first indication of its quality.

ANTIVIBRATION SYSTEMS

Maybe you think that tools should be kept as trim and light as possible, free of any unnecessary gadgetry or extra weight. Parp sympathizes with this attitude and likes the clean feel of a precision tool, one that incorporates nothing unrelated to the function of the thing. Good sense tells us that good design is exactly that.

But chain saws are not simple hand tools. They are complex and potentially dangerous machines that have hazardous side effects that are not immediately apparent.

TVD is an example. (If you're a logger, you might know it as "white fingers.") TVD, or traumatic vasospastic disease, is a common and extremely uncomfortable problem for many loggers. It's caused by operating a vibrating tool for long hours. If an operator already has trouble with TVD, any work with a chain saw not equipped with an antivibration system will aggravate the problem beyond endurance. Besides being sheer torture, TVD can put the strongest logger on unemployment. (Some recent medical theories indicate that TVD and long periods of operating a vibrating tool may be related to the onset of early arthritis.)

The typical healthy chain saw owner who uses a saw occasionally doesn't have to worry about TVD. But you do have to worry about comfort and the safe efficiency that comfort promotes. For several years, many chain saw manufacturers have incorporated special designs to reduce the vibrating of the engine and to prevent vibrations from reaching the operator's hands. In general, this is accomplished by cushioning the handles with rubber blocks. There are other, more complex systems, but the rubber mounting blocks work as well as anything.

Antivibration systems do add some weight to chain saws, and the rubber blocks do need to be cleaned often and replaced occasionally. It's well worth the trouble. Even if you don't have TVD, the vibration of an undamped saw will wear you out very quickly. Parp says that if you're buying anything larger than a minisaw, be sure it has an antivibration system.

HEATED HANDLES

Even with good gloves, the cold steel of unheated chain saw handles can be uncomfortable in the winter. The rest of your body may be over-heated from exertion, but those handles can freeze to your gloves and dangerously sap the warmth from your hands, clear to the bone.

And that brings up TVD again. If a vibrating tool is held by hands that are cold or wet, TVD is more likely to occur. And if the operator already has TVD, cold hands will aggravate it quickly, even with a machine equipped with an antivibration system.

If you use your chain saw less than full-time, you won't need heated handles. But Parp says good, rubber-insulated handles are a must for everyone. If you're going to be cutting a lot of wood all day in the winter, heated handles will be a welcome accessory. They should probably not be a deciding factor in your choice of a chain saw, but if they're an option on the saw you want, and if you live or work in a cold area, get the heated handles.

There are two common heating systems for chain saw handles. The first and oldest is exhaust heating. In this system, exhaust from the saw's engine is channeled through passageways in the handles. This can cause problems. The exhaust leaves carbon deposits in the tubing of the handles and also makes the handles oily and sooty after a while. When the carbon deposits become extreme, the engine's exhaust system is impaired. This heating system is also very difficult to regulate.

The other method is a modern electrical heating system with heat rods or coils permanently installed in the handles. The current is usually supplied by a separate generator that's an integral part of the ignition. You can usually turn such heating systems on and off.

Unfortunately, heated handles are still not available on most chain saws built for the consumer market.

AUTOMATIC OILING

It used to be true that no logger would buy a chain saw with an automatic oiling system. Now, however, few loggers would buy a saw *without* one—although they may also demand a manual override to provide extra lubrication for tough cutting. Automatic oiling systems have become much more durable and dependable in recent years, and the development of adjustable automatic oiling systems has done a lot to overcome professional prejudice against them. On any saw above the minisaw class, the automatic oiler should be adjustable for different kinds of cutting under different conditions. If you buy a chain saw with an adjustable automatic oiling system, you should study your owner's manual before changing the preliminary setting. Some of these adjustments are ridiculously delicate and it's possible to damage some automatic oilers with an incorrect adjustment or by forcing the adjustment. Also, take care that your saw doesn't run out of chain oil before it runs out of gas. If it does, you could burn your chain before you notice. If you discover this happening, start out with a full oil supply, but with less than a full tank of gas—or adjust the oiler accordingly.

Automatic oiling systems are directly or indirectly connected to the crankshaft of the engine. Sometimes the connection is a worm gear and sometimes it's an eccentric or cam—a sort of lopsided circular lobe attached off-center to the crankshaft. As engine speed increases, the worm gear or eccentric automatically operates the oil pump and increases the amount of oil delivered to the chain. On some saws, notably the European makes, these systems are easy to replace or repair. On other saws, repair is almost impossible.

Parp still prefers to have that manual override when the going gets rough, but an automatic oiling system sure saves a lot of thumb work. It also saves chain.

ANTIKICKBACK DEVICES

Parp happens to believe that no industry works as hard to minimize or eliminate hazards as the chain saw industry. Completely on their own, with no governmental or private pressure, chain saw manufacturers began safety research early in the history of chain saw development. It would have been easier to have said that the chain saw is an inherently dangerous machine and let it go at that.

But long before Detroit ever heard of Ralph Nader, Andreas Stihl was already dreaming of ways to make a safer chain saw, a lightweight machine that would be safe enough for the average backyard woodsperson. And Stihl wasn't the only one. Very significant safety innovations have been achieved by Jonsered, Homelite, McCulloch, and Husqvarna.

All together, these companies have introduced or improved a very impressive array of mechanical and design features intended to minimize the hazards of cutting wood. Operating a chain saw today, in Parp's opinion, is no more dangerous than operating an ax, and considerably less dangerous than driving one of those Detroit monsters.

Homelite, for example, offers a beautifully simple device called the Safe-T-Tip. This innovation made everybody else wonder why they didn't think of it first. It's an extremely effective device that really does eliminate kickback—when it's properly installed.

Kickback happens when the chain hangs up as it speeds around and down the upper nose of the bar. The chain catches in the wood and the whole saw then makes an upward arc, back toward the operator.

When you're running a chain saw, engine torque is transferred to the chain. This is the turning energy that cuts the wood. If the chain hits a solid object unintentionally, or if the chain takes too large a cut, it stops for an instant. The engine torque is then transferred to the guide bar and the chain saw, as a rotation around the center of mass. Since this mass includes you, it can make a mess out of *your* mass. That's what this kickback fuss is all about.

Safe-T-Tip installation

Homelite's Safe-T-Tip is a one-piece steel guard that fastens to the nose of the bar and prevents the chain from hitting anything as it passes the nose. It is an effective device and is especially useful when you're cutting single logs on your woodpile. It can easily be removed when you need to use the full length of the bar. Shut off the engine first. The Safe-T-Tip does *not* prevent, however, the push or pull that occurs when the chain catches at the center of the bottom or the top of the bar.

The most common kickback safety devices actually do not prevent kickback. For several years, most manufacturers have offered optional brake systems for most chain saw models. These brake systems help prevent *injury* from kickback by stopping either the chain or the engine or both within a split second after kickback occurs.

The very dangerous kickback zone

Contact with solid object in the kickback zone

Most dangerous kickback zone

Upper 90° quadrant of guide bar tip

These brake systems typically consist of a hand guard or lever mounted immediately in front of the front handle. The lever is connected to a device—usually a steel band or a brake block—that contacts or surrounds the clutch. When kickback occurs, the operator's left hand bumps the lever. The lever then activates the brake and instantly stops the chain.

Some brake systems stop both the engine and the chain. In that case, the lever must be reset before the engine can be started again. Other systems stop only the chain.

Some engineers say that a system that stops both the engine and the chain is safest. However, a brake system that stops only the chain may be used as a convenience. This system allows the operator to lock the chain and move about more or less safely with the saw while the engine is still running. (Once in a while, technology makes a safety rule obsolete, but Parp is still cautious.)

Chain brake in action

HAND PROTECTION

Chain breakage is not a common experience for the occasional chain saw user, especially if good chain-sharpening and maintenance procedures are practiced. But when a chain does break, it breaks in use, while speeding around the guide bar. The broken ends can then snap toward the operator, possibly causing injury to the hands.

Most of today's chain saws include a left (or front) hand guard as standard equipment. Often, this handle is also the chain-brake lever. A broken chain can snap back to reach the operator's left hand at the front handle, but a front hand guard will prevent this.

A broken chain is more likely to injure the operator's right hand because the chain is already moving down and back when it breaks. Most saws incorporate a chain-catcher pin that prevents the end of the bottom half of a broken chain from reaching the operator's body.

But even with a chain-catcher pin to stop the chain from reaching the body, the end of the chain can still snap across the operator's right hand. Only a right (or rear) hand guard will absolutely prevent this. And a right hand guard is doubly useful during limbing operations.

Parp urges the combination of an antikickback device such as a chain brake, together with a chain-catcher pin and front and rear hand guards for maximum protection.

Left hand guard; in some models this is also a chain-brake lever in case the left hand slips off during kickback.

Right hand guard; in case the chain may still reach the right hand

Chain-catcher pin

If the chain should break, it wraps itself around the catcher pin and cannot reach the operator.

Safety features

The Jonsereds 520 SP showing front and rear handguards

TRIGGER INTERLOCK

Another good safety feature that has become common is the trigger interlock system. A trigger interlock is a safety catch that theoretically makes it impossible to rev the engine speed unintentionally above idle, to cutting speed.

Most trigger interlocks consist of a latch or locking lever mounted on the top of the rear handle, above the trigger. When the latch is locked, the trigger cannot be moved. To move the trigger, you have to squeeze the latch at the same time. Theoretically, this makes it possible for the operator to carry an idling chain saw without fear that a branch or something will catch the trigger and accelerate the engine. It also makes it safer to adjust the carburetor while the engine is running.

Parp certainly recommends selecting a saw with a trigger interlock safety system, but he also cautions that it will not always prevent the chain from moving accidentally. Two-cycle engines are given to erratic behavior, especially when they get old. Your saw may appear to be idling smoothly and perfectly, with the chain absolutely still, when the engine suddenly revs, causing the chain to jump. If the chain happens to be resting against your leg or side, it will cut. And it can cut incredibly deep, incredibly fast, with one short burst of the engine.

Even with a trigger interlock system and a chain brake, Parp says don't walk with a running chain saw.

ELECTRONIC IGNITION

These days, most high-quality chain saws are available with optional electronic ignitions.

Until the development of the electronic ignition, all hand-start chain saws incorporated the standard breaker point ignition. This kind of ignition needs occasional service, as part of a periodic tune-up. To service a standard ignition you replace the points and condenser. When the points or the breaker plate are moved or altered, the timing of the spark is also altered and must be readjusted. Furthermore, in order to replace the breaker points and condenser, you must open the assembly that contains them. Not only is this assembly susceptible to dirt and contamina-

A conventional (breaker point) ignition system

tion when it's open, it's also susceptible to dirt at all other times simply because it *can* be opened. And there is always a lot of dirt around a working chain saw.

The electronic or breakerless ignition is a one-piece unit with no moving parts. You never need to do anything inside, so the unit can be permanently sealed against dirt, moisture, and temperature changes. Also, the timing of the spark is electronically controlled, permanently. All of this represents a great improvement in chain saw design, especially for the occasional user who would rather not do any tune-ups.

Electronic ignition should not be confused with electric start. A few years ago, a number of leading chain saw manufacturers experimented with electric starting systems intended to replace the standard, hand-crank rope-pull starters. It didn't work.

Electronic ignitions do work, and in most cases they work very well. They are more expensive to replace when they do fail, but the odds are good. On the other hand, if you prefer to do all your own mechanical work, choose a standard ignition.

Electronic (breakerless) ignition

DECOMPRESSION VALVE

A decompression valve, or compression release, is a convenience feature that chiefly appears on large-displacement chain saws.

It allows the operator to open a valve in the engine to release some pressure during cranking. If an engine has a displacement of five cubic inches or so, it can be hard to pull the starter rope against the pressure that builds up in the combustion chamber. If the saw includes a compression release, you just push a button that stays in until the engine fires. When the saw is running, you pull the button out to allow full compression—or you pull and then you push. Some compression releases are automatic and release when the throttle trigger is squeezed.

REPLACEABLE SPROCKET NOSE

One of the most consistent, troublesome, annoying, and expensive problems for professional loggers is the damaged guide bar. Guide bars must be made of a steel that can withstand the heat of chain friction, as well as the heat that builds up in the log being cut. But any steel that can stand heat is a hard steel and is therefore susceptible to chipping and breaking.

Most guide bar breaks occur at the nose of the bar. A few years ago, the Windsor Machine Company, a large manufacturer of guide bars, decided to tackle this problem. They developed a guide bar with a replaceable sprocket nose. When a break occurs at the nose of the bar, only

Replaceable sprocket-nose guide bar

that part is replaced—at considerably less expense than an entire bar. The sprocket itself, enclosed in the replaceable nose, also lengthens chain and bar life by accurately guiding the chain around the nose of the bar. This increases the speed and efficiency of the saw, and decreases the heat buildup in the bar and chain. It also decreases the drag on the engine and on the bar and provides better all-around performance.

Several companies now produce replaceable sprocket-nose bars, and Parp suggests that they are a good investment if you use a bar 16" or longer, especially if you do a lot of cutting in heavy timber or under rough conditions.

AUTOMATIC SHARPENING

Most of the features and accessories mentioned in this chapter are items that Parp would want in a new saw of his own. But automatic sharpening?

Parp has no serious objection to letting machines do his hard work— if they are able. But a built-in automatic sharpening system adds weight right where you don't need it. It also adds another gadget that can go wrong—easily, according to the expert repair people.

Futhermore, an automatic sharpening device doesn't begin to replace hand sharpening. At best, it saves a few seconds of on-the-job touching up. Is that worth even an extra ounce? Even the manufacturers of these things say you shouldn't use them very many times before you sharpen the chain correctly, with a file and file guide. And if the chain is not adjusted to the correct tension, the system will actually dull the chain.

Parp says don't go for this one. Buy a high-quality saw with no extra weight and carry a good clamp-on file guide so you can control the sharpening for the wood you cut and the age of your chain. You'll come to know your saw better, and to understand why so few professionals would even *borrow* a saw with an automatic sharpening device. It isn't worth its weight.

CHAIN GUARD, CARRYING CASE, AND TOOL KIT

Any new chain saw should come with a good tool kit that includes a combination wrench for the bar nuts, spark plug, and chain-tensioning screw. Ideally, the tool kit should also include a device for locking the crankshaft when you change the sprocket, and a clutch wrench. If the saw has a sprocket nose or roller nose, the manufacturer should supply a special grease gun designed to meet the daily lubrication requirements. The tool kit should certainly include a file guide and depth gauge, files, a chain repair kit, and an extra air filter. And the owner's manual.

Now it helps a lot, says Parp, if you have a carrying case with room enough for all this stuff, plus the extra items you can't ask a chain saw manufacturer to supply. Keeping it all together, and portable, is far better than having separate toolboxes or an overflowing glove compartment. A large carrying case is a good investment, especially if you can also use it to carry all your accessories, replacement parts, and field service tools. For long-term storage, nothing beats a case designed especially for your saw.

In addition, a protective chain cover will make your saw safer to carry or leave around without the case. A chain guard slips over the chain itself and leaves the rest of the saw visible for service and cleaning. A combination carrying case and chain guard is the best idea—but, so far, only one manufacturer, McCulloch, has produced such a thing. It's easy, however, to buy the two items separately and use them together. Even with a good storage case, you should also have a chain guard. They're very inexpensive. If your dealer doesn't sell them, you can mail-order one from Zip Penn or Bailey's.

MANUFACTURING STANDARDS

Obviously, the most important of the features and accessories mentioned in this chapter are those that make working with a chain saw safer. In Sweden, a study of chain saw injuries among professional loggers showed that saw-related injuries decreased remarkably when the significant safety features appeared on most chain saws.

But the safety of a chain saw doesn't depend entirely on the safety devices it includes. Good balance, in Parp's opinion, is a significant safety consideration. If a saw is lightweight, well-balanced, and easy to operate, you will get a lot less fatigued and frustrated while you're working. A good weight-to-power ratio and good balance are qualities found only in the best chain saws. Again, good design is an important indication of these qualities. Parp suggests that if you look for high standards of manufacturing quality in chain saws, you'll find the saws that are the safest and easiest to handle.

CHAPTER 4

HOW TO BUY A USED CHAIN SAW

SHOULD YOU BUY A USED CHAIN SAW?

If you ask a logger for advice on buying a used chain saw, chances are he'll tell you not to do it—unless *he* happens to have one for sale. Nearly all seasoned professionals say the same thing: Never buy a used chain saw. And in the world of the professional, that's excellent advice.

When a logger discards a chain saw, it is indeed used. It's been used at least eight hours a day, at least five days a week for an average of 18 months or more. Maybe a tree has fallen on it, it's been dropped in a lake, an apprentice has burned the bar, or it's just been run to death. And, of course, all the "professional" mistakes have seriously contributed to the saw's demise. Used crankcase oil has been reclaimed to lubricate the bar and chain. It's been stored in a semidry state, or with its gas tank full of stale fuel. It has been hand-sharpened too often by an over-confident expert. Obviously, the professional advice to avoid used chain saws is good advice, considering the treatment most saws receive from most professionals.

But few used chain saws are discarded refugees from a logging camp. Those saws are usually junked or tossed in a spare-parts can, never to be touched again.

Most of the used chain saws that you're likely to run across were traded in on newer models, or on an electric fireplace. Most used chain saws are found along with new saws in dealer showrooms, where they've been sharpened, thoroughly cleaned, and possibly even reconditioned and are ready for many hours of average use.

Other serviceable saws can be found at farm or estate auctions, garage sales, and pawn shops, or through the want ads. Often, these saws were hardly used at all, and the original owner didn't have time to do any serious damage. But damage can occur very quickly, with very little use, and you will have to learn how to identify saws that have been improperly used, even if it was for only an hour or so. We'll cover the most important symptoms later in this chapter.

As it happens, Parp has considerable experience with used chain saws and, as a result, tends to agree with the professional advice against them. But not everyone is in a position to buy a new chain saw, and all the advice in the world won't change that. There are beginning farmers who need to clear brush and young homesteaders who need firewood, and there are others who, feeling the energy crunch, want to supplement their fuel usage with a little stove wood. Many of these people simply can't spend the bundle required to buy a really dependable new chain saw in the size and class they require.

A used chain saw that works can make life easier *now*, but the dim prospect of a savings account large enough for a new chain saw will do nothing to keep you warm meanwhile.

So how do you buy a used chain saw?

DETERMINE YOUR NEEDS

If you didn't read Chapter 2, "How to Buy a New Chain Saw," you might do so now. It will give you a good idea of the types and sizes of saws available and of their best uses.

In any case, you've decided to look for a used chain saw . . . and that's a considerably different and more complicated matter than buying a new saw.

At this point, Parp is busting me in the ribs to caution you against used *electric* chain saws. Since new electric chain saws can be so much less expensive than gasoline models, and since electric saws are fatally damaged so easily, let's take Parp's advice and avoid them altogether. We'll confine our discussion to used gasoline-engine chain saws.

Do you need a used chain saw in order to fell standing dead trees, then to cut the trees into logs to load into your pickup, and then to cut them at home to fit your stoves? Are you a homesteader or something like one?

If you heat and cook with wood a great deal, you will use your saw a great deal. You will at the very least use it solidly for a month in the summer and for at least one day a week through the rest of the year. You will certainly need a full-size saw with an engine displacement of 3.5 to 4 cubic inches or more. And you will need a saw that has a fuel capacity of more than one pint so that you won't have to refuel twice for each pickup full of wood. You will also want a bar 16" or 20" long.

No matter how much or how little you expect to use your chain saw, you must first consider the wood you'll be cutting. The best advice is to get the smallest and lightest saw suitable to the work you'll encounter most. But that's not very complete or satisfactory advice. How can you know how small a saw can be and still be acceptable? On the other hand, you won't need or want a bar as large as the diameter of the largest tree around, since you probably won't be felling that tree anyway. You want a bar long enough, and an engine strong enough, to conveniently cut most of the logs you'll be handling. Remember that a chain saw will cut a tree or log *twice* the size of its bar. Also remember that as you're working on your woodpile, cutting long logs into short pieces for chopping, your work will be doubled if your bar isn't long enough to cut most of the logs in a single pass.

You're shopping for a used chain saw, so you're not likely to have as much choice as a shopper for a new saw would have—all the more reason why you should determine your needs within general guidelines *before* you begin to shop. Otherwise, you could end up with a real bargain on a fine, well-kept saw that's all wrong for the work you need to do. There are some really surprising used saw bargains, and they can be hard to resist if you haven't determined your needs first. (See Chapter 2 for more tips on deciding what kind of saw you need.)

HOW MUCH SHOULD YOU PAY?

The gasoline chain saw is still a relatively new consumer item, and the modern chain saw incorporates many recent technical advances. This means, for one thing, that used chain saw prices are still arbitrary, unpredictable, and unstable. The generally accepted rule is that any used power tool in good condition is priced at about 50 percent or 60 percent of its original retail value.

In various parts of the country, Parp has run across one particular brand of used saw, a model of his choice, at prices ranging from $85 to $225. The original retail price of the saw was $411.50. Each saw was of the same model year and in reasonably good condition.

Bear in mind that prices and values of used chain saws are definitely affected by season. Fall is certainly the worst time to buy a used chain saw. That's when the prices are highest, obviously. That's also when the typical person will discover that the saw that was stored in the garage since the end of the previous wood-cutting season is full of varnish. Lots of other people will decide for other reasons that last year's saw isn't good enough for this year. They'll all trade them in. The cheap ones and the best ones go first, but they're all overpriced. The saws that are left until spring or that are not traded in until spring will cost a lot less than they would have in the fall. And many of the saws that are passed up in the fall will be good medium-duty saws, ignored by most choppers because of their weight, but well maintained by the previous, probably serious, owners.

Weight is another important consideration that affects the price of a used chain saw. Almost universally, a lighter chain saw retains more of its original value than does a heavier one. There are several reasons for this. Chiefly, most people simply prefer the lighter, easier-to-use saws. Also, most dealers automatically assume that a heavier saw has seen harder use than has a lighter saw. Very often this is true, and you should test and examine any large used saw before you buy it. But it's also often true that larger saws were owned previously by more serious (though not professional) woodspersons, or at least by people who are experienced with power tools. Some of these people do maintain their equipment well, and most of them know enough to avoid the worst and most obvious mistakes.

If you've decided that you need a used chain saw in the medium-duty class, and if you shop for it in late spring or early summer, chances are you'll get a better-than-average deal. Otherwise, the best used saws cost the most. That's because the saws that are well maintained are owned by people who realize their value. Such saws usually won't come cheap, especially in autumn.

To review briefly, we've seen that minisaws and lightweights cost more, comparatively, than do medium-duty or production saws. On the other hand, used medium-duty saws in good condition are often the best deals because they're somewhat less popular. Parp again urges caution regarding used production saws. And avoid older chain saws—those huge monsters with the 15- or 30-pound bodies and long, wide bars. The best bargains cost the most, and the more the saw weighs, the less it's worth. Of course, there's the occasional steal . . .

Chain saws are designed for one specific purpose: cutting trees. And if that isn't scary enough, there's the whole business of a portable gasoline engine that you're supposed to hold between your hands while it sputters and coughs. They're not very delicate tools, and many people, rather than appreciating the chain saw as a really admirable design achievement, have a different and considerably more sensible reaction. They're scared to death of the things, whether they're running them or somebody else is.

Once in a while, one of these people somehow ends up with a new chain saw. Often the saw never sees use at all. Parp has a friend who found one at a garage sale. It was in the original package with the bar and chain still disassembled. This kind of situation shows all the signs of a real steal.

So the first thing you do in shopping for a used chain saw is to tell all your most unlikely friends about your interest. Mention it to the relatives, also, and to the mailman. And put notes on the bulletin boards in the laundromat, grocery store, drugstore, and hardware store. All of your sane friends will pretend they didn't notice.

SOURCES

NEW SAW DEALERS

As noted before, most used chain saws are trade-ins and so will be found in dealer showrooms. Most dealers at least clean and sharpen a used saw before offering it for sale, and if you find in a dealer's showroom a used saw that is dirty and has a dull chain, you should try another dealer. Dealers are usually well-informed on the true market value of a used saw, so you may expect to find that the dealer's prices are not too far off, one way or the other. Very few dealers will ask $200 for a saw worth only $100, and a dealer's showroom is no place to expect a real steal, though it does happen. A good bargain is common.

If you do shop in dealers' showrooms, you might keep in mind that if a customer is satisfied with a particular saw, he or she is more likely to trade it in on another from the same manufacturer. Obviously, there are exceptions, and reasons other than lack of satisfaction cause people to switch brands. It's still a good rule, though.

There are several real advantages to buying a used chain saw from a dealer. Again, such a dealer is likely to be very knowledgeable about saws in general. A dealer is also likely to be a chain saw mechanic or to have one in the shop. It's a great help to be able to take a limping chain saw to the person you bought it from and pick it up later that day or in just a day or two. They know the saw when you bring it in, especially if they sell the same saw brand-new. The dealer or the mechanic is also familiar with repair methods for that particular saw and will have the most commonly required parts in stock. Surprisingly, specialized chain saw dealers are established in almost all areas, including many areas where there have been no forests for decades.

If there is no specialized chain saw dealer in your area, the next best bet is the local hardware store that sells chain saws, either from stock or on special order. Most hardware stores that deal in new saws also accept trade-ins. And most hardware dealers that sell chain saws also carry cutting chains, chain-sharpening tools, two-cycle engine oil, and other parts, tools, and accessories, in stock or by order.

HARDLY USED HOMEOWNER TYPES

Your local newspaper publishes ads for estate auctions, farm auctions, neighborhood sales, and garage sales. These are the most likely places to buy hardly used chain saws, especially minisaws, at reasonable prices.

Many people who buy or are given chain saws have very little or even no use for them. In recent years, minisaws and lightweight saws have become popular Christmas presents and retirement gifts. Nearly 20 percent of the chain saws sold every year are purchased as gifts. An amazing number of these saws are never used at all, and some have never even had fuel in their tanks. These are the saws to watch for.

You can spot them immediately at garage sales. If the chain is sharp and the bar is clean and new-looking, you can bet on the saw being as good as new. If there are the slightest scratches, or if the chain has been sharpened, you can judge how much it has been used by examining the chain, and by employing the various little tests that we'll cover soon. Parp has turned up some amazing values at garage sales, including one $450 professional medium-duty saw in new condition, with all new accessories, a case, and an owner's manual, for $110. Don't expect to find such buys very often, especially as more people become aware of the value of chain saws as tools. And it takes only one serious mistake to ruin a new chain saw. If the owner used it only once but failed to use the proper fuel or two-cycle engine oil, the saw may appear to be in excellent condition but may be full of varnish. Don't buy a used saw without starting it.

RENTAL SHOPS

Rental shops, those large stores that offer everything from sickroom equipment to backhoes, usually offer chain saws as well. These shops generally operate under one of two opposing philosophies.

One rental philosophy assumes that people are unintelligent and destructive. This kind of shop carries the cheapest equipment available, figuring that it won't last anyway. Consequently, their chain saws aren't much good to start with and are no good at all after a few customers have used them. This kind of shop will also do only minimal maintenance and service to their equipment. Chain saws require good care in order to go on working. You should be able to identify these shops by the merchandise they have on hand.

The other kind of rental shop buys the best equipment it can find and then maintains it with adequate to excellent care and service. When a saw comes back, it is cleaned, sharpened, tuned if necessary, and tested before it goes back out. This kind of shop tries not to let equipment turn into junk. Accordingly, they will regularly offer chain saws for sale at reasonable prices based on estimated hours of use. These shops can be excellent sources for good, dependable used chain saws.

Rental shops price used chain saws primarily according to age and weight. Weight is an especially significant factor here. In a rental shop, large medium-duty saws with few hours of service will frequently sell for as little as a used minisaw. Rental shop minisaws, on the other hand, are often sold at 75 percent of the original retail value. Shop around and be careful. Rental shops don't have a fast turnover in used equipment for sale, so a saw that you're considering may well sit there for several weeks, giving you plenty of time to be sure it's what you want.

Incidentally, a few rental shops surveyed stated that they don't sell their equipment at all. They wait until it's just about gone. When a saw fails, they give it to the last customer who rents it.

LOCAL GOVERNMENT AND BUSINESSES

Many government agencies use chain saws. County road crews use chain saws for clearing new roads or for removing fallen trees. Chain saws are used for rescue work and construction, for building and clearing trails, and for maintaining forests, parks, and agricultural projects. Some colleges have chain saws in storage rooms, and they occasionally turn up in surplus sales. Utility companies and other quasi-governmental organizations use chain saws extensively. All of these sources periodically hold public auctions at which one may buy a used chain saw for very little money. These auctions are always well advertised, and the public usually has a chance to examine, but not to operate, the equipment to be sold. Bidding is subsequently held on a number basis, and you just take your chances.

Private businesses or professionals using chain saws as a main tool nearly always have one for sale. Tree surgeons and nursery operators are notable as sources for used minisaws or lightweights. Obviously, one must be careful here, but there are tree surgeons who maintain their saws at peak performance and sell them all at the end of each season as a matter of policy. If you don't have much capital and you want a lightweight professional-quality saw, this can be an excellent source.

On the other hand, many tree surgeons are sloppy about the maintenance of their saws. Even that can work to your advantage. Parp tells of some professionals who don't clean spark plugs. When their saws fail, they sell them or drop them in a barrel in the back of the shop. You can gamble on a junker like that and sometimes do very well.

And then there's the real professional castoff, a logger's used saw. Many loggers use medium-duty saws, so we're not necessarily talking about huge 30-pound saws with 40" bars. The Stihl 045 is a very popular logging saw, and it's even on the light side of the medium-duty class. The Homelite 650 and Husqvarna 380 are two other examples. You'll be able to tell if the saw is a little too tired for professional use but just fine for your woodpile.

GETTING THE MOST FOR YOUR MONEY

When you consider buying a used chain saw, look first at the type and size. Don't hustle yourself into something you don't need just because it's available. Determine what you need first, as discussed earlier in this chapter, and don't buy anything that doesn't conform to your conclusions.

Next, look at the general condition of the saw. If it obviously hasn't been kept clean, you can stop right there. A chain saw that's been run while dirty is likely to have other, much more serious problems. For one thing, a thick coat of dirt and grease will cause the saw to overheat.

If the saw is clean and appears to have been well cared for, look more closely for signs of improper use or poor maintenance. Examine the chain, bar, and sprocket. If the chain's cutters are dull or if they have not been filed uniformly, if the bar is bent or burned, or if the sprocket is badly worn, you can bet the owner hasn't taken good care of the saw, and you don't want it (except maybe for parts). Any single problem, like a bent bar, might be easily remedied, but the point is that you're looking for signs of bad maintenance or improper use. If you find them, the chances are that the saw is ruined.

There are other little things to look at before you even start the engine. First, look carefully for stripped or missing bolts or nuts. If any bolts or nuts are missing, try to determine if it's because of stripped threads. If not, replace them and be sure they stay put while the saw is in operation. If threads are stripped, consider whether or not you will be able to correct the problem yourself or if you can afford to have a mechanic do it for you. If you can't correct the problem one way or the other, look for another saw.

Sometimes the screw that adjusts the tension for the chain becomes stripped or misshapen. If so, you won't be able to keep the chain properly adjusted. On most saws, it's an easy job to replace the entire chain-tensioning mechanism or just the screw itself. On other saws, it's a job for a master mechanic or even the factory. In either case, a damaged chain-tensioning mechanism indicates hard use and possible abuse—so, if you're not gambling on a junker, forget it.

Next, remove the top plate that covers the area of the carburetor. Inside, there should be a fine-mesh filter screen. This is the air filter. If it's missing, don't buy the saw except as junk. The filter should be there, and it'll probably be a little dirty, maybe even clogged. Don't be concerned about normal dirt and slight clogging. Just clean the filter before you start the saw. But if the filter is clogged and the incoming dirt and dust seem to be collecting around the sides of the air box and below the air filter enough to get into the carburetor, gross neglect is indicated, and you can bet it isn't limited to the air filter. The air filter of a chain saw must be cleaned every working day, or even more often, with kerosene or air pressure. The air entering the carburetor has to be clean, or the abrasive effect of dust, dirt, and sawdust will clog and choke the machine or grind it to death.

Another little thing to look at is the oil used for chain lubrication. Get some on your finger and see if it feels gritty. If it feels dirty and old, it may be used crankcase oil. In itself, that may not be so serious—you could easily just start using new oil yourself. But we're looking at little things, indications of improper use or lack of maintenance. All these factors will affect whether or not you want the machine, and for what price. Of course, you can also ask the owner specific questions about the machine. "What kind of oil do you use?" If the questions are specific, most people will be honest.

Examine the condition of the spark plug cover or connection and the spark plug cable. If the material appears dry, frayed, or damaged, it will have to be replaced and may indicate that other ignition problems are present or will soon develop. Also look at the starter pull rope. If it's hanging loosely from the saw, either the rewind is improperly installed or it needs to be retensioned. If it's frayed, figure that the saw either has been run for many hours or is hard to start.

CHAIN, BAR, AND SPROCKET: A CLOSER LOOK

For complete information on how to sharpen, maintain, and replace the chain, bar, and sprocket once you have a chain saw, see Chapter 8. For now, we're going to look for specific problems that have already developed and at symptoms that indicate abuse of a used chain saw. If you do find a used saw with a damaged or badly worn or improperly maintained cutting attachment, you must then decide if the problem is severe enough to stop you from buying the saw, or if the saw itself is still good enough and the price reasonable enough to justify replacing the attachment entirely. Very minor abuse or error may be corrected with proper care and filing, but it has to be pretty minor.

The first thing to look at is the bar. The chain is still on, so you can't see the grooves, but you can see the hard tip and blade portion. If you see chips or cracks, the bar is no good and is dangerous to operate as is. Chips or cracks at the tip or near the sprocket indicate that the chain was run too tight or that the bar was used to pry logs apart. Damage along the top or sides of the rails indicates that the chain was run too loose.

If you see signs of burning (dark blue or black streaks or stains), the saw has probably been forced through wood with a dull chain or has been run without oil—or both. A burned bar is a very serious symptom that nearly always indicates a junker. If the bar is badly burned, the engine or clutch may be damaged also.

If the bar has a sprocket nose or a roller nose, find out if it has been properly greased and maintained. Ask the owner how often you have to grease a thing like that. If he says, "Once in a while," he's wrong. It's every working day. For a final look at the bar while it's still on the saw, set the saw down so you can look directly at the end of the bar. Check to see if it's bent or twisted. If it is and you buy it anyway, you'll have to replace the bar, chain, *and* sprocket to correct the problem. There's no cheaper way.

Now let's take a closer look at the chain itself. Using a ruler, measure the length of several cutters on each side. If the cutters on one side are longer than the cutters on the other side, the chain has not been sharpened uniformly, and the saw will not cut straight. To make the saw cut straight again, you'll have to file all the other cutters back to match the smallest one. You'll probably have to file the bar rails square, too. Also check the depth gauges with a depth-gauge tool to be sure they are uniform. If they're all too high, the chain has not been cutting efficiently and has caused drag that has worn on the engine. If they're not uniform, that's even worse, and it's a sure sign of bad maintenance. In any of these cases, certain parts or pieces of the chain itself may have cracked or may soon break.

Next, remove the bar and chain from the saw. While you're at it, double-check those studs and nuts that fasten the bar to the saw. Be very sure they're not stripped or loose in the casting. And look at the outside of the nuts. If they appear chewed or rounded, the wrong tool has been used on them. It's a very common problem and is quite easy to correct, but, again, it does indicate abuse. Don't use anything on those nuts except a quality wrench that's exactly the right size. Pliers or adjustable wrenches or cheap open-end wrenches will ruin them fast. Use a socket wrench, a good box wrench, or (last choice) the tool that came with the saw.

When you have the bar and chain removed from the saw, look at the sprocket. If the sprocket is chewed or worn or damaged, it must be replaced; even minor wear on the teeth (particularly the tips) changes the pitch of the sprocket. Look for dirt around the sprocket, in the groove of the bar, and on the parts of the chain you've just exposed. Here's where a superficial cleaning job will be revealed.

Now hold the bar up without the chain and examine the grooves. At the tail end, where the chain enters the grooves, they should be slightly funneled out so the chain won't catch on them. Except for this funneling, the rails should be straight, parallel, and uniform all around the bar. Filing, of course, is a part of normal maintenance, but the filing must be uniform and accurate. If it isn't, other problems will be present. Check the depth of the rails against the drive-link tangs of the chain. The chain should ride on the rails with clearance below the tangs. Now hold the bar up without the chain to double-check for bends or pinched-together sections. The groove should be of equal width all around. Remember that you must replace or repair a bent bar in order to cut efficiently, safely, and accurately.

While the bar is off the saw, look at the hole in the saw that delivers oil to the bar and chain. If the saw has a manual oiler or an automatic oiler with manual override, push the oiler control button. You should see a strong spurt of oil come from the hole. (Don't look *too* close.) If the saw has only an automatic oiling system, you'll have to wait until the saw is running before you can check the pump.

Finally, take a look at the entire chain. Check the drive links for damage. If you find any problems, compare them to the "Saw Chain Troubleshooting Guide" at the end of Chapter 8. That way you can determine the probable cause of the damage and decide if it indicates a problem too serious to correct. And look for any parts of the chain that may have been replaced. Notice if they have been properly filed to match the old pieces. This is essential.

If you find you must replace the chain, bar, and sprocket, figure in that cost as part of the price of the saw.

ENGINE PERFORMANCE

First, read Chapters 5 and 6 and familiarize yourself with the proper way to start a chain saw. Have the owner start it first, to show you any little tricks for that particular model. If it doesn't start, we're talking about a junker, more than likely. If it does start, it should run fairly smoothly, both while idling and while at full throttle. (But don't race a chain saw for more than a few moments when you're not cutting.)

Chain saw exhaust is normally dark, and a steady, popping sound is also normal with two-cycle engines. But the engine should sound healthy and dependable and should not smoke or pop excessively. If you've never heard a chain saw run before, it may be hard to tell if it's running properly or not. Parp hopes you've prepared by having a friend or dealer demonstrate a new saw first.

There are three major concerns that you should try to check out during your examination of a used saw: You need to determine if the ignition is working properly and is delivering sufficient spark, you need to know if the saw still has enough compression to last for a while, and you need to know how well the saw performs under load. If you have time to do a complete check, study Chapter 12 and become familiar with troubleshooting techniques. If not, proceed as follows:

If the saw starts easily, it's getting sufficient spark, and you can prob-ably count on the ignition parts lasting for a while. If it doesn't start, refer to the troubleshooting procedures or go back to the want ads.

If the saw will not idle smoothly immediately after starting, it's possi-ble that it has been stored too long without starting and that the seals have dried. Less severe problems, such as an incorrect carburetor ad-justment or a fouled spark plug, may also cause a saw to idle roughly—but in these cases the idle will not improve as the engine runs. An en-gine with dried seals will usually idle smoothly once it's thoroughly warmed up.

Now let the saw warm up for a while. Before you cut, check the chain-oil system with the engine running. Lean a piece of cardboard or some-thing up against the log. Aim the front of the chain saw directly at it, about six inches away. If the saw has an automatic oiling system, just rev the engine moderately. If the saw has manual oiling, push the oiler, rev moderately, and push the oiler again. If the oiler system is working properly, a fine spray of oil will leave the end of the bar where the chain speeds around the tip, and will appear on the cardboard. If the saw has an automatic oiling system with a manual override, test both functions separately, as above.

Now do some cutting on a 10"- or 12"-diameter log. If you're not used to chain saws, cut only about one-third of the way into the log. From idle, increase the speed of the saw just as the chain touches the wood. (It's like engaging the clutch and stepping on the gas at the same time.) Do several cuts until you're satisfied that the saw operates under load as well as it does at idle. If it doesn't, serious problems are indicated that could range anywhere from bad timing to carburetor problems to worn rings. If you're still interested in the saw, refer to the Appendix.

If the saw started easily and ran well under load, you can assume that most of your worries about performance are answered. Lots of things could be wrong or could soon go wrong, but at this point you can take a chance that the saw will be satisfactory. If you have time, however, you should now turn the saw off and let it sit for a few minutes. Then start it again, following the instructions outlined in Chapter 6 (page 102). It should start easily if you don't flood it, and it will *probably* start un-choked and with the throttle at idle. It should continue to run smooth-ly at idle and with slight to moderate revving as long as the fuel holds out. If it does all this satisfactorily, you just might have found a depend-able used chain saw. If you have any reservations at all, you should not buy the saw—or you should offer a lower price or follow the trouble-shooting procedures in order to determine the probable trouble and roughly estimate the cost and difficulty of repair.

It may, at this point, be worth your while to make a quick compression test as a final check, especially if the saw seemed a little weak or rough at high speed and under a working load. There's an easy way to do this.

With most chain saws, it's easy to remove the starter housing and flywheel cover. If the fuel tank is also built into this assembly, as it is on many saws, you only have to be careful not to damage the fuel line. Remove the flywheel cover and disconnect the fuel line if necessary. Then turn the flywheel until you feel pressure. Then give the flywheel a quick spin. If it snaps back strongly, compression is good. If it keeps going or stops weakly without snapping back, the compression is low; or the compression could be normal but the compression-release valve may not be seating properly. If the saw passes this test satisfactorily, if it starts easily cold or warm, if it runs well under a load, and if the chain, bar, sprocket, and general appearance of the saw are satisfactory, it's still a gamble, but the odds are decent.

GAMBLING ON A JUNKER

You can improve the odds by looking for saws that have been worn out but not beaten to death. The condition of the chain will often give you enough information to decide which of these baskets a particular saw goes into. If the chain has been used very little and treated very badly (see the "Saw Chain Troubleshooting Guide" at the end of Chapter 8), the poor saw was probably beaten to death. If the chain is worn-out but still looks as if it has been well cared for, filed uniformly, and kept sharp, chances are the saw is just tired and a reconditioning will wake it up. If that's the case, and you can get it cheap enough, that's the junker to buy.

To recondition the saw you'll need to be able to buy parts. The more recent the model is and the more common, the more likely it is that you'll be able to complete the job and then keep the saw running for a year or two afterward. Parp says that five years is maximum chain saw longevity in most cases. If it's a production saw that's popular with loggers year after year, it might be a little older. But it's a junker anyway, and you're a gambler.

In many cases you can obtain a shop manual for a used saw from the saw's manufacturer. That will make the recycling infinitely easier. Plan on storing the junker for up to three months while you wait for the book, which will cost about $10.

While you're waiting, take the saw completely through the troubleshooting procedures in Chapter 9 and study all the repairs covered in this book. Also obtain *The Chain Saw Service Manual* (Intertec

Publishing Corporation) and any other repair book that seems appropriate. Then practice dismantling the saw and putting it back together, going a little further each time. As you're doing this, clean, repair, and replace *all* the parts that you possibly can.

It's at this point that you'll wish you had a barrel of saws for spare parts. If you can find a county or government garage or a tree surgeon who has used that kind of saw for a few years, you just might be able to buy a never-used parts barrel or even a few identical junkers. If so, you'll probably have everything you need except gaskets, rings, and some ignition parts. These you can buy or mail-order from a parts distributor or from the original manufacturer. Some dealers will sell you "used parts assemblies," including starter assemblies, carburetors, oil pumps, and mufflers.

Many saw users make no repairs whatsoever and do very little maintenance. It's not uncommon to find an otherwise serviceable saw that's been discarded because of a broken starter spring. In almost every parts barrel, you can find a good saw, though it might be in the form of a piece here and a piece there, waiting to be assembled. If the starter spring was broken, you can pull the entire starter assembly and housing off another saw of the same model that has worn rings. If the bar is broken as well, that's only a little more trouble. If you're interested and determined, it's entirely possible to scrounge enough parts in almost any town to put together two or three good saws and start a firewood business. Familiarize yourself with the major components of all chain saws, and study this book and *The Chain Saw Service Manual*; you'll be an expert scrounger-restorer in no time.

ACCESSORIES FOR A USED CHAIN SAW

It is not only easy to find substitutes for the tools that come with a new chain saw, but Parp says it's necessary as well. A good 3/8"-drive socket set is a reasonable investment in any case. With it, you'll be able to work efficiently on any chain saw. Almost any large screwdriver is better than the screwdriver end of the "scrench" that comes with new saws. And a good hex-wrench set is inexpensive.

If the saw has a roller nose, get a small grease gun with a small needle adapter at your local hardware store. Zip Penn (see the Appendix) sells an inexpensive model. The depth gauge that comes with saws is exactly the same as the model in the hardware stores. Just get the right size. File guides are generally not supplied with new saws anyway, and if they are, they're the hand-held type. Invest in a high-quality clamp-on type guide, or get a 12-volt electric sharpener if you can afford it. Parp uses a Granberg electric sharpener, which he carries on all woodin' trips in order to maintain chains in the field. It works off a 12-volt vehicle battery and is engineered for accurate chain grinding. Of course, an electric bench grinder built especially for saw chain is the best sharpener.

Be sure to get a chain protector or guard. Chain guards are inexpensive and will protect you, your saw chain, and the backseat. A full case is nice, but it isn't really necessary. Just get a chain guard and cover up the saw when it's stored.

Getting an owner's manual is not always easy. The big chain saw companies are pretty good about this and will supply the book if they have it. If not, start calling the professional chain saw users in your area. When you find one that uses your brand of saw, ask if he has any old manuals lying around. He probably will. You can sometimes benefit from one covering a similar model of different year, as long as it's from the same company.

If you have trouble obtaining parts and supplies from the chain saw's original manufacturer, you may have to write some letters or visit the older established parts distributors, warranty stations, or dealers for that particular saw. They will often have some odd, really old stuff in stock.

The entire subject of used chain saws can be a fascinating pursuit in itself. It can also be a way of making a living, either with a business that puts used saws to work selling firewood or with a business that deals in used chain saws.

A little shop, some wood, some open space—that's freedom.

CHAPTER 5

AN ERSATZ OWNER'S MANUAL

Don't start it yet. First, let's cover a few more basics and make sure that your new or used saw is complete and in good condition for safe operation. We're going to check it in as if we'd just received it on a job where it has to perform professionally.

Your saw's first days at home are important. It's all too possible to damage a new chain saw in just one day of improper use. But this chapter is short, and in a few minutes we can go on to Chapter 6, which is where we fire up that new machine and finally mingle the smells of gasoline and oil and fresh sawdust. (Ah, says Parp. The very thought takes him back to the woodpiles of yesterday and away from the typewriter of this week. He sees the standing dead beckoning with their widow-makers in the green forests of tomorrow, where this book becomes a thing to carry instead of a full-time job.)

Chain-brake lever and hand guard

Saw chain
Guide bar
Oil filler cap
Starter grip
Fuel filler cap
Ignition ON/OFF switch

Handle arm
Guide line for felling direction
Spark plug connecting boot
Half-throttle lock button
Throttle lever lock

Throttle trigger
Carburetor cover
Choke lever

Parts of the chain saw

INSPECTION AND ASSEMBLY OF A NEW CHAIN SAW

First, of course, unpack your saw, the bar and chain, and the owner's manual. Take time to read your owner's manual thoroughly. Much of this chapter is intended to supplement your owner's manual or to serve as a general substitute. With a new saw, the owner's manual should contain a list of components, parts, supplies, and tools that the manufacturer *intended* to include with the saw. Carefully check for each of these items and examine them for breakage or flaws. Especially check the outer edges of the bar and all parts of the cutting chain for burrs or roughness. Wear gloves when handling the chain. You can file any slight roughness or minor burrs until they're smooth, or you can remove them with emery cloth, being careful to work in the cutting direction. If you find large burrs, steel slivers, or a lot of roughness, refer to Chapter 8 for proper filing techniques—then file the chain and bar as if they had been through a hard day's work. The chain and bar of a new saw should, of course, be perfect, so if yours are bad, take them back.

Inside the fuel tank of most chain saws, there is a fuel pick-up tube with a filter in the open end. If your owner's manual indicates such a filter on your saw, remove the fuel tank filler cap. Then, using a piece of bent wire, carefully fish out the end of the fuel pick-up tube. It's usually bell- or cylinder-shaped and made of black rubber. If yours is a new saw, we're only checking to be sure the filter is there and that it's secure.

Hook out the fuel line
end to clean filter.

If yours is a used saw, remove the filter by twisting it free. Clean it with solvent and be sure it's dry before you put it back. If it seems clogged or at all greasy, you should replace it with a new filter. Do *not* attempt to clean it with water. When you replace it, push it in with a twisting motion. Never operate a chain saw without a fuel filter installed.

Inside the chain-oil tank, there's a similar device. It's the oil pick-up tube and filter. Used-saw owners should also remove and clean the oil filter. Don't twist or break the oil line.

If you are checking into a used chain saw, you should read this chapter and follow *all* maintenance procedures before using your saw. Be especially careful to clean thoroughly all sawdust guards and cooling fins, the spark arrester, muffler, and the exhaust ports, according to the recommended procedures.

Whether your saw is new or used, you should now check *all* screws, nuts, and bolts to be sure they are tight. Don't forget to check the screws that secure the handle. These are often loose on new saws, and a loose screw that flies out during your first cutting session can make you wish you'd bought a propane space heater.

Now, just as we checked the fuel filter, let's make sure we have a clean air filter. First, be very sure that the entire top or cover plate of your saw is perfectly clean and free of all sawdust, loose screws, tools, oil, grease, and so on. If it's a used saw, be sure you have completely cleaned the entire saw. Then remove the top cover plate and clean carefully all around the air filter and the air box. If dirt gets into the air box, it can do a lot of damage very quickly. If your saw is new, you shouldn't have to do any cleaning, but it's best to be certain. If your saw is new, you should only have to glance at the filter to be sure it's there, clean, and securely in place. If your saw is used, remove and clean the filter with kerosene and blow it dry with compressed air. (Always keep an extra air filter on hand. You'll need it.) Make sure all fasteners are tight as you replace the air filter and the top plate cover. Never operate a chain saw without a clean air filter properly installed.

Air filters and the like are often best cleaned by blowing them out with compressed air, and you can make your own source of compressed air easily and cheaply. Obtain an old truck tire that is worn out but will still hold air. Attach an air hose, which you can buy at most hardware stores and major service stations. You can either attach a hand-operated valve or use the push valve that comes with the hose. Just hold the hose against the work so that the valve needle is pushed in. This method is every bit as effective as using an air compressor. You should never, of course, blow out an air filter while it's on the saw, since you'd be blowing the dirt through the air filter and straight into the carburetor.

Parp's cautions regarding the fuel filter and the air filter are not just echos from an owner's manual. Dirt is the first enemy of the small engine. Most of the really first-rate professional small-engine mechanics that Parp knows work in atmospheres of laboratory cleanliness that remind one of a surgeon's operating room. There are good reasons for this. The smallest amount of dirt that enters the air box will go straight to the carburetor and clog its tiny passages. Also, dirt coming from the fuel line or air box can eventually build up in the crankcase or in the cylinder. There, its abrasive effect will quickly score the sides of the cylinder and burn out the piston rings. All of this is mechanically very serious indeed. Mechanics means nothing more than making things fit and work together properly. Anything that gets in the way or interferes or causes wear constitutes bad mechanics. Dirt is the number one contributor to bad mechanics.

INSTALLING BAR AND CHAIN

After you've found that you have all the components, parts, tools, and supplies that you need for your saw and after you've read the owner's manual if you have one, *and* after you're satisfied that your saw is clean and in good condition, it's time to install the bar and chain and do the first adjustments—called "cold-tensioning."

(First, it's a good idea, though, to soak the chain overnight in a bath of clean, new 10-weight nondetergent oil. This will assure maximum chain lubrication during the crucial break-in period. Used chains should be cleaned in solvent first, to remove all pitch, and then soaked in oil overnight before using.)

There's a plate attached with a nut (or nuts) to the lower right-hand front side of almost all saws. This is the clutch guard and chain sprocket cover. Remove the nut and washers, and remove the clutch guard. Oops; first switch the ignition switch to OFF. If your new saw has fiber or cardboard spacing washers on the bar bolts, remove and discard them.

Now locate the inside bar protector plate. Minisaws often have only one bar protector plate, the inside one, and the clutch guard serves as the other. Almost all other saws have two bar protector plates that sandwich the bar and chain. Very few saws have none at all, so if you don't find one, check your owner's manual. It should be easy to identify the inside plate if there are two. It's the one with more holes in it. One of these holes is for the chain oil. In any case, one will fit over the bolts with the flanges facing the saw's body, and the other won't.

Install the inside bar protector plate over the bar bolts with the plate flanges away from the bar and the edges pointing toward the saw's body.

The fundamental procedure for installing the bar and chain when preparing a new saw

Flip ignition switch to OFF.

Hook chain over clutch and onto sprocket.

Chain-tension adjusting screw

Chain direction

Wear gloves when handling the chain.

Now straighten any kinks in the chain and lay it out in a loop. The cutting edges of the teeth must face in the direction of chain rotation: On the bottom of the loop, the teeth must face the engine; on the top of the loop, the teeth must face *away from* the engine, toward the nose of the bar.

Lay the bar in the loop of chain so that the nose is pointed away from the saw. Put the chain's drive-link tangs into the grooves of the bar so that the chain is snug around the nose and sides of the bar. This will make a loop at the tail of the bar. This loop will go over the sprocket as you install the bar and chain.

Now hold the chain in place on the bar as you pick up the bar and loop the chain over and onto the sprocket. The bar bolts should now be through the mounting slot on the bar. If there is only one bar bolt, there will also be a fixed pin that will project through the long slot in the bar. Turn and fit the bar and chain so that the chain-tensioning pin fits into its proper hole in the bar. The hole will often be distinguished by shape; *i.e.*, a square pin takes a square hole. In any case, it should be apparent. If necessary, turn the chain-tensioning screw until you can mount the bar properly. Be sure that the bar is mounted flush against the inside bar protector plate and mounting pad. Now hold the bar flush and place the outside bar protector plate or the clutch cover/chain guard over the bar bolts. Replace all washers and nuts and tighten them just enough to hold the bar snugly in position. Some saws, notably certain models made by Skil, have the chain-tensioning screw and mechanism built into the outer chain-and-clutch cover, rather than in the main part of the saw's body. In this case, you have to move the bar as you install the chain cover in order to position the chain-tension pin properly through the hole in the bar. The chain will slip around awkwardly, but it can be done.

An alternate method of installing the cutting attachment is to install the bar first and then to put the chain on while the bar is on the saw. You may find that this makes it easier to handle a large bar and chain. To use this method, first turn the chain-tensioning screw until the tension pin is almost all the way back. Then place the bar over the bolts with the tension pin through the proper hole in the bar. Hold the bar in this position while you loop the chain over the sprocket. Then start the chain in the top groove of the bar. Continue thus with the chain until all of the drive-link tangs are properly seated in the grooves of the bar. You may have to turn the adjusting screw until the chain is positioned at both ends—over the sprocket and over the nose of the bar. Then replace the outer bar protector plate and the clutch guard and chain/sprocket cover. Tighten the nuts to hold the assembly and proceed to adjust the chain tension as follows.

COLD-TENSIONING

You adjust a cold chain differently than you do a warm chain. Ideally, you should always adjust the chain when it's cold, but that's not always possible, as we shall see. In any case, the most important chain adjustment is the cold-tensioning procedure. This first adjustment will determine how well your chain will hold tension later and how long it will last.

First be sure the bar-mounting nuts are loose enough to allow the bar to be moved by hand. For now, we're going to adjust the chain quite snugly. Hold the nose of the bar up and tighten the chain-adjusting screw with a long screwdriver that fits the screw. Get the chain as tight as it

Adjusting pins positioned in
corresponding holes in the
guide bar

Clutch
guard
nuts

Bar flush
against
mounting pad

*Turn the mounting nuts down until snug,
yet loose enough that the bar can still
slide.*

*Tension the saw chain by turning the
screw clockwise while holding up the bar
nose.*

The straps must
touch bar along
bottom . . .

Chain
from
nose

. . . but the chain must
move freely when pulled
by hand.

*This "cold-tension setting" is complete
when the clutch guard nuts are tightened
securely.*

Too much chain sag!

can be and still move freely along the bar. With a gloved hand, pull the chain forward and along the top of the bar. Adjust the tensioning screw until the chain is taut but moves without binding. To remove any kinks, snap the chain by pulling it away from the bar and letting it go. Do this several times and, if the chain develops slack, readjust the tension until it's snug. When all the tie straps are just touching the bar along the entire lower edge of the bar, and the chain moves freely, the tension is correct.

While still holding the bar nose up, tighten the bar nuts to lock the cutting attachment securely at this cold setting. Then double-check the tension by moving the chain in the proper direction of rotation. Again, it should fit snugly but should move freely with no binding. That's all there is to it. You've got it together. (For warm-chain adjusting procedures, see the next chapter.)

INSPECTING A USED SAW FOR WORN PARTS

SPROCKET

We've already discussed the air and fuel filters. When you bought your used saw, you probably took a good look at the sprocket. If not, you should inspect it now. (And new-saw owners should inspect the sprocket often.) A worn sprocket will ruin a new chain fast, will make it impossible to keep your chain sharp, will cause excessive wear on the bar, and will make your cutting inefficient and unsafe. Check the sprocket carefully. If there are any grooves or scars, you'll have to replace it. Chain manufacturers recommend that you change the sprocket with every second chain. The best thing is to start with two chains and alternate them. When you replace the chains, get a new sprocket. You should always have at least one extra sprocket and chain on hand.

REPLACING SPROCKET

One of Parp's few gripes against chain saw manufacturers is their occasional tendency to behave like Detroit's car manufacturers. The whole business of sprocket replacement is a typical example. Chain saw manufacturers understandably want you to visit their authorized repair centers often. Not so understandably, many of them attempt to force you into this by making it seem very difficult to replace your own sprocket. Some companies say in their official owner's manuals that you *must* take your saw to an authorized service outlet in order to have a sprocket replaced.

All this is because, in order to replace the sprocket, you have to lock the crankshaft against turning. Some companies make doing this relatively easy. Skil, for example, provides a simple hole in the bottom of the saw below the flywheel. To lock the crankshaft, you insert a small punch or steel rod through the hole and into the flywheel.

The European manufacturers are generally more considerate when it comes to things like this. Jonsered gets the kudos for a simple and ingenious device they call a counterhold. It's a tool made of shaped, flat steel that locks the crankshaft easily at the clutch side of the machine. Other companies, notably Stihl, provide a crankshaft-locking screw with every chain saw. To use this kind of device, remove the spark plug and insert the locking screw in the cylinder at the spark plug hole. Screw it in by hand until it butts against the piston. This locks the crankshaft. Professional mechanics often accomplish the same thing by using a spanner wrench to hold the clutch.

Whatever kind of saw you have, there is *some* way to lock the crankshaft. It's not always easy to find out how to do it, however. Parp suggests you simply ask around, about your particular saw, until you find someone who knows how and is willing to tell you.

To replace the sprocket, set the ignition switch to OFF. Then remove clutch cover, bar, and chain. Pull out the starter rope far enough to wrap the rope three times around the handle; this protects the rope from breaking when you tighten the clutch. Lock the crankshaft according to the manufacturer's recommended procedure, or use a spanner wrench and socket set. Then remove the clutch nut by turning it *clockwise*. It has a left-hand thread. Then remove the clutch, sprocket bearing, and sprocket from the crankshaft. Take careful note of the exact assembly of all these parts as well as any retaining washers. You can now install your new sprocket.

Before you reassemble your saw, clean the crankshaft, the bearings, and all exposed parts with a clean, oil-soaked cloth. You must also repack the clutch bearings with a high-quality waterproof grease. Inspect the bearings carefully and replace them if necessary. Put some oil on the crankshaft behind the clutch. Then reassemble in exactly the reverse order of disassembly.

GUIDE BAR

Very often, the guide bar on a used chain saw is worn and should be replaced or filed to the proper shape. To file a bar, place it in a vice and use a flat file to make the rails of the bar straight, flat, and uniform. When you're done, be sure the chain's drive-link tangs still have clearance inside the grooves. The chain should ride on the rails, and the tangs should not contact the bottom of the groove. If the chain won't ride or seat properly on a clean bar, chances are the bar needs to be regrooved.

There isn't much you can do yourself, usually, with a badly worn bar. If, however, you happen to be starting a chain saw-related business such as logging or selling firewood, you may want to buy an expensive machine for rebuilding bars and regrinding the grooves. You'll have to rebuild a lot of bars to make it worthwhile.

An inexpensive but brand-new bar, chain, and sprocket set is far better than a once-high-quality cutting attachment that has been ruined. And don't be shocked at your own mistakes. Unfortunately, almost everyone goes through at least one cutting assembly—if not an entire chain saw—before learning good maintenance and uniform filing techniques. That's one good reason to start with a used chain saw.

SPARK PLUG

The spark plug, like many modern mechanical devices, is an amazingly durable item. A new spark plug is also a real bargain. But as long as your saw is running well, you should leave the spark plug in place. It'll let you know when it needs cleaning—or, if you like schedules, you can remove, inspect, and clean and regap or replace the spark plug after every 50 hours of use.

If the saw begins to run roughly, remove the spark plug and clean it with a medium-hard wire brush or a hand file, or with a hydrohone process. Never sandblast or power-brush a spark plug—the residue can ruin your engine. Use a spark plug wrench or a good deep-well socket to remove the spark plug. Do not use pliers. When you replace the spark plug, start it with your fingers and screw it in by hand to be sure you don't strip the threads. You can tighten it, moderately, with your wrench. After cleaning, set the spark plug gap. Most chain saw spark plugs are gapped either to .025 or to .030. If you're not sure which it should be, call a dealer who sells your brand of saw. A new saw, of course, comes with all specifications in the owner's manual.

To gap a spark plug, you need a good feeler gauge. This tool has dozens of uses and is essential for chain saw maintenance and repairs. A feeler gauge is a set of either wire gauges or flat metal or plastic blades of precise and marked thicknesses. The gauges are used for measuring the distances between parts. Whenever you clean or install a spark plug, even a new one, you must set the gap between the electrodes. The gap must be precise.

To set a spark plug gap, insert a feeler gauge of the proper thickness between the two electrodes. The gauge must be held straight to get an accurate reading. Carefully bend the outside electrode—the L-shaped one—until the feeler blade just touches both electrodes. It should move freely, even though it is touching both surfaces. Once the gap is set, be

When testing the ignition system, insert a 1/4" metal rod into the spark plug boot to contact the spring connector inside; turn starting switch to ON, hold boot with rod in it 1/4" away from metal housing, then pull starter cord to create a spark in the air gap. (Wear heavy gloves!)

1/4" air gap

Switch turned ON

careful not to bump the electrode or disturb the setting.

In an emergency, an old spark plug may sometimes be reused if you clean it well and reset the gap. Often, however, a spark plug will be fouled or damaged in such a way that you can't detect the problem visually. Considering how inexpensive they are, it's always best to install a new plug.

Before you replace your spark plug, test the ignition system as follows: Insert a metal rod or screw into the spark plug boot to connect with the spring or contact inside. Hold this together firmly, with your fingers protected by the insulation. Hold the rod or screw close to the metal edge of the muffler or some other bare metal contact or engine ground on your saw. Allow a gap of about 1/4" between the rod and the metal. Then with the switch ON, pull the starter rope to crank the engine. (Be sure electronic ignition systems are properly grounded and that the spark can jump; they can be ruined if the spark has nowhere to go. Protect yourself from shock, since electronic systems pack a tremendous wallop.) You should see a strong blue or white spark. If so, your ignition system is probably good. If the spark is weak, or if there's no spark at all, your ignition system needs service, and the problem is probably in the magneto.

When a spark plug fails, you should try to determine the cause. They are pretty tough little gadgets, but poor maintenance or improper fuel can kill them fast.

Look at the electrodes to find the symptoms. If the electrodes are black to dark gray or tan, the plug is just old, and no problems are indicated. If the electrodes and the bottom of the plug show heavy oily or sooty black deposits or are heavily carboned, something is wrong. Either the fuel mix is incorrect, or the ignition is weak, or it's the wrong spark plug. If the deposits are light gray, the plug's porcelain looks blistered, and the electrodes or other parts appear melted or burned, the engine is running too hot. This may be caused by defective engine seals, by an air leak in the fuel system, or by an incorrect carburetor setting. If the deposits are yellow and ashy and are bridging parts of the plug, it's likely that improper ingredients containing additives have been used in the fuel mix.

In any of these unusual situations, you should avoid using the saw until the trouble is identified and corrected.

STARTER ROPE

The hardest part is getting to it—and that's not hard. Disassemble the saw only as much as is needed in order to remove the starter housing. That's where the rope goes in. On some saws, you'll have to remove the front handle. On others, the fuel tank may be built into the starter housing. If so, just be careful not to damage the fuel line; it will have a fitted plastic connection that you can take apart easily once the housing is unscrewed and partly removed from the body of the saw. Take care not to get dirt into the fuel line.

The ignition switch should be OFF. Remove the screws anchoring the starter housing assembly. If necessary, remove the front handle. Also, if necessary, disconnect the fuel line.

Inside the housing, you will see the pulley or rotor to which the rope attaches. In the center of this, you'll see the starter axle. The rotor or pulley is usually secured to the starter axle by a small circular clip. (You must release the tension on the starter spring before attempting to lift off the rotor or pulley. The energy contained in a wound spring is tremendous. Either untie the knot in the starter grip to release the cord or unwind the cord from the drum.) Hold the pulley down while you remove the clip. Then very carefully lift the rotor 1/2" or less from its proper position. The object is to avoid releasing the starter spring that is just under the pulley. Use a screwdriver to push the spring down firmly and hold it there. Now you can lift the rotor or pulley off the axle. Remove the old rope, and then thread in a new rope, using a single, simple overhand knot to secure it in the pulley (a figure eight knot is better if there is room in the rotor cavity). Thread the other end out through the cord hole in the housing and through the starter grip. Secure it with a double knot. Wind most of the new rope onto the pulley, then reposition the pulley on the axle. Rotate the pulley until it engages the rewind spring. Then lock it all in place with the circular clip or lock washer.

REWIND SPRING

To replace the rewind spring, remove the rope and pulley as described above. Then dislodge the old spring by giving the back of the housing a sharp blow. Discard the old spring safely—either taped up securely or wrapped in a rag. Put the new spring into place. The proper installation will be obvious from the shape and direction of the die-cast portion of the housing that holds the outer end of the spring. You can put it in only one way. Just be sure to keep the spring in place, especially after you remove the wire loop or clip that holds it together. If the retainer is a wire loop or clip, it will come off *as you force the spring into place*. Don't remove it first. Rewind springs have tremendous stored energy, and they release it explosively. Some mechanics wear eye protection when working with rewind springs. If the spring should come loose, you can still use it; just install it clockwise from outside to inside and then get the bandages.

When the spring is in place, reassemble the rope pulley and retaining clip as described above. Oil the spring lightly with an AFT-type oil. Then set the tension for the spring.

TENSIONING THE SPRING

To reset the proper tension, have the rope wound onto the rotor and hold the rotor in place. Pull out the starter handle to put stress on the spring. Then make a loop in the rope inside the housing, using a screwdriver as a lever if necessary. Now wind the rope twice around the pretensioned rotor. The tension is correct if the rotor still has about half a turn left after the rope is pulled all the way out. Too much tension will deprive the spring of a long life.

STARTING CLEAN

And speaking of long lives, your chain saw won't have one unless you keep it clean. Not only will dirt and debris get into the engine, as Parp said before, but it will also cause your saw to overheat and the bar and chain to burn up by preventing proper lubrication.

Since this chapter is serving as an ersatz owner's manual, Parp will detail some basic cleaning procedures here so you can refer to them when you need them—and so you can get started clean.

We found in Chapter 1 that the chain saw is an air-cooled machine. Every single piece of the shining metal that covers your saw's body is an essential part of the cooling system. So are all those funny looking fins and vents and ports and vanes that you see here and there. All of that metal has to be kept as clean as possible, inside and outside.

EXHAUST GUARDS AND COOLING FINS

All around the starter housing you'll see holes and vents of various sizes and shapes. This whole assembly is intended to allow cooling air to reach the engine and to keep out sawdust and other foreign matter. To clean the assembly, remove the housing from the saw and use an old toothbrush, a wooden scraper, and a soft cleaning brush. When all the sawdust, wood chips, and dirt are scraped out, use a dry, soft cloth to wipe the entire assembly, inside and out. Reach as far as you can and do as good a job as you can. Compressed air is a real help here.

While the housing is off, thoroughly scrape any cooling fins on the cylinder that may be exposed. This is essential. The slightest amount of dirt on those fins will increase the running temperature of the engine dramatically. Similarly, clean all the vanes on the flywheel and any other engine parts that are exposed. Get into the habit of thoroughly cleaning anything you can reach after each cutting session, as well as each time you remove or disassemble any part of the saw.

EXHAUST SYSTEM

At the other end of the saw is the muffler or spark arrester. You should frequently disassemble and thoroughly clean all the parts in this area.

Remove the screws holding the muffler or exhaust area cover and spark arrester. Clean off carbon deposits by using a scraper, washing with a toothbrush and solvent, or soaking the metal parts in clean solvent.

While the muffler is off, clean the exhaust ports in the engine—but first slowly pull the starter rope (ignition OFF) until the piston completely covers the exhaust port from inside. You'll be able to see it. Use only a *wooden* scraper to clean the ports. (Anything metal will scratch the piston or the rings.) When you're done, turn the saw so that the exhaust ports are down, and blow away the dirt and scrapings. Be very careful not to allow any dirt, scrapings, or loose particles to stay on the ports or to enter the cylinder. Finish up with the toothbrush, carefully.

DECOMPRESSION VALVE

If your saw is equipped with a decompression valve, it will have to be serviced occasionally. If it fails to close during acceleration, it needs attention. While you're at it, you should also clean the decompression passage. Remove the valve. Remove any loose particles or dirt. Then remove the decompression passage plug screw. Using the starter rope, slowly move the piston until the piston skirt blocks the passage from the inside. Use a wooden scraper to remove all carbon deposits, then blow away all the dirt and particles. Do not disturb the saw after cleaning until it is fully reassembled. Clean the valve seat and the valve assembly (metal parts only) with solvent. Again, blow away all dirt and particles and reassemble.

CHAIN OILER

It's very easy to clean the little hole behind the tail of the bar where the oil comes out: Give a little push on the oiler control to clean any clogs, then clean out the hole with a bent wire or stick.

It's a good idea to schedule a periodic cleaning of the oil strainer screen (if your machine has one) and of the oil tank itself. If there is an oil strainer screen, it will probably be accessible through an assembly in the side of the oil tank. Drain the oil tank and remove the screws, cap, gasket, and screen. Clean the screen with kerosene and replace it. Then half-fill the oil tank with kerosene and shake to clean out the tank itself. Fill it up with fresh bar lubricant and test to be sure the system is working properly.

The bar holds the real secret of proper chain lubrication: Both the holes at the tail of the bar, and the groove of the bar itself, must be frequently and thoroughly cleaned. Use a bent wire or small stick for the holes, and use a toothbrush for the bar grooves. Be careful to get all the oil-soaked sawdust out of the grooves, paying special attention to the tail of the bar. Both the groove and the funneled tail should be immaculate when you're finished; they should gleam. And, of course, the chain itself should be carefully cleaned with solvent and soaked in clean 10-weight nondetergent oil after every use. Parp knows that all this sounds like a lot of trouble. But, as Stihl said recently in one of their in-house publications, "Never buy anything with a handle on it. It means work."

SHORT-TERM STORAGE

To keep your saw in top condition during storage periods (a month or less), you should take certain steps to be sure your saw will be ready to work when you are.

The first thing to do is to clean the exterior of the saw thoroughly. If the chain and other cutting assembly parts are coated with oily sawdust, remove the bar and chain and clean them, using solvent if necessary. Be sure to grease the sprocket nose if your bar is equipped with one. After cleaning and sharpening the chain, apply a good coat of bar oil and reassemble the bar and chain. Clean the air filter next, and remove any dirt that may have collected in the air box around the filter and carburetor. Now top off the fuel tank with the correct fuel-oil mixture and fill the chain-oil reservoir. Check all screws and fasteners carefully to be sure that everything is tight. These steps make up a good regular maintenance schedule that will help keep your saw running its best and can help you spot problems before they become serious or even dangerous.

LONG-TERM MAINTENANCE AND STORAGE

When you store your chain saw for a long period of time, 30 days or more, you must protect it against rust and corrosion, inside and out.

The first thing you should do is completely clean your saw and perform all maintenance procedures. Never store a saw that's in bad running condition without correcting the problem first. And since you're going to store your saw after it's cleaned and inspected, drain the fuel tank first.

When the fuel tank is drained, start the saw and run it at idling speed until the engine stops. This will remove almost all the remaining fuel from the fuel system. Fuel stabilizers do not protect a stored saw against corrosion, moisture absorption, or varnish for very long.

When all the fuel has been run out of the system, remove the spark plug and pour a teaspoonful of two-cycle engine oil through the spark plug hole into the combustion chamber. Then pull the starter rope slowly several times to distribute the oil evenly throughout the engine. Replace the spark plug tightly. Drain and clean the chain-oil tank.

After sharpening the chain, remove and clean it and the bar in solvent. Store the chain in a covered container completely submerged in clean, 10-weight oil. (An empty coffee can with a plastic top is ideal for chain storage.)

Apply a heavy coat of bar oil or grease over the entire bar and be sure plenty of oil gets into the chain groove. The bar, of course, must be cleaned first. Wrap the bar in heavy paper—such as butcher's paper—or in cloth.

Clean the outside of the chain saw's body with automotive cleaner and then apply a good protective coat of automotive body wax. If you don't have a saw case, cover and wrap the entire saw with a lightly oiled cloth. Store the saw and the bar in a cool, dry place. Never store a chain saw near any heat source, chemicals, or fuel supplies.

To take the saw back out of storage, remove the spark plug and briskly pull the starter rope to clear the excess oil out of the cylinder. Clean and gap the spark plug, or install a new plug. Fill the fuel and chain lubrication tanks and follow the standard starting procedure.

Even with all the precautions mentioned here, it's best not to store any gasoline power tool longer than 60 days without removing it from storage and working with it for a while. In any case, most of us are glad to get out the old chain saw every month or so and spend a pleasant afternoon cutting wood. Whenever you do that, take your saw all the way through the complete cleaning and maintenance procedures before you store it again. It's the only way to keep a chain saw in good condition.

A FOND MEMORY

Parp has an inexplicably fond memory of one of his early used chain saws, a particularly temperamental model. He was wintering far from any chain saw dealer and badly wanted to keep his little monster running. He used it every day, and every day it had to be completely cleaned or it would go on strike.

So there was Parp, long after dark, on a mountain that should have been peaceful, with his old toothbrush and various scrapers and rags and kerosene, surrounded by little tiny chain saw parts, cleaning, cleaning, cleaning. That saw had to be completely disassembled and thoroughly cleaned and reassembled every night. Every night. Parp got so he could even do it sober.

CHAPTER 6
MAKING IT GO

Let's start out this chapter with still more attention to the hazards and dangers of operating a chain saw and to the safety precautions that can help protect you from those hazards.

HAZARDS

The problem is that the many aspects of chain saw work present many different kinds of potential threats to your health and safety. First, of course, is the obvious danger of the cutting attachment itself. It is meant to cut wood. It will also cut meat. When you operate a chain saw, you must constantly be alert to the potential of that cutting attachment, and you must take whatever precautions you can. Lots of things can go wrong.

Kickback is the most common cause of wounds. It causes 30 percent of all chain saw injuries. Kickback occurs when the chain, as it speeds

Kickback!

When nose strikes *any* solid object

Kickback!

When incorrectly starting to bore

If nose of saw hits bottom of saw cut
when reinserted into previous cut

Kickback!

Situations known to cause saw to kick back toward operator

around the upper part of the nose of the bar, comes into contact with something solid. When the chain is at the upper third of the nose, it can't cut efficiently. Since it can't cut, the power of the chain's movement forces the bar back and up, in the direction of the operator. Whenever you use the nose of the bar, either accidentally or intentionally, the risk of kickback is highest. If for any reason you have to cut with the nose of the bar, be sure to start the cut with the lower part of the nose and be sure the saw is running at high speed as the chain touches the work. You should definitely avoid boring or using the nose of the bar before you are familiar with operating chain saws.

There are various antikickback devices available for many chain saws. Most of these devices can be back-fitted; in other words, if you own a McCulloch chain saw without a McCulloch chain brake, you can take your saw to a McCulloch dealer and he or she can install a chain brake for you. This is true of most brands of chain saws and most antikickback devices.

But the best way to avoid kickback is to be aware of its causes and avoid those circumstances. When you operate your chain saw, be alert for kickback at all times. Always cut with your left elbow locked or with your arm as straight as possible. Cut only one log at a time. Take every precaution to be sure that the nose of your bar does not touch anything. Always cut as close to the engine end of the bar as possible. Use your saw's bumper spikes to grip the wood and to provide pivot and balance for your saw.

Another problem caused by the chain itself is the pull or push that occurs as the chain catches in the work at the middle of the bar. Push occurs when the top of the bar hits the work; the chain catches in the work and the saw is forced violently back toward the operator. Similar-

Push and pull reactions

ly, pull occurs when the work is forward of the bumper spike; the chain catches in the work and violently pulls the saw forward until the spike hits the work. These two hazards are most likely to occur if the saw is not running at full speed as the chain hits the work, or if the operator isn't holding the saw firmly.

Certain safety precautions can help prevent chain-caused injuries. Competence and alertness are the operator's best protection. Next is proper clothing. Safety clothing is available, chiefly from the European chain saw manufacturers. Such clothing is limited in its ability to protect the operator if a fast-running chain actually hits the clothing. But it *can* absorb the first shock and give you time to react. European loggers always wear these protective garments. For most of us, however, ordinary snug work clothes are best. You should certainly avoid wearing bulky or loose coats, sweaters, or gloves when you're working with a chain saw. Trousers should be snug and cuffless. Parp prefers ordinary jeans. Those Scandinavian loggers in full dress look like Martians, even if they don't get hurt as often as U.S. loggers do.

The cutting chain can also cause injuries when it breaks. A chain-catching pin built into the saw can protect the operator by stopping the chain before it flies into the body. Hand guards for the front handle and for the rear handle also help. Even when a chain catcher stops the broken chain, the end can still reach the operator's right hand. Many recent chain saw designs incorporate a large guard to protect the right hand. Snug leather gloves can also help. Either goggles or a face mask and a hard hat protect the operator's eyes, face, and head from flying chain.

In addition to the cutting attachment, other aspects of the chain saw present hazards to the safety and health of the operator. Noise and vibration can be much more serious than they might seem. All the best modern chain saws incorporate designs that are intended to minimize vibration and noise. But you should take further precautions. Any prolonged session of chain saw work increases the chance that vibration and noise will endanger your health. You should, if possible, avoid working for more than six hours in one day. For most of us, that's no problem. The wood still has to be split and stacked, and there are valleys to look at, fish to catch, and things to think about. And that's good. On those rare occasions when you must operate your saw for extended periods, or if you're about to become a logger, at least be sure to wear ear protection and take frequent breaks. Parp tells of getting that awful ringing in his ears and not being able to get rid of it for three days. It really is extremely unpleasant, and it can do a lot of damage before you know it. Good, inexpensive, professional earplugs are available from Bailey's (see the Appendix).

Plane
of
chain
rotation

Body entirely
to the left of
chain rotation

Hearing protectors

Hard hat

Always wear a face shield,
goggles, or safety glasses.

Grab the front handle bar with
your left hand, like you mean it,
and keep your elbow unbent for
best control.

Before cutting, be sure the saw
is running at top speed; then
begin cutting at the base of the
guide bar.

Use saws equipped with a
kickback guard/chain brake.

Stand on solid ground with
your weight balanced on
both feet in this diagonal
stance.

Thumb on
underside of
handlebar!

Protective
gloves

Be sure to keep the
chain sharp.

Never let
the tip of the
saw hit the
ground, as this
causes kickback
and dulls the
chain.

Protection-type
work shoes must
allow you to stand
comfortably and
securely.

Be safety-minded!

Never bend your
left elbow!
Kickback cannot
be controlled
when left elbow
is extremely bent.

Never stand directly
behind the saw blade.

As for the vibration, stop working when it starts to bother you (after four or five hours or so). Never operate a chain saw when you're fatigued. Even if there's no danger of "white fingers" in your case, that vibration can cause your muscles to turn to jelly without warning. It's a temporary condition, of course, similar to writer's cramp, but it can be very dangerous if you and your saw are in a bad position or if kickback catches you by surprise.

Other dangers from the saw itself are related to the fuel. Obviously, gasoline is extremely flammable. Always move your saw at least ten feet from the fueling point before you start it. The heat of the saw and unexpected sparks from the saw or the chain can start a big fire fast, and the saw can explode. Don't take that fact lightly. It has happened. Always store fuel in properly marked containers that are designed for that purpose. Keep the containers tightly sealed and safely stored away from any open fire or heat source. If you spill fuel on your clothing, don't operate your saw until you change. If the fuel cap should come off while you're running your saw, immediately switch the ignition OFF, or kill the engine by choking it to full choke. Never use gasoline for cleaning.

Another potential danger from the fuel is the poisonous exhaust. No one should ever operate a gasoline chain saw in a closed area. The poison gases are odorless, tasteless, and invisible.

Not all of the danger comes from the saw itself. A whole new list of dangers comes from the wood. Before you cut any wood, you should study the techniques described in this book, in your owner's manual, and in other available literature. Pay special attention to the pictures and memorize the theories. A lot of research and experience are behind them.

Proper cutting techniques can help protect you from most of the dangers coming from the wood. They can help keep trees from falling in the wrong direction, stressed limbs from snapping your head off, and rolling logs from crushing your legs. But proper cutting techniques can't protect you from the falling limbs that we call widow-makers. Obviously, large dead limbs are dangerous. The vibration of your saw in the tree's trunk can cause these large dead limbs to fall down on you. Parp's only suggestion is to avoid cutting under limbs that might fall or to have a watching helper warn you when one falls. You can rehearse signals to facilitate your escape.

Small falling limbs are the ones that can surprise you with their speed, power, and deadly sharp points. They come down like spears and can penetrate several inches of frozen ground or anything else that happens to be in the way. All Parp can say, faintly, is that felling trees is dangerous. If you're not up to it, buy logs or mill-end slabs and use your chain saw to cut them up on saw bucks. If you *are* going to cut down trees, you should most certainly study the tree, use recommended cutting techniques, stay alert, and wear a hard hat at all times. When you hear something snap and start to fall, leave your saw and retreat quickly.

MIXING THE FUEL

Never operate a chain saw on gasoline alone. The engine receives its only lubrication from the two-cycle engine oil that you mix with the gasoline. Running a chain saw without oil burns it up and causes its parts to seize.

Start with a container designed and labeled for gasoline. If you're not going to do a lot of cutting, a one-gallon can will probably be enough. If you're beginning a season of wood gathering or a lot of clearing work, you may want a five-gallon container. Parp recommends that the container be equipped with a removable, flexible pouring spout that is properly fitted with a clean, fine-mesh filter. Clearly relabel the container as chain saw fuel and avoid using it for anything else.

You should have two clean, rust-free funnels: one for the fuel and one for the chain-and-bar oil. Use these funnels when you fill the saw's fuel and oil tanks. The *fuel* funnel should be fitted with a filter. Do not switch the funnels. Label or mark them in some permanent way.

The gasoline must be clean, fresh regular-grade of from 85 to 90 octane. Never use white gas, high-octane gasoline, or any other substitute fuel.

You should also know that there is a difference between summer fuel and winter fuel. In the summer, petroleum companies blend their fuel so that it doesn't evaporate quickly in warm temperatures. The tendency of a fuel to evaporate is called *volatility*. Winter fuel is more volatile than summer fuel in order to make it easier to ignite. If you use summer gasoline after the weather turns cold, your chain saw will be much harder to start. If you use winter gasoline after the weather turns warm, you will lose a great deal to evaporation, and your saw will run slightly hotter. The only real control over fuel volatility is to buy it in small quantities for the season, and to keep it stored properly.

The engine oil must be clean, new two-cycle engine oil and preferably should be exactly the type specified by your saw's manufacturer. Manufacturers' specifications vary widely, especially between U. S. and European machines. If you have an owner's manual for your saw, you should ignore Parp's mixing instructions and follow your owner's manual to the letter. If you don't have an owner's manual, try to determine the manufacturer's fuel-mix recommendations some other way: Call a dealer who sells that kind of saw, ask the previous owner, or find someone else who knows. As a last resort, follow these general guidelines.

For Homelite, Skil, and most other U.S. chain saws, the proper mix is 16:1—that is, 16 parts gasoline to 1 part two-cycle engine oil labeled SAE-30-MS. If you use so-called "premium" two-cycle engine oil, you must adjust accordingly. If you use Homelite Premium SAE-40, the proper mix is 32 parts of gasoline to 1 part engine oil. If your saw requires a 16:1 mix, that means you add half a pint of any SAE-30-MS two-cycle engine oil to each gallon of gasoline. If your saw requires a 16:1 mix and you use a premium oil, add one-fourth of a pint of premium SAE-40 two-cycle engine oil to each gallon of gasoline.

McCulloch chain saws and some other U.S. saws require a 20:1 mix. McCulloch recommends that you use their McCulloch 40:1 Two-Cycle Custom Lubricant. This, again, is a premium two-cycle engine oil, and you must adjust the mixture accordingly. If you use that oil, you add three ounces of McCulloch 40:1 oil to each gallon of gasoline. If you can't get McCullouch's premium oil, use a good SAE-40 two-cycle oil. In that case, you add six ounces of oil to each gallon of gasoline.

Stihl and most other manufacturers outside the United States specify a 25:1 mixture if you use SAE-30-MS two-cycle engine oil. That means you add one-half pint of SAE-30-MS to each 1-1/2 gallons of gasoline. If you use Stihl's own oil, the proper mix is 40:1. That's three ounces of oil to every gallon of gasoline.

Never use anything other than two-cycle engine oil in the engine of a chain saw. Other oils contain additives that turn into glue at high temperatures.

Now that you have your fuel container and two-cycle engine oil, partly fill your container with gasoline. Add the precisely measured amount of oil for the amount of fuel you're mixing, and shake the container well to mix the oil with this partial quantity of gasoline. Then add the rest of the gasoline. Cap the container and shake it well to thoroughly mix the ingredients, giving an extra few shakes in cold weather. Never attempt to mix the oil and the gasoline in your chain saw's fuel tank.

Your fuel is mixed.

STABILIZING THE FUEL

If you'll be using your chain saw only occasionally, or if you're going to store it for a month or two, you should stabilize the fuel while it's still fresh. Unstabilized fuel will separate quite rapidly and can, in time, cause corrosion and gummy deposits. If you're going to store your saw for a long period of time, follow the long-term storage procedure described earlier. Some people simply stabilize the fuel before storing a saw, but a saw containing stabilized fuel must be started periodically and run for a few minutes to adequately protect the internal parts. Incidentally, if a saw has been sitting for more than 20 minutes, always give it a good shake before starting it.

There are several products on the market that help stabilize two-cycle fuel for short periods of storage. These are ideal if you use your saw occasionally but regularly. They keep the oil and gasoline from separating. They do not keep the gasoline fresh, and that's why Parp doesn't recommend them for long-term storage.

Make sure your ignition switch is OFF. Use your clean filter funnel to carefully fill your saw's fuel tank. Close the fuel container, tighten the saw's fuel filler cap securely, and move away from the area. Wipe off your saw to clean away spilled fuel. Your saw is now halfway toward being ready to use.

LUBRICATING THE BAR AND CHAIN

Parp hopes that you have already soaked your chain in clean 10-weight, nondetergent, nonadditive oil—or in commercial bar-and-chain lubricant. The chain should be clean, sharp, and well lubricated. Used-saw owners should clean, sharpen, and reclean the chain before using it.

Your bar and chain are now properly installed on your chain saw. (See the previous chapter for instructions.) The chain's side straps are touching along the bottom edge of the bar, but the chain moves easily by hand. Now, squirt enough oil on the bar and chain to thoroughly drench them. (Don't get it all over the saw, though.)

Next, fill the chain-oil tank with oil. Parp urges you to use good chain-and-bar lubricant. It costs a lot less than a new cutting attachment or a new chain saw. Never use reclaimed or used oil or crankcase oil, no matter what anybody tells you. Crankcase oil is worn-out and contains shavings, additives, and dirt that can ruin your chain. Parp is starting to repeat himself, so he mumbles to refer you to Chapter 1. You don't have to use the bar-and-chain lubricant that has your saw's brand name on it; any good bar and chain lubricant will do, and so will any new nondetergent, nonadditive motor oil. In the chain-oil tank, use SAE-30 when the weather is warm (over 40°F) and SAE-10 when it's colder. In extremely cold weather, mix two parts chain oil with one part kerosene and use 30 percent more lubricant mix per work minute than you would use if it were straight oil. Make it a habit always to fill both tanks— gas and chain-oil—at the same time. If your chain is being properly lubricated by the oiling system, the oil tank will need filling every time you need a refuel, or more often.

If your saw has a manual oiler or a manual override, test it again to be sure it's working. Check the chain tension again, and snap the chain a few times to be sure. If necessary, readjust for proper cold tension.

HOW TO HANDLE A CHAIN SAW

Now practice holding your chain saw and simulate a working stance. Space your feet far enough apart to permit a firm but comfortable balance. Grab the handles as if you mean it. Hold the saw firmly with both hands, with your thumbs curled around the handles. When you're bucking a log or working on the woodpile, you should keep your left elbow locked or your left arm as straight as possible. Then if the saw does kick back, you have more strength behind it to protect you. The saw will throw your arm up, on a pivot from your shoulder, instead of collapsing your arm backward with the saw coming straight at you.

It's not a contradiction to say that you should work close to your saw. Don't be afraid of it. If your right arm is stretched, you will tire quickly and increase the chance of kickback. Hold the saw firmly and work close to it. When it's possible or convenient, as in limbing, keep the work between you and the cutting attachment of your saw.

Practice moving with and holding your saw until you are comfortable doing so. Also, become familiar with the location of all controls—especially the ignition switch, or "kill" switch, and the oiler control. If your saw has no ON/OFF switch, you must kill the engine by fully choking it. Get used to reaching that choke control. There will be many times when you'll want to turn that thing off fast without looking at it—when you're watching a tree fall unexpectedly, for example.

HOW TO START A GASOLINE CHAIN SAW

The fuel tank is filled with the proper mixture of regular gasoline and two-cycle engine oil. The oil tank is full of bar-and-chain lubricant, and the oiler is working properly. If it's a new saw or a new chain, you've drenched the chain with additional oil—either with clean 10-weight non-detergent, nonadditive oil or with the same chain-and-bar lubricant that you put in the tank. The bar and chain are "cold-tensioned." All nuts, bolts, and screws are tight. Your eyes, ears, hands, and head are protected with safety gear. You've moved at least ten feet from the fueling area and further from all fuel containers. No one else is near you, and you are on the ground, standing in a safe area free of underbrush, boulders, or stray logs.

Place your saw on a clean piece of ground. Close the choke all the way. That means you pull the choke control button or lever all the way out, or in the direction of the arrow, or toward the word CHOKE. We say, "close the choke" because as you move the choke control, a plate closes off the top of the carburetor. Anyway, close the choke. Usually, this means pulling it.

Proper stance for starting a chain saw
after all preliminary steps have been taken

If your saw has an ON/OFF or ignition switch—or "short-circuit switch" as the Europeans call it—flip it to ON, to START, or away from the word STOP—whatever applies to your saw.

If your saw has a decompression valve, a DSP valve, or a compression release, move it to the ON, START or OPEN position. In other words, push it in. This control relieves the pressure against the piston and makes it much easier to start larger chain saws.

Almost all modern chain saws are equipped with a throttle latch. This is a button or lever near the trigger, usually on the right side of the rear handle. On some saws, this latch will automatically half-open the throttle when you push it in. You have to squeeze the throttle control or trigger and then push in the throttle latch button. This locks the trigger at the half-throttle position. If your saw has a trigger interlock system, you'll have to use your grip to depress simultaneously the trigger and the safety catch on the top of the handle. Then you can set the throttle with the throttle latch.

If you have a standard, full-size chain saw with a rear handle, put the toe of your right work boot in the handle and press down, stepping on the handle. If you just kicked loose the throttle latch, reset it again. If yours is a minisaw, steady the rear of the saw with your right knee. Keep all other parts of the body away from the saw.

Now look around carefully. Be sure the kids or your husband or somebody didn't sneak up on you. Be sure that the cutting attachment of your saw isn't touching anything, anyplace.

Take hold of the starter rope handle with your left hand. Get a firm grip with a relaxed arm. Pull the starter rope out until you feel resistance.

Without stopping, use more strength as you meet the resistance and *briskly* pull the rope to give the engine a swift, cranking spin. Don't pull the rope *all* the way out and don't let go. Hold onto the rope, and it will rewind smoothly. Don't let it snap back. Repeat this procedure until the engine starts.

After the engine has fired (sputtered as if it were about to start), move the choke control to half-choke whether or not the engine kept running after firing. If the engine stalled, repeat the starting procedure with the choke control at half-choke. If the engine continued to run, let it run at half-choke for half a minute and then move the choke to the OPEN position, or all the way in or down. Let the saw warm at half-throttle and half-choke for a few minutes. Do not race the engine.

Normally, a chain saw that has just been fueled will need three to five cranks of the starter rope to prime the engine. In cold weather it might take more cranking. A well-tuned chain saw that has been run recently will often start with one crank. A warm chain saw, recently operated, will also usually start with the choke open, or OFF, and the throttle trigger at rest, undepressed.

After half a minute or so, be sure the choke is open, OFF, away from the words START or CHOKE, or pushed all the way back in. Keep your left hand firmly gripping the front handle. With your right hand, press the trigger a little—just enough to disengage the throttle latch. Release the trigger. Your chain saw is now idling.

If it stalled, try again. If it still won't idle, read ahead to adjust your carburetor according to Parp's instructions or according to your owner's manual—then repeat the starting procedure until your chain saw idles properly, without the chain moving.

"Hey!" you may say. "This thing is shaking me to death, and it's about to blow up." Yeah. Wait till you see what it does to *wood*.

FIRST CUT

After your saw is warmed and idling smoothly, turn it off. Get a good-sized log, at least 12″ in diameter, and plan on cutting only partway into it, say a third or so, for practice. Don't cut more than halfway through the log until you know what you're doing.

Have the log firmly supported on the ground, with no part of the log not fully supported. Stand on the uphill side of the log. If your saw or chain is new, add extra oil by hand at this time. Use the same kind of oil that's in your saw's chain-oil tank. Restart your saw on the ground, not on the log. Be sure the cutting attachment isn't touching anything. Never start a chain saw when it is resting on a log or with the chain touching wood.

Hold the saw firmly in both hands, with the engine at idle. Bring the cutting attachment up above the log, with the nose of the bar pointing up slightly. Bring the body of the saw down slowly, still at idle, so that the bumper spike engages the wood. The chain still should not be touching the wood.

If you have a manual oiler or a manual override, pump it like crazy. At the same time, squeeze the trigger as you pivot the saw on the bumper spike. The engine and the chain must be going full speed when the chain touches the wood. The idea is to coordinate the downward pivot of the cutting attachment with the increasing engine speed so that you hit full speed and power just a split second before the chain hits the wood. That will prevent the saw from racing in the air, and will also save you from having the saw pulled violently forward by a slow-running chain.

As you cut, let the saw do most of the work. Don't force the saw into the wood. Pivot the saw on the bumper spike. Keep your left elbow straight but hold the saw firmly, while standing close to it. Use *plenty* of oil; pump the oiler every ten seconds to break in a new saw. Keep your body just slightly to the left of the plane of chain rotation. Don't be afraid. *You* are in charge.

As the saw cuts down into the log, the nose of the bar will drop. When the cutting attachment has pivoted below horizontal, so that the nose is lower than the tail of the bar, move the saw so that the bumper spike grips lower on the log. About now you should be a third of the way through the log. Bring the bar up out of the cut, while simultaneously releasing the throttle trigger. If you accepted Parp's suggestions verbatim, your cutting attachment is not stuck in the log. If your bar is pinched because you cut too far, use a wedge or crowbar to widen the kerf enough to remove the saw. (Turn your saw off first so the moving chain isn't damaged by the wedge or bar.) Don't use the saw's guide bar to pry the saw loose, and don't try to cut your way out.

If you didn't pinch the guide bar, your saw is still running at idle and is removed from the cut. Without touching it, glance at the chain. If it's sagging, stop now, kill the saw, and go on to the next section. If it isn't sagging, repeat the cutting procedure described above at another place on the log. Do this two or three times to heat the saw and the cutting attachment thoroughly. Be sure to use plenty of oil. If you have a manual oiler, pump it every ten seconds while the chain is cutting. If you have an automatic oiler with a manual override, pump it every 20 seconds. Be sure to keep the saw going full speed. If you cut at less than full speed, the clutch will wear out very quickly. When you remove the saw from the last cut, turn it off.

READJUSTING THE BAR AND CHAIN

Examine your chain while it's still hot. A hot chain stretches, and there should be a slight sag, so that the side straps in the bottom middle are not quite touching the bar. The drive-link tangs should be just visible and riding well up in the groove of the bar.

The best advice is never to adjust the chain while it's still hot. You should let it cool completely. But we can't always take the time we should to do things right, so . . .

To tension a warm chain, turn your saw OFF. Pull the chain around the bar and snap it a few times while pumping the manual oiler. Then lay the palm of your glove flat on top of the chain and give it as fast a spin around the bar as you can. If the sag is very slight, with the side straps almost touching along the bottom rails of the bar, the tension is satisfactory. If it's too tight or too loose, you must reset the tension.

Loosen the nuts on the bar bolts just enough to be able to move the bar. Hold the nose of the bar up while you turn the chain-tensioning screw clockwise. When the side straps are almost touching at the bottom middle of the bar, the tension is approximately correct. Keep holding the nose of the bar up while you tighten the nuts on the bar bolts.

But again, instead of adjusting while the chain is hot, take a few minutes to let it cool first, if you can. Then simply follow the instructions for cold-tensioning.

There is one rule that no experienced chain saw operator ever breaks: *Never touch the chain or attempt to adjust tension while the engine is running.*

HOW TO ADJUST THE CARBURETOR

You will need to adjust your chain saw's carburetor in any of the following situations:

1. While breaking in a new chain saw.
2. After breaking in a chain saw (after about an hour of actual cutting time with a new chain saw).
3. If the chain rotates when the saw is at idle.
4. If the saw stalls easily or fails to idle smoothly.
5. If the saw runs rough at high speed.
6. At an altitude different from the saw's place of manufacture, or after a change in altitude.

If your chain saw is new, it certainly should have had proper preliminary carburetor adjustment on delivery. If it didn't, let your dealer do it for you, if possible. Otherwise, follow your owner's manual or the steps below.

If your new saw bears a notice that the carburetor is altered for high-altitude operation, and you are going to a low-altitude area, arrange for your dealer to change the carburetor's circuit plate or jet size. A high-altitude saw will overheat at low altitudes.

If your saw has been adjusted for low-altitude operation and you will be operating it at a *high* altitude, have your dealer or mechanic determine the necessary carburetor changes. You may need to replace the standard circuit plate with a high-altitude circuit plate.

Chain saw carburetors are all very much alike, although there can be some differences, especially between U.S. and European carburetors. However, almost all European chain saws imported to the United States have U.S.-make carburetors.

All chain saw carburetors are adjustable, in different ways, from the outside, and any chain saw owner can and must occasionally perform these adjustments. You make the adjustments by altering two or three screws, depending on the saw.

The three screws are universally labeled as follows:

1. "H" is the high-speed mixture needle adjustment. (This is the screw that may be "missing" on some saws.)
2. "L" is the low-speed mixture needle adjustment.
3. "I" or "T" is the idle or throttle speed adjustment.

The H, or high-speed mixture needle, is the main adjustment screw and affects the mixture of fuel at speeds faster than idle. The L, or low-speed mixture needle, adjusts the fuel mixture at idle and is also called the idle *mixture* screw. Do not confuse it with the I, or T, which is always a large and predominant screw. The I or T alters the idle speed of the engine but does not affect the fuel mixture itself. It is the screw you will adjust most often, and is less delicate and crucial than either of the mixture adjustments.

Make all of these adjustments with extreme caution. It's easy to damage a carburetor by turning the mixture adjustment screws too far. Use a good screwdriver that fits. Make all carburetor adjustments with the engine warm and the air filter clean. The normal preliminary setting for these adjustments on U.S. and Canadian saws, and most European saws, is as follows:

1. Gently turn the low-speed mixture needle (L) all the way in, until it just barely touches the seat. Then turn it back one full turn.
2. Do the same with the high-speed mixture needle (H).
3. Start the engine and allow it to idle.
4. Carefully turn the idle speed adjustment screw (I or T) until the saw idles smoothly. If the chain rotates at idle, turn the idle-speed adjustment screw counterclockwise until the engine idles smoothly

with the chain motionless. If the saw stalls and fails to idle, turn the idle-speed screw clockwise, half a turn at a time, and each time restart the engine until it idles properly.

5. If the engine tends to stall when you increase the speed, open the low-speed needle (L) slightly.

6. If the engine tends to race and adjusting the idle-speed screw (Step 4) does not correct the situation, open the high-speed needle (H) slightly. If that makes the exhaust smoky under acceleration, you've gone too far. Go back to Step 1.

Carburetor box cover removed

Short screw

Long screw

High-speed adjust-ment screw: 1¼ turns open is the normal adjustment.

Low-speed adjustment screw: Three-quarters to 1 t< open is normal adjustment.

Air filter

Carburetor

Slower   Faster

Idle-speed adjustment screw: The engine should idle with-out stopping and without moving the chain.

Carburetor adjustment screws are used to allow maximum performance and lowest fuel consumption. Check adjustments only on a warm engine with a clean air filter. Remember, the air filter easily becomes clogged with sawdust, resulting in a loss in power, so clean it daily.

After all these adjustments, the high-speed needle (H) must be at least three-quarters of a turn out from the bottom, and the low-speed needle (L) must be at least one full turn out from the bottom. If these needles are adjusted closer than this, the engine will race, and damage may occur.

In the event that all attempts fail and the above steps don't result in proper operation at idle and acceleration, you may have one of the carburetors that require different preliminary settings. If your saw is a European-make minisaw, *decrease* the initial settings of the high-speed and low-speed needles (H and L) by one-eighth to one-quarter turn.

If your saw is a U.S.-make minisaw, *increase* the initial setting of the idle *mixture* adjusting screw by one-quarter turn. (This applies only if your U.S. minisaw has only one screw for adjusting idle mixture and has a fixed high-speed needle that cannot be adjusted by the operator.)

Chain saw carburetors are quite universal, and repair or rebuilding kits are readily available. When your carburetor needs it, you'll be able to rebuild it yourself. The job is tedious but not difficult, provided you obtain a high-quality kit from the carburetor's manufacturer and carefully follow all instructions.

Your carburetor should perform perfectly, with minor adjustments, as long as you keep dirt from falling into it and keep the air filter clean. Change the filter frequently. If you move from one altitude to another, simply follow the adjustment procedure as noted above, from the beginning, unless your saw bears a notice that your carburetor was specifically built for certain altitude conditions.

MAKE A SAWBUCK AND CUT SOME FIREWOOD

You'll need a sawbuck to help make your woodcutting easier. It's best to have a helper for this project. When you're finished, the helper will be replaced by the completed sawbuck—which is all the help you really need for working on your woodpile or for doing easy cutting jobs.

Parp assumes you'll be using your chain saw primarily for cutting firewood, and that you already have some wood around.

Find some logs about four inches in diameter and several feet long. Until your sawbuck is finished, you'll need some way to hold one end of each log while you cut the other. That's where the helper comes in. If no helper is available, you can use heavier logs to hold one end of the work.

Place the first log so that most of its weight is resting on a flat surface and one end is extending, unsupported, at about the level of your knees or a little higher. Get the log level with the ground. Have your helper

Four-legged sawbuck

hold the supported end of the log firmly, or brace it with heavier logs. Be sure it's braced sufficiently to prevent that end of the log from moving when you apply your chain saw to the other end.

Working in this manner and observing all safety precautions, cut two pieces of log, each three feet long. Since the logs are only four inches in diameter, you should be able to cut straight through from the top of the log without the log splitting. Be careful of the cut pieces as they fall. Don't try to catch them. If you move or stop work for a few minutes, or pause to adjust the work, turn your saw OFF.

You *can* notch the logs for assembly. (See Chapter 11 for the best notching techniques.) Leave about a foot of log above the notches.

Now assemble the two three-foot pieces into an X, crossed at about a foot from the top. You can lash them together with rawhide or heavy cord, or you can fasten them together with two long spikes (large nails) or lag screws. This is the simplest and best sawbuck to use for cutting firewood on your woodpile. It can be easily transported or stored.

You can make the same kind of sawbuck using 2 X 6 lumber cut to three-foot lengths and fastened together with one bolt and a wing nut. That makes it easy to fold it up for storage. Be very careful when you apply your chain saw to the lumber. If you're inexperienced, the chain can catch in the edges of the lumber and give you a bad pull.

To use your sawbuck, just stand it up and let the work form its third leg; it will look like an elongated tripod. Cut on the free side of the sawbuck, of course, and avoid hitting it with any part of your saw. As you cut logs into splitting lengths, set your saw down and lift the end of the log to move the sawbuck back. Work on smaller logs while you're gaining experience; logs that are about eight inches in diameter are easy to handle and will provide good firewood. Work on the uphill side of the wood, watch out for falling pieces, and don't move with a running chain saw. Follow all safety rules and use plenty of oil on the chain.

Just when you start to realize that you're really having fun, you'll discover that you already have a large pile of cut firewood. When your arms get tired, take a long break or stop for the day.

WORKING WITH A GASOLINE CHAIN SAW

Lots of people say that a chain saw is only as safe as its operator. Parp hates other people's clichés as much as he does his own, and that par-

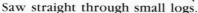

Saw straight through small logs.   Pivot saw at bumper for thicker logs.

When cutting firewood-length pieces from a raised end,
there is no stress, so undercutting isn't necessary.

ticular one is false, anyway. A chain saw is somewhat more dangerous than its operator.

You can take all the precautions and follow all the rules and *still* have accidents. The risk is minimized, but it's still there. That's why it's a good idea always to work with a partner, or to have someone nearby who will hear you scream if something horrible happens. Any experienced woodsperson will recognize that as common sense.

But a good woodsperson, even though sensible, is primarily a *woods*-person, and part of the reason you have a gasoline chain saw is the need for solitude and self-reliance. When the saw is turned off and it's time for a break, you want to look up at the blue sky and the gray rock, or you want to feel the closeness of silent snow falling, or you want to drowse on the warm grass. You don't want to talk to anyone, or to be distracted from contemplation by the proximity of another, no matter how quiet or compatible he or she may be.

So chances are you'll often be alone with your chain saw. If so, carry a whistle, a good loud one. If you get pinned by a tree, cut yourself, or break a leg, you can blast on the whistle. Chances are someone will hear you, almost wherever you are. If you're further away than that, you probably know what you're doing; in any case, you knew the chance you were taking and figured it was worth it. Parp certainly understands. Anyway, you have your first aid kit and your whistle (or a gun), and you are as careful as you can reasonably be. After that, it's up to everything else.

When you're actually in the woods and working with your chain saw, the hardest thing to manage is your footing. Try to shut off the saw whenever you move, and try to clear any area where you're going to work. It's impossible to maintain a difficult balance and use a chain saw at the same time.

If you drive off to the woods with your pickup truck to get a load of logs, take along all the tools you're likely to need. Take extra fuel and all the extra maintenance parts—such as air filters, spark plugs, and an extra chain and sprocket. Start with a sharp chain and a clean saw. After every hour of work, stop and service your saw. That means you fill the fuel and oil tanks, clean or change the air filter, touch up the chain, and wipe off the saw. If you discover or suspect any problem with your chain saw, stop working until you have diagnosed and corrected the problem.

Take frequent breaks. Listen to the living trees around you and don't cut their lives short for firewood. They are sentient creatures. They are also the voices of the wind and the earth.

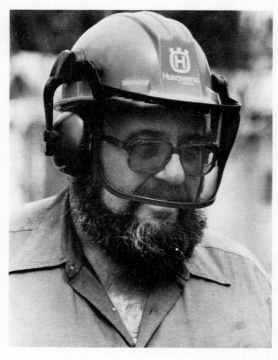

Don't forget your safety gear!

CHAPTER 7
MORE ABOUT ELECTRIC CHAIN SAWS

In the years since the original *Barnacle Parp's Chain Saw Guide* was first published, numerous new electric models have appeared on the chain saw market. Many of these newer models are from Japanese and Italian manufacturers whose products, both gasoline- and electric-powered, have gained strength in the American marketplace in recent years. Others are new models from the more familiar U.S. and European manufacturers—such as Homelite, Stihl, McCulloch, and Pioneer. Nearly all of the new models are intended for general consumer use. Previously, only a few of the electric models were aimed at the consumer, and these tended to be very cheap saws, made with far too much plastic. Most quality electric saws were designed chiefly for commercial use by industry, especially builders, and government agencies or utilities. These days, there are far more models designed and priced for home or consumer use.

THE NEW ELECTRICS

When it comes to the new electric chain saws designed expressly for the consumer market and for home and yard use, McCulloch, Homelite, and Stihl are in the lead, with McCulloch the clear leader for a number of good reasons. These companies have in recent years greatly improved the overall quality of their products in the consumer price range. Even the smallest of the electrics available from any of these manufacturers is well designed and well built and is a good value. New lightweight materials for the body and some improved designs in handles, sprockets, bars, and low-profile, low-kickback cutting chains contribute to the solid feel and efficiency of the present models.

These new saws are well suited to most home and yard tasks—such as trimming and shaping trees, pruning, fence building, light carpentry, and easy firewood cutting.

ADVANTAGES AND CHIEF USES OF ELECTRIC CHAIN SAWS

The chief advantage of the electric chain saw over the gasoline-engine models is that the electric saw is much quieter to use. Also, the electric saw does not require the use of volatile fuels or the mixing of fuel. This makes the electric saw much cleaner, easier, and more pleasant to use in the backyard or small woodlot where electric power is available. Because of this, the chief domestic uses for the electric saw are pruning, trimming, general yard and small orchard use, and—for the heavy-duty models—construction such as on a cabin or rural homesite where power is available. And because the electric saw emits no poisonous fumes, it may be safely used indoors or in confined areas where the use of a gasoline saw would be ill-advised and dangerous.

DISADVANTAGES AND LIMITATIONS OF ELECTRIC CHAIN SAWS

The disadvantages and limitations of electric chain saws mirror their advantages and best applications. The first and most obvious limitation and disadvantage is, of course, the power requirement. And power is frequently undependable or expensive in rural areas. Also, power tools cannot be used or stored safely in wet conditions. And then there's that power cord that you must always be aware of so as not to cut it in half, which is a very bad thing to have happen. Finally, electric saws in general tend to be far less powerful than similarly priced gasoline models. There are some extremely powerful commercial electric saws available, such as the Stihl E-30, but even these cost much more than would a gasoline model with comparable guts.

All things considered, most people who are thinking of buying an electric chain saw should plan on using it casually, around the house or in the backyard. Parp says that if what you need is a real firewood saw, opt for the best gasoline-engine model you can afford. You'll be glad to have the extra boost.

TYPES AND SIZES OF ELECTRIC CHAIN SAWS

Electric chain saw motors are usually rated in terms of horsepower, which is about as subjective as even our consumer-based pop sciences ever get, since one manufacturer's horse may be another's frog. Be that as it may, horsepower ratings are what we get from most of the industry.

CONSUMER MODELS

Most electric saws for the consumer market have motors ranging from about 1.5 to 2.0 horsepower. That is not a wide range. The chain speed that results is actually the same for motors of 1.5, 1.75, and 2.0 horsepower—at least for the consumer models. The chain speed is nearly always 2,000 feet per second.

Consumer electric saws usually weigh from about 8.5 pounds on up to about 10.5 pounds. The average or usual length of bar supplied with these saws is 12″, but the smaller models have 10″ bars that Parp says are useless for anything but the lightest trimming jobs. Top-of-the-line consumer electric chain saws from most manufacturers have a maximum bar length of 14″.

PROFESSIONAL MODELS

Compared to similar gasoline-engine models, electric chain saws that are designed and built for heavy-duty, professional use tend to be quite expensive in terms of the power available. Unlike the consumer models described above, the motors used in the professional saws carry a kilowatt rating, which at least gives us a more objective basis for comparing models. In the professional category, motors range from about 1.9 kw (roughly equal to 2.5 horsepower) on up to about 2.7 kw (roughly 5 horsepower).

Pro electric bar lengths come as short as you wish and, at least on some saws, go all the way up to 36″. The same saws range in weight from less than 20 pounds up to 40 pounds or more, depending on the size of the cutting attachment. Electric saws do not live up to the high power-to-weight ratio standards set by the gasoline-engine saws.

NOTE: Before buying a professional-level electric chain saw, be sure that you can meet the power requirements specified by the manufacturer. Many of these saws require three-phase power; others may require 220-volt lines.

HOW TO USE AN ELECTRIC CHAIN SAW IN THE WOODS

Now for the impossible. How does a person take an electric chain saw into the forest for cutting firewood? On that question hangs a Parp tale.

In the town of Alamosa, Colorado, not far from Parp's neck of the woods, there is a remarkable store called 'Tween Taos And Aspen. This unique enterprise holds, under one very small roof, virtually anything and everything the earnest back-to-the-lander or homesteader might ever need in the way of bulk foods, unusual cooking utensils, wood-burning stoves and water heaters, farming tools, and alternative clothing. And all at prices that would put a nearby discount store out of business if the general public knew. But the most remarkable aspect of 'Tween Taos And Aspen is not its enormous resources and nearly un-American prices, but the degree of knowledge that owner Bill has about everything he sells.

It was Bill who first showed Parp how to run an elecric chain saw in the woods without an extension cord.

For years, Parp tended to dismiss electric saws from serious consideration for all but the lightest backyard cutting chores. Then one fine high-country spring day, Parp drove his ancient pickup "down valley" to see what was new 'Tween Taos And Aspen. When Parp arrived, Bill held out a strange-looking contraption and said, "Here's your new saw, Parp."

"Whoa now, Bill," Parp replied, noting that he'd never before run into a chain saw called Brute. "That thing sure looks electric to me, although, otherwise, it looks almost like a real chain saw. But you know how I feel about umbilical cords."

"Dummy," said Bill, "grab that battery and follow me." He hesitated. "On second thought, I'll get it myself." Whereupon he picked up the odd-looking saw in one hand and the battery in the other and led the way to his sawhorse out back. There he attached the saw's long electrical leads to the battery, flipped a switch, and quickly bucked a very large log into four blocks.

"Wow!" said Parp. "That thing really cuts. But what about hauling that battery up and down hillsides and across snags? Must weigh half a ton."

"It's lighter than that five-gallon can of yours, at least when the can's full of gas—not to mention your engine oil and tools and extra spark plugs."

"Hmm, you've got a point there," Parp conceded. Then he grinned. "But what about when the battery wears down?"

"Well, you are thick today, aren't you? This here is a marine-grade battery. A good one. It can be recharged and run down over and over with no problem, any number of times. So all you gotta do when it's getting a little low is take it back to your truck, hook it up, and turn over your engine. There's always enough power left to start a pickup, even yours. And then, in ten minutes or so, it's fully charged again."

"Well, Bill," Parp said. "Every time I come here I learn something new, and this is truly amazing. I've always figured it couldn't be done unless someone came out with a solar-powered saw. But I'm still not sure I want to haul that battery around the mountains."

"Okay," said Bill, flipping the switch. "But just listen to that blessed quiet."

WORKING WITH AN ELECTRIC CHAIN SAW

Everything Parp has said about safety with gasoline-engine saws applies to electric chain saws as well. In addition, don't use more than one length of extension cord, and don't stand in or on anything wet. Don't work in wet weather. Disconnect the saw before making any adjustments or performing any maintenance. If you use an electric saw for pruning or trimming, don't cut over your head, no matter how light the saw may seem.

MAINTAINING ELECTRIC CHAIN SAWS

Except for the power cord and the motor itself, the maintenance of an electric saw is nearly identical to the maintenance requirements of a gasoline-engine saw. That is, the cleaning, sharpening, and chain lubrication tasks are the same. But that's where the similarity ends, because maintaining an electric motor involves no spark plugs, points, condensers, coils, or other gadgets necessary to gasoline engines. However, electric motors must at all times be kept clean and dry, with the emphasis on dry. Never use an electric chain saw in wet, or even damp, conditions. To avoid excess strain on the motor and related assemblies, maintain your bar and chain in good cutting condition as described in the next chapter. In addition to general maintenance of the bar, chain, and sprocket, the following maintenance rules apply to all electric-motor appliances:

1. Always keep the motor housing clean and free of accumulated oil and grease.
2. Frequently check screws and connections to be sure they are tight and not covered with oil and grease.
3. Clean the motor's air-cooling passages daily, or more often when cutting in extremely dirty or dusty conditions.
4. Replace worn bearings as needed.
5. Check wiring. Look for frayed or worn wiring and for bare sections of wire. Clean or replace as necessary.
6. Clean start-switch contacts daily and polish them periodically with a fine abrasive paper. Do not use emery cloth because of its coarseness.
7. Lubricate the motor according to the manufacturer's specifications. Too much oil, or the wrong type of oil, can be as bad as too little.

STORING YOUR ELECTRIC CHAIN SAW

Obviously, there are far fewer things to worry about when you store an electric chain saw, either for a short time or for a full year or more. There is no fuel tank to drain, no spark plugs to protect from corrosion. But you cannot simply throw your saw into a closet and forget it, either.

A stored electric saw should be protected from dust, dirt, moisture, and the possibility of spilled liquids. If the storage is to be long-term, you should remove the bar and chain and clean them thoroughly. The chain should be sharpened and well oiled to keep it from rusting, and then stored in a plastic bag or a can. The bar should be covered with a light coat of oil, and it can then be hung from a nail. For the saw itself, wipe the exterior clean and remove any wood chips, sawdust, or oil from the body as well as from the area of the sprocket and chain adjustment mechanism. Never leave your saw connected to power when it's not in use.

Parp has recently noticed that the electric chain saw has become the most common tool used in urban situations for all kinds of backyard cutting chores. This has certainly made it easier to sleep in on a Saturday morning. Ah, that wonderful quiet.

CHAPTER 8

KEEPING IT SHARP

A LIST OF TOOLS

In order to sharpen and service saw chain, you need these tools and supplies:

1. Spare chain loops or chain in reels.
2. File guide or chain grinder.
3. Depth gauge or jointer.
4. Chain file or grinding wheel to fit your chain.
5. Flat safety-edge file for depth gauges.
6. Solvent or kerosene.
7. Clean oil for chain bath.
8. Measuring rule or calipers.
9. Chain breaker.
10. Chain rivet spinner.
11. Flat 8″ file for bar.
12. Grease.
13. Grease gun for roller-nose or sprocket-nose bars.
14. Toothbrush.
15. Rags.
16. Gloves.
17. Hand tools.

TYPES OF SAW CHAIN

There are several types of saw chain available from numerous manufacturers. Although no manufacturer produces all of the different kinds of chain available, any particular chain generally can be replaced with a chain made by a different company. No matter what kind or size of chain saw you have, a variety of chains is available to fit it. You don't always have to use the brand or type of chain that came with your saw, but generally you do have to use the same size in a replacement chain, unless you change the bar and sprocket as well.

There are four basic shapes of saw chain cutters. The first and most common is the *rounded chipper* shape that helped facilitate the development of the modern, lightweight chain saw. The round chipper tooth, which is traditional, became the standard before industry engineers realized that a squared cutter is more efficient. A rounded cutter has advantages: It's easy to maintain and may be sharpened with a round file. Most consumer saws are supplied with chipper chain as standard equipment.

When the engineers realized the advantages of squared cutters, a compromise design appeared. Commonly called *semichisel*, this cutter has a semisquare cutting edge. It may be sharpened with a round file.

The most efficient shape for a cutter is the *squared chisel* shape that is common on professional saws. This shape removes more wood with each cut and never cuts the same cross grain twice. It's more difficult to maintain since the filing must be done precisely with a flat, bevel-edge chisel file. However, if you use a clamp-on file guide, this chain is as easy to sharpen as chipper chain.

Chipper cutter

A round or chipper-type cutter must sever the same wood fiber several times as it passes through.

Chisel cutter

A square-shaped or chisel cutter severs the wood fiber with a single pass. This means faster cutting action and less work for both the engine and the operator.

The fourth cutter shape is used only on saws that have a built-in automatic sharpening system. This cutter has a distinctive clawlike shape that sticks up to allow the stone in the automatic sharpener to reach the cutting edges. But it's difficult to maintain properly and cuts less efficiently than the manufacturers claim. It's also expensive.

Although Parp recommends a clamp-on file guide for all saw chains, the rounded chipper and semichisel types may be sharpened with the common hand-held file guide. All authorities agree that a clamp-on sharpener is mandatory for true chisel chains. One of the best recent developments in chain is the Stihl Oilomatic Injected saw chain. This chain features oil channels built into the drive links. The channels carry oil directly to the rivets and other chain parts. The cutters are available in

Stihl Oilomatic® chains have a built-in oil channel in the drive link for better lubrication of the chain.

chisel, semichisel, and chipper designs. Also, the chain comes pre-stretched and very sharp, eliminating many break-in problems.

Any of the various types of saw chain may be linked in different ways for special purposes. These differences are usually created by increasing or decreasing the space between the cutters, or by changing the shape of the side strap or drive link as is done in most safety chains. Sometimes the shape of the depth gauge is also altered.

Standard chain in any type consists of cutters separated by one set of side straps sandwiching the drive links. The side straps are nearly flat across the top, and the distance between any two cutters is only slightly more than the length of a side strap. This configuration is by far the most practical, and all others are for special uses only.

Skip chain is a special-purpose chain with greater distance between the cutters. This distance is achieved by adding extra side straps, and the result allows for maximum chip clearance and less engine strain when very long guide bars are used in softwoods.

Standard chain
The popular chisel-style chain

Skip chain
For softwoods

Full-house chain
For cutting soft metals such as aluminum

Ripping chain is designed for speed in ripping logs into boards and is ideal for use with a lumber-making attachment or mill. For this chain, chipper-style cutters are reground to make narrow cuts. The design is based on the first chains developed for the early chain saws. They were called scratcher chains and worked more like pointed slicers than like the chip-cutting teeth of today's chain. Ripping chain should not be used for crosscuts, as in bucking or felling.

Full-house chain is a very limited special-purpose chain designed for cutting soft metals like aluminum. As the name implies, there is no spacing between the cutters. Full-house chain should not be used on wood.

Safety chain came about when the chain manufacturers themselves tried to do something about kickback. This chain utilizes specially designed side straps or drive links. Depending on the manufacturer, either the drive link or the side strap has a high curve or rise that is supposed to keep the chain from catching in the wood. These chains are considerably less efficient than other designs and greatly increase the amount

Oregon® XtraGUARD® 72SG safety chain. Follow the manufacturer's sharpening instructions.

Oregon® XtraGUARD® 91SG safety chain. Follow the manufacturer's sharpening instructions.

of time it takes to cut a log. They do decrease somewhat the force of kickback, but not its frequency. Parp believes that a combination of caution and a chain brake are the operator's best protection against kickback.

PARTS OF A SAW CHAIN

Let's take a closer look at the parts of a chain and how those parts work, so we can have a better idea of how to keep them working properly.

The *cutter* is the most obvious part of any saw chain. It's the sharp part, of course, and it's the part that sticks up above the rest of the chain.

But the cutter itself has "parts," even though it is all of one piece. The *depth gauge* is the little tooth right in front of the cutting edge. As the chain moves through the wood, the depth gauge guides the wood up into the cutter at exactly the right height. If the depth gauge is too high, the chain won't cut. If it's too low, the cutter will be choked by the wood and will catch. The relationship between the cutter and the depth gauge may vary slightly under certain circumstances, but the relationship must remain fairly close to the original factory design; otherwise, the chain won't cut properly. If you make a change in either the cutter or the depth gauge, you change their relationship. As a cutter is sharpened, it becomes lower. A cutter can be sharpened only two or three times, lightly, before the depth gauge must be lowered. If you tend to file the cutters more than lightly, the depth gauges must be filed down and reshaped every time you sharpen the chain. The depth gauges must, of course, always be lower than the cutting edge.

Between the depth gauge and the cutting edge is the *gullet* of the cutter. As the name implies, the gullet affects the chain's ability to eat wood. When the cutting edge chips or chisels a bite of wood, the bite is forced out of the cutter between the cutting edge and the back of the gullet. Gullets should be cleaned with a round file before every fifth sharpening.

Side straps or *tie straps* are the chain pieces that link the rest of the chain and hold it together with rivets. The side straps endure the most friction and wear from contact with the guide bar. As a result, they are subject to burrs and breakage. Side straps should be frequently and carefully examined. Burrs can be removed, lightly, with a safety-edge file, but any other damage should be viewed as a symptom of error or weakness and should be diagnosed according to Parp's "Saw Chain Troubleshooting Guide" (see page 148). If tie straps become burred or peened to the point where they are tight and inflexible, the chain must be replaced. Such damage is always caused by a worn sprocket, improper chain tension, or badly worn guide bar rails. If the cause isn't corrected, any new chain will quickly be ruined in operation.

Parts of the chain

The last part of your saw chain is the *drive link*. Again, the name tells us the primary function of this part—it drives the chain.

As the engine turns the crankshaft, the crankshaft turns a sprocket or gear assembly attached to the crankshaft. As the sprocket turns, its parts engage the drive links of the chain to rotate it around the guide bar. The sprocket and the chain must match perfectly, and as soon as sprocket wear becomes serious, symptoms will appear on the drive links. Always replace your sprocket before that happens.

At first glance, anyone might think that the hook at the front of the drive links is the part engaged by the sprocket. But, of course, it's going in the wrong direction. The sprocket engages the other side of the drive-link tang, and pushes against most of the tang surface opposite the hook. If that surface becomes damaged, the drive link is ruined and must be replaced. The hook is a different story. Its only job is to help clean the grooves of the bar. Once in a while you'll have to clean the hook with a round file. Be sure to maintain the original shape of the hook.

As a chain wears, it stretches. If a chain has a long life, it will frequently stretch so far that it can't be adjusted properly with the chain-tensioning screw. Before this happens, you might be able to remove a link in the chain to correct the problem. At that time, however, you must check the fit of the chain with the sprocket. If it doesn't match correctly, the chain should be replaced. If the stretched chain has damaged the sprocket, then it, too, must be replaced.

The entire cutting attachment is a precise assembly, and all of its parts must meet and work together perfectly. No damage or wear can be isolated. It will always affect the rest of the attachment, resulting in greater damage that affects other, seemingly unrelated, parts. Any noticeable damage or wear must be thoroughly diagnosed—from effect to cause—and corrected before further use of the saw. Never operate a chain saw that is working less than perfectly or that shows any signs of mechanical damage whatsoever. It's dangerous.

CHAIN MAINTENANCE TOOLS

It's possible to sharpen a chain with a hand-held file and no file guide at all. It's also possible to lower the depth gauges without a jointer. It's even possible to do so fairly accurately, but most of us are not that expert. In any case, it's faster and easier to use the proper tools.

There are three basic kinds of file guide. The first is a hand-held device usually called a *file holder*. It looks as if *all* it does is hold the file, but it does have etched guidelines. As you file, you keep the guidelines parallel with the bar. This helps you maintain the correct filing angle. File holders are the cheapest and most commonly available tools for sharpening chain.

Clamp-on file guides are actually designed as guides, not as holders. These tools, or jigs, are available in many sizes, styles, and price ranges. The better designs clamp *onto* the guide bar and include a small vise that locks a portion of the chain. The filing angle is set with a dial and then locked in place. The file is held by a swing that you move away from the chain on the backstroke. These tools are extremely accurate, versatile, and durable. Get one, says Parp.

If you want to be professional about it, you can get an *electric chain grinder*. These, of course, are more expensive, but they are still among the real bargains in our high-octane economy. If you use chain saws al-

Oregon® Precision Filing Guide

most constantly, if you sell firewood, or if you want to service chain saws in your shop, you'll want an electric chain grinder. There are many different models available, ranging from $60 to $1,500 or more. VIP Industries has developed a portable model that operates off a vehicle's generator. It can also be set up in a shop and is designed to sharpen the chain while it's still on the saw.

Bell Industries, formerly Nielson, offers one grinder in the mid-price range—the KB101—that will sharpen any chipper or chisel chain that requires a round file, and is capable of sharpening an unbroken loop chain as small as 6″. Most other shop grinders are more limited, and shorter chains must be broken in order to fit them onto the filing vise. Bell's KB101 is a high-quality, dependable machine.

A professional-quality chain grinder does the most accurate sharpening and is much easier and faster than any other sharpener. It's a good investment for a small business.

The Silvey SDM4 is a precise chain grinder. It will accurately sharpen true chisel chain, and it'll outlive almost any other machine. Understandably, it costs over $1,500. You can lease one from Bailey's, however,

Bell KB101 chain grinder   Bell KB1A chain grinder

for a small monthly fee. Silvey also makes a chipper-chain shop grinder that allows you to leave your chain on the bar. Silvey's are definitely professional models, and the round-chain grinder costs about $450. Another very popular chain grinder for chisel chain is the Simington 450. It costs about $500.

Since you must lower the depth gauges as you file back the cutters, you need a *jointer* to measure the relative heights of the depth gauges and the cutters. There are many simple devices available for this crucial measurement, and none of them is very expensive. The most common ones are called *filemates* or *gaugits*. These are usually fixed tools for specific chains, and you need a different one for each size chain. Zip Penn sells a more versatile model, simply called Depth Gauge (part number Z-570), that has five different settings controlled with a dial. This particular tool has the advantage of allowing you to adjust the depth for different cutting operations and conditions, as well as for different chains. Priced at less than the cost of two six-packs, it's the most expensive saw chain jointer Parp knows of. The Depth Gauge is pocket-size and accurate.

Sometimes a chain stretches so far that it can no longer be adjusted to the proper tension. Sometimes a chain breaks. Sometimes a single link is damaged by abrasion, or cracks because of an unusual weakness. In these and other cases, you need chain repair tools. Adequate tools to do each of the required jobs come in both shop models and hand or tool-box models.

The cheapest combination of chain repair tools is a ball peen hammer and a punch for removing rivets. The job can be done with these simple tools, but more specialized tools make the work easier and more accurate.

For breaking chain, all sorts of pocket *chain breakers* are usually available at very low cost. These consist of a small anvil with channels to fit various chain sizes. You still use a hammer and punch to remove the rivets, but the anvil holds the chain steady and the channel forms a slot for the punched-out rivet. After the old part is removed, you put the replacement in position on the chain breaker and form the rivet heads with your hammer.

A somewhat more expensive, but far superior, hand tool is the Granberg Break-N-Mend. This tool, as its name implies, both removes the rivets and replaces them. It even restores old rivets so they may be re-

Oregon® Pocket Chain Breaker

used. It forms perfect rivet heads without hammering, and includes an adjustable anvil for all chain sizes, as well as a rivet spinner. Parp suggests it is the best all-around chain repair tool for most chain saw users.

If you use a chain saw professionally, if you have a shop to work in, or if you want to make a profit on sharpening, selling, and repairing chain, you will want the shop tools designed to repair chains professionally. Many companies manufacture specialized bench tools for this purpose. *Bench spinners* and *bench breakers* are a one-time investment and are tools that anyone can use with ease and accuracy. These tools have cost about $30 each for many years. They'll probably go up soon. They are hand-powered precision tools that can be set up anywhere by bolting them to a bench, and they are exactly what the biggest professional shops use. Nothing better has appeared as yet and probably never will. Again, Granberg's chain shop tools are among the best and are readily available.

We have reviewed, briefly, the main types of tools available for sharpening, jointing, breaking, and mending saw chain. Since damaged sprockets cannot be repaired, the only remaining component of the cutting attachment is the bar itself. For almost all chain saw users, it's far easier and cheaper to replace a badly worn or damaged bar than to repair it. In almost all cases, that's Parp's advice. But there are machines available to renew or rebuild guide bars. In some cases, one of these machines

Granberg/Firmont Break-N-Mend

Granberg/Firmont Grind-N-Joint

OREGON® 110-Volt Electric Sure Sharp®

can be a good addition to a large professional chain saw shop. Specialty Motors manufactures the best of these, called the Barshop. It's capable of turning large, old guide bars into small, new ones. It can also regroove worn bars, square the rails, close grooves to standard size, and polish like new. It costs about $1,000. With new guide bar prices as low as $20, this machine would have to work long and hard to pay for itself. It is, of course, a high-quality product.

It's a lot of fun to do things professionally. Many companies sell saw chain in reels of 25, 50, or 100 feet. With a bench grinder, a bench breaker, and a bench spinner with a few reels of chain, anyone can easily set up a nice little chain sales and repair shop. You can produce custom chains to fit any saw, for any cutting purpose. Or you can buy one reel of chain to fit your own saw and have the comfortable feeling of being well stocked for a long time. And you can equip a truck with professional tools to do the same jobs on location. A chain-maintenance business is one of the easiest and least expensive enterprises to establish and maintain, and it's usually a fast route to prestige in any wood-oriented community.

FILES AND FILE SIZES

The cutters of a chain saw require special files made especially for sharpening saw chain. Most chains on most saws are still the chipper type and require a round file of the correct size. All hardware stores carry these special round files, and they're always called chain saw files. They're not tapered and they're not rat-tails. Before you do anything to a saw chain, find out exactly what size and kind of file that chain requires and never attempt to use anything else. Using the wrong file will ruin a chain.

The best source of information about your chain is the owner's manual. If you don't have an owner's manual or if the chain on your saw is different from the original, you should check with your local dealer.

HOW TO SHARPEN A SAW CHAIN

CHIPPER CHAIN

The question Parp hears most is, "When should I sharpen my saw chain?" And you know the answer. "Anytime it needs it." Your chain needs sharpening whenever the saw cuts slowly, whenever you notice that cutting is becoming more difficult, and whenever fine sawdust—rather than proper chips—can be pulled from the cut. And that can happen incredibly often, depending on a number of factors. The best method is to keep your chain sharp and never let it get dull.

If your chain is new, it might not need sharpening (*might* not). Chain manufacturers often sharpen the cutters before assembling the chain. When the individual chains are assembled, the cutters are usually dulled in the process. A few manufacturers avoid this problem in various ways, but it's something to watch for.

If your chain is dull or used or doesn't seem quite as sharp as it should be, have it sharpened professionally before you use it. Then you'll start sharp and with proper angles, and it'll be easier to keep it that way.

In use, a chain normally needs touching up after every hour of cutting. It needs complete sharpening after eight hours of cutting. Any chain should be professionally sharpened, by you or by someone else, after every 40 hours of cutting. That's why, if you plan to use your saw a lot, you should get the best sharpening equipment you can and learn how to use it expertly. It'll save you time and money. Keep in mind, too, that saw chain technology is constantly changing. Check your manufacturer's recommendations for the correct filing angle for your chain.

To sharpen a chipper chain, first examine the chain carefully for damage. Any damaged links should be replaced before you sharpen the rest of the chain. If you're leaving the chain on the bar, adjust it to the correct tension. But it's better to use a vise. If you have a clamp-on file guide, it should have a built-in vise to hold the chain steady. If not, remove the chain from the bar and put it in a vise for sharpening. No one can accurately sharpen a loose chain.

Next, find the shortest cutter tooth on your chain. Use a ruler to measure. In order to cut straight and to avoid excess wear and stretch, each cutter and depth gauge must be the same. Uniformity is the important factor in chain saw performance. The shortest, lowest, smallest cutter must be sharpened first, and then all the others must be filed to match it exactly. The short cutter serves as a guide for filing all the other cutters.

When you've found the shortest cutter, attach or align your file guide so the file will move from the inside of the cutter to the outside. Set your file guide to the correct filing angle. In almost all cases, the correct angle is 35°, and all file guides carry a 35° indicator for chipper chain. The 35° angle is best for chipper chain in all woods, and adjustments for specific woods should involve the height of the depth gauge and not the top plate or cutter angle. The only exception applies to saws used only in frozen hardwood. For this application, file the cutters at 30°. If you use one chain in the winter and another in the summer, sharpen your winter chain at 30° and your summer chain at 35°.

Hold the file level or hold it with the handle no more than 5° lower than the tip of the file. Do not change the angle of the file from horizontal. Keep it constantly level or maintain a constant 5° from horizontal. About one-fifth to one-tenth of the file's diameter should be above the cutter. File lightly with a steady hand. Remove only enough steel to sharpen the tooth or correct any problems. Move the file away from the cutter on the backstroke. In other words, file only on the forward stroke, from the inside to the outside. Check your work carefully and proceed slowly until you are familiar with the entire operation. If the chain has previously been sharpened incorrectly or at the

Oil inlet hole

Remember to keep the oil inlet holes from clogging with sawdust by cleaning them with a hooked wire.

File and
file holder

*Hold the file level. Press against the cutter and make two
or three light strokes forward.*

Always file from inside to outside of cutter.

Keep angle index par-
allel with chain to keep
top plates even.

35°

*File your way around chain, completing one direc-
tion of filing before switching sides.*

35°

Finish filing the other cutters from the other side.

60°

*60° top-plate
cutting
angle*

90°

*90° side-plate
angle for
"chipper
chain"*

wrong angle, or if the cutter has been damaged by abrasion, file until all such problems disappear.

When the shortest cutter is sharp, loosen your file guide or vise and move the chain to align the next cutter on the same side of the chain. Proceed in this way until all the cutters on one side are sharp and uniform. Then remove and reverse your file guide, or turn the saw around, to sharpen the cutters on the other side. Again, use that same, shortest tooth as a guide to sharpen the others. All teeth on both sides must be uniform. If the cutters on one side are shorter than on the other side, the saw will cut crooked.

Note that you measure a cutter by measuring the *length* of its top plate. If all the top plates are the same length, they will also be the same height. That's what the ruler is for.

When you've sharpened all the cutters, examine them again for uniformity and burrs. If you find slight burrs on the cutting edges, rub them with a piece of wood to smooth them out. If the burrs are more than slight, you held the file at too great an angle. You should also compare your cutters with the pictures in this book, or with a new cutter. The angles should be the same.

After you've finished all the cutters, check the height of the depth gauges with your jointer or filemate. If the depth gauges project up through the slot in your jointer, file them level. Use only a flat safety-edge file and leave the jointer in place as you file each depth gauge. Be careful not to hit the cutters or other chain parts. Even with a safety-edge file, you can damage a cutter if you hit it.

When all depth gauges are level and uniform, round off the front corners to restore the original shape. All depth gauges should be filed every second or third sharpening and checked before cutting with a used chain. Do not ''sharpen'' depth gauges: They do no cutting themselves. Their sole purpose is to determine the depth at which the cutters cut the wood.

Finally, clean and lightly file the drive-link tangs on the front face only, to restore the cleaning hook. Be sure to maintain the exact original shape of the tangs. Their purpose is to clean the grooves of your guide bar.

Parp has repeatedly recommended Granberg's File-N-Joint throughout this book. Granberg is the leader in research and development of chain saw tools and accessories. Their products are very high quality and are dependable, accurate, and reasonable. There are a number of other clamp-on sharpeners available, including the Oregon® Precision Filing Guide. Parp suggests you carefully compare the quality and accuracy of any other clamp-on sharpener. Other guides that compare favorably are those made and sold by the European saw manufacturers,

Preset left-hand cutter

Top plate
Side plate
Depth gauge

Positioning tab
rests on cutter
top plate; tighten
C-clamp snugly.

Guard link

Place top file cutter midway on bar.

Support legs
fit over middle
of cutter to be
filed.

Hold file
level at all
times.

*File depth gauge until file
slides easily.*

Measure
side-plate
projection—
it should
be 1/32".

*File cutter
from inside
toward the
outside of
the chain.*

*Gullets are also filed from
the inside to the outside at
a 24° angle to the perpendicular of the chain.*

Proper depth gauge setting

*Place "gaugit" on chain
to check gauge setting.*

*If depth gauge projects,
file it level.*

*Then round off the front corner
to maintain the original shape.*

and they're usually hard to find.

To use the File-N-Joint, leave the chain on the bar and place the File-N-Joint over the bar and chain. The sharpener clamps to the bar—but first you have to tighten the screw that adjusts and locks the chain clamp just above the tops of the rivets in the chain. The chain clamp acts as a vise. Then hold the File-N-Joint parallel to the bar and tighten it with the inside knob.

Now loosen the chain-vise screw slightly, so that the chain is held snugly but still moves freely. Then move a cutter into position against the chain stop and set the angle-dial to the correct top-plate angle for your chain. Another dial adjusts the height so that one-fifth to one-tenth of the circumference of the file protrudes above the cutter. This is one of the reasons why using a File-N-Joint is so much better than hand filing, especially for the beginner; it's very hard to hand-hold a file at the correct height and the correct angle at the same time.

You can then adjust the cutter length—stop to match your shortest cutter. Since you use the same setting to file all the cutters, all the cutters are precisely uniform in height and top-plate angle. Then you can use your File-N-Joint to set your depth gauges with the same accuracy. Use the settings and angles recommended in your owner's manual or in this chapter. Be sure to make all settings with care, or this tool will consistently repeat your errors.

CHAIN TYPES REQUIRING ROUND FILE

Most of the instructions for sharpening chipper chain apply to these chains as well. However, instead of holding or setting your file level, or with the handle 5° below horizontal, hold the handle of the file lower than the tip to maintain a constant angle of 10° from horizontal. The correct top-plate angle for all semichisel chains of 1/4″ or .325″ pitch is 30°. The angle for all other chain sizes of these types is 35°, just as it was for chipper chain. Also lower the depth gauges in the same manner as for chipper chain. Clean and lightly file the drive-link tangs, using a round file to restore the front hook section only.

CHISEL CHAIN

A true chisel chain can be identified by a perfectly flat top plate and a squared cutting edge. If the edge looks round inside, it's either a chipper chain or a semichisel chain and should be sharpened with a round file, as above.

Before every fifth sharpening, clean the gullets of your chisel chain with a round file that would fit a chisel cutter of the same pitch.

Chipper chains are sharpened with a beveled chisel-chain file. Use a file guide to maintain a 20° top-plate angle on new chains. Gradually increase this angle as the cutters get shorter. The beveled corner of the file should fit into the front corner of the cutter—and you file *downward*, against the cutting edge instead of toward it. The file moves from the front toward the rear of the cutter. Depth gauges are lowered just as they are for chipper chains. Clean and lightly file the drive-link tangs with a round file to maintain the original shape.

Keep drive-link tangs sharp. Use a round file to sharpen the tang so it will clean the bar groove of sawdust.

Chisel-chain file

Round file for cleaning gullets

Safety-edge flat file for setting depth gauges

45°–55°

Check depth gauge every third sharpening

90°

20°

Never do this.

Clean out gullets before every fifth sharpening. Always round off depth gauges.

Hold round file level and at a 20° angle to the perpendicular of the cutter.

CHAINS FOR AUTOMATIC SHARPENERS

These are the chains installed on saws equipped with "automatic" or built-in self-sharpening devices. The cutters and depth gauges are set at extreme angles to meet the sharpening stone in the system. The side plates of these chains must be hand-sharpened since the built-in stone doesn't touch them. Manufacturers generally recommend that the side plates be hand-sharpened every fifth time the system is used. Parp says sharpen them every other time.

Be sure to keep your sharpening system clean and free of sawdust. You should always remove packed sawdust from the inside housing before using the system. Use a screwdriver or a long wooden scraper.

To adjust the stone, turn the adjusting screw until sparks appear during sharpening. Be sure to retract the stone when not sharpening.

On all automatic sharpening systems, there is a handle, knob, or some other device for oscillating the stone. You must use this control to oscillate the stone for the entire duration of the sharpening operation. This control moves the stone from side to side to fully sharpen both left and right cutters.

Whenever you replace your chain, always install a new sharpening stone and tighten the locking nut securely.

SPECIAL FILING

You might decide to experiment with your depth gauges. If you do, you should have more than one chain, and you should determine each chain's specific application. You should then avoid using a chain under conditions inconsistent with its special filing.

For example, if you live in an area of hardwood forests and long cold winters, you might want a winter chain (for cutting frozen hardwood). To get efficient work from your chain under these conditions, leave your depth gauges higher than specified in the chart. If you want to change a 3/8"-pitch chipper chain to a hardwood winter chain, stop filing the depth gauges until they are somewhat higher than .020". Try .017" for a while, or gradually decrease the depth-gauge distance until the cutting seems most efficient. A frozen hardwood chipper chain should also be filed at a top-plate angle of 30°, rather than 35°.

For a summer softwood chain, lower your depth gauges .02" or .03" below the specified setting.

If you use your saw with a mill, or do a lot of ripping—as when building a cabin—you should have a special chain just for ripping. The best way to get one is to special-order it, either from your dealer or from Zip Penn or Bailey's. You can also make your own ripping chain: Refile the cutters on any chain to a 15° top-plate angle instead of the standard

35°. Do the filing with a round file, no matter what type chain you use.

A very specialized chain is *boring* chain, a type seldom used by non-professionals. To make one, file the tails of the cutters of a chisel chain at a 45° angle. For most of us, though, the little boring that we ever need to do can easily be done with a standard chain. For that matter, a standard chain will serve most of us very well most of the time. Parp has cut a lot of frozen wood and has never bothered to file a winter chain. It's always sunny where a Parp lives.

When a saw chain is used only for ripping, *change the filing angles as shown above.*

When a chisel chain is used for boring, *taper the tails of the cutters to increase boring efficiency.*

CHAIN REPAIRS

Once you have the tools, correct chain repair procedures are quite obvious. Again, though, uniformity is a major concern. When you replace any chain part, it must be filed to match all the corresponding parts in the chain. The bottom edges of the side straps and cutters ride on the guide bar rails and therefore wear down in use. New parts must be filed to match before they are installed, and drive-link tangs as well must be filed to match the rest of the chain.

Granberg's Break-N-Mend (see photo page 129) is a dependable and accurate combination hand tool that breaks chain, restores old rivets, and spins new rivet heads. To use it to remove rivets, place the side link between the movable anvils and adjust the knurled nut to fit lightly. The side of the drive link (center link) rests on top of the anvils. You then adjust the tension of the punch by turning the knurled nut in the han-

Right

Wrong

Fit chain into the smallest slot of the chain breaker so that the cutter is on top. Punch out the rivets of the damaged part.

Put preset part on a flat surface.

Install chain on the new part.

The dimple on the strap faces out. Form the rivet head with a round hammer.

File off the bottom of the new part to match the worn parts. Then file a new cutter back to match the worn cutters.

dle. Then squeeze the handle to punch out the rivet. That breaks the chain so you can replace the damaged parts.

The first anvil of the Break-N-Mend is a spinning anvil that allows you to reshape a used rivet. Place the old rivet in the recess of the spinning anvil—head up—and squeeze the handle. The rivet comes out looking new.

To reassemble the chain, place the new pieces and the rivet into the recess of the spinning anvil, rivet head down. Adjust the pressure, and close the handle to form a new rivet head. A little oil makes the spinning easier. File the new parts to match the corresponding worn parts of your chain.

If you use a pocket chain breaker or some other kind of anvil, place the damaged section of your chain over the channel that fits your chain. Place the chain on the breaker so that the affected cutter is on top, not underneath (see page 141). Use a punch to knock out the rivet. Be sure not to use excessive force. Drive from the cutter to the side strap underneath. File the new parts to match the corresponding worn parts of your chain. *Cutter top plates and depth gauges should be filed after assembling the chain, but the bottoms of cutters and tie straps must be filed first.* Put the new part in position on a flat part in your chain repair tool and install the chain over it. Form rivet heads with a ball peen hammer or a rock.

GUIDE BAR MAINTENANCE

As indicated earlier, the guide bar groove should be cleaned thoroughly and often. Use a toothbrush as much as possible, but if the dirt or pitch is hard, you can remove it with the end of a file, a wooden scraper, or the guide bar scraper on your filemate. Whenever you remove your bar, turn it over. Rotating a bar distributes the wear evenly and helps prevent the groove from getting wider on one side. Guide bars should be separately oiled after cleaning.

As your bar gets older, check frequently to determine drive-link tang clearance. The tangs must not touch the bottom of the groove. The chain rides with the shoulders of the tie straps and cutters on the rails of the bar, not with the tangs scraping the bottom of the groove.

If a saw gets hung up or pinched in a cut, the rails can be pinched together, and cracks or splits will sometimes occur. If they're small, you can weld them—if the bar doesn't have hardened rails or a stellite tip. It's best to replace the bar, but slight bends or kinks can be straightened by pressing it or by laying it on a hard, flat surface and pounding it lightly. Note that the grooves at the tail of the bar should be funnel-shaped. If they become flattened, file them open with a flat file.

Good   Uneven height   Burred

Worn from chain   Spread rails   Shallow groove;
being too loose   grind deeper

When your guide bar rails become rough or worn, lightly file them smooth with a flat file. Take care to file them evenly and be sure to check drive-link tang clearance afterward. If the tangs bottom in the groove, the bar must be professionally reground or else replaced. Parp says replaced.

Roller-nose or sprocket-nose bars must be greased daily. That's daily, every time you use the saw, even if it's only for two hours. Clean the nose and the grease holes, and pump the grease with a needle-nose grease gun. Keep pumping until grease comes out all around the roller. Watch the sides of the roller nose for burrs and remove them with a flat file. Disposable chain saw grease guns are available from your dealer or from the mail-order houses.

Whenever you work with your bar or chain, be sure to check and clean the oil holes carefully.

SPROCKETS

Never install a new chain on a worn sprocket. Sprockets are set to the same pitch as the chain and must match perfectly for good performance. Gauges are available for measuring sprocket pitch. If you use plenty of lubrication in your cutting, if you keep all cutting attachments parts clean and properly filed, if your chain, bar, and sprocket match correctly, and if correct chain tension has been maintained, each sprocket should last through two chains. Anytime you change chain sizes or types, you must also change the sprocket, even if the old one is still in good shape. Many companies sell sets that consist of bar, chain, and sprocket. Parp

Sprocket pitch too large   *Sprocket pitch too small*

says that's the best way to renew your cutting attachment. (See the "Troubleshooting Guide" in the Appendix for sprocket-related cutting problems.) Grease the sprocket bearings every time you remove your sprocket.

Since both chains and sprockets change with wear, the most economical solution is to start with one new sprocket and two or three new chains. Alternate the chains to keep the wear equal. In this way, the sprocket and chains will age together, and the sprocket should last as long as the chains do. When you replace the chains, replace the sprocket at the same time.

TOUCHING UP ON THE JOB

If you work steadily at cutting, even the best softwood will take the edge off a chain in an hour or two. To extend that time, as well as bar and chain life, use plenty of oil. Always watch for grit or sand in the bark, as abrasive material dulls a chain very quickly.

Whenever you take a break, check the edges of your cutters. You can easily and quickly restore them to near perfection with two or three light passes of a file in a file holder. Be careful to maintain the correct angles. Depth gauges rarely need lowering in the course of a day's work.

TROUBLESHOOTING

Occasionally, in one of your periodic examinations of your chain, you might find a problem with some part, such as a cutter. When you do, compare the problem part to the "Saw Chain Troubleshooting Guide" on pages 148 and 149. You should be able to identify the problem and thus discover its probable cause and remedy.

But not all cutting problems are immediately apparent, especially if chain saws are new to you. It's impossible here to cover completely all the potential saw chain problems, but if you experience a performance problem, try to identify it from the following paragraphs.

Chain cuts crooked; cuts at an angle; engine drags: If your bar and sprocket are in good shape, these problems are caused by filing the cutters at different angles or by inconsistent filing pressure from tooth to tooth. A chain that is sharper or longer on one side will pull to that side. Refile to restore uniform cutters, and reset the depth gauges. Check bar rails and tang clearance.

Chain dulls quickly: The most common cause of this problem is thin or feathered cutting edges caused by holding the file handle too low or by pressing down too hard on the file. A misaligned, worn, or wrong-pitch sprocket will also cause the chain to wear or dull quickly. Check the sprocket for wear and for the correct size. Refile cutters using lighter strokes with the file held level or at a slighter angle, no more than 5° from horizontal. Also check and lower the depth gauges, and check the chain tension often.

Chain has been filed but won't cut; powders wood instead of chipping it: Blunt cutting edges are produced by holding the file too high on the face of the tooth or by holding the handle too high. Refile with a clamp-on file guide.

Chain binds; requires pressure to cut: Incorrect top-plate angle is caused by holding the file at an incorrect angle (less than 35°) or height (producing back slope), or by letting it drift during the filing stroke. Depth gauges left too high will also cause this condition. Refile with a steady hand.

Chain overheats; scrapes wood instead of cutting: If you're using sufficient oil, this problem is usually caused by a back slope of the cutters. This happens when you hold the handle of the file too low, while simultaneously filing too high on the tooth. Have the chain reground professionally.

Chain grabs and jerks; cuts rough: This is caused by a forward hook on the cutters produced by excessive downward filing pressure with the top of the file too high on the tooth. Have the chain reground professionally.

Cutters dig too far into the wood, or take only thin slices: Both of these problems are caused by incorrectly set depth gauges. Check the depth gauge setting. Refile and reshape the depth gauges if they're too low, and file back the cutters.

Chain slops in guide bar; overheats; cuts crooked: The bar rails are probably spread too far, or the drive links are bottoming in the groove. If the rails are spread, pound them back into shape, using a bar-groove gauge, and try again. If the problem persists, or if the drive links are bottoming in the groove, the bar must be replaced or regrooved on a bar-rebuilding machine. Parp says replace both the bar and sprocket, and regrind the chain.

Whenever these or any other cutting problems occur, you should remove the bar and chain from the saw and clean them in solvent. Then examine the chain carefully and compare its parts to the drawings in the "Saw Chain Troubleshooting Guide" at the end of this chapter. The chart should help you to identify the cause or causes of your troubles. When you know the cause, you'll also know the remedy.

ORDERING AND REPLACING SAW CHAIN, BAR, AND SPROCKET

Your dealer can order any replacement part for your chain saw if you can supply accurate information on the saw's brand, model number, type, and size. The size of a cutting attachment is usually stated as a measurement of the actual bar cutting length from the front of the saw's body to the tip of the bar. It's also often helpful to know the overall length of the bar itself, from tail to tip. It's best to make note of the drive-link count of the original chain and scratch this number somewhere on the saw for reference.

Most chains carry a code number stamped on the drive link. This code indicates the gauge of the chain. In addition, the pitch of the chain is often stamped on the cutters or depth gauges. If you know this information and the number of links in your chain when it was new, you can easily order a replacement chain that is prefitted to your bar. Or you can order the chain, bar, and sprocket as a set.

Most dealers carry or can order more than one brand of chain. First, of course, they carry the brand of chain made by or for the saws they sell. They often sell a cheaper brand of chain as well, or chain they cut themselves from bulk reels.

You can also mail-order chain from Zip Penn or Bailey's, either in reels or in closed loops to fit your saw. Bailey's sells the high-quality Oregon Saw Chain at a discount. If you place a large order, Bailey's will give you a special package deal. If you're way out in the woods or if you're starting a chain saw business, this is the way to go.

To order chain for your saw or to change brands, find your chain on the "Saw Chain Conversion Chart" in the Appendix. The chart will tell you which other companies produce similar chains. You can also switch to another brand or type of chain, as long as it fits your bar and sprocket. Be sure it does.

CHAIN MAINTENANCE CHECKLIST

1. Clean the chain in solvent before and after sharpening.
2. File cutters at the correct angle.
3. Check and lower the depth gauges often.
4. Soak chain in clean oil between uses.
5. Use sufficient oil when cutting.
6. Check the bar and sprocket condition frequently. If damaged, repair or replace immediately.
7. Avoid hitting dirt or abrasive material when cutting.
8. Check the condition of chain parts frequently. Compare with the "Saw Chain Troubleshooting Guide."
9. Never force a dull chain to cut. Severe damage will result to the chain, bar, sprocket, and clutch.
10. Check and set the chain tension often. Allow no sag in any kind of chain on any kind of saw under any conditions. With standard bars, set the tension so the side straps just touch the rails along the entire bottom length of the bar. With roller-nose or sprocket-nose bars, set the tension tighter. Also increase the tension to sharpen the chain on the bar.
11. Keep bar grooves clean and oil holes open.
12. Keep bar rails flat and uniform.
13. Check for drive-link tang clearance in bar grooves.
14. Clean bar daily when used.
15. Grease roller-nose and sprocket-nose bars daily when used.
16. Check roller nose for burrs. Remove with file.
17. Sharpen front lower hook portion of drive-link tangs.
18. Grease sprocket bearing whenever sprocket is removed.

SAW CHAIN TROUBLESHOOTING GUIDE

WEAR—CUTTERS AND TIE STRAPS

CONDITION: Cracks under rear rivet holes on cutters and opposing tie straps.
CAUSE: Excessive pressure on dull or misfiled cutters. Common during winter.
REMEDY: File chain correctly. Use oil freely.

CONDITION: Light damage on cutting edges of top and/or side plates.
CAUSE: Cutters hit sand or dirt, other foreign material.
REMEDY: File cutters to remove all damaged area.

CONDITION: Excessive wear on bottom of cutters and tie straps.
CAUSE: Depth gauges too high. Cutting edge cannot get into wood.
REMEDY: Lower depth gauges to proper setting. Keep cutters filed correctly.

CONDITION: Peening on front corner of cutters and intermediate tie straps. Causes tight joints.
CAUSE: Chain striking bar entry. Sprocket too small, or loose chain tension.
REMEDY: Use proper bar and sprocket. Adjust chain tension correctly.

CONDITION: Peening on bottom of cutters and tie straps causes tight joints.
CAUSE: Loose chain tension. Result of dull cutters and forcing dull chain into wood.
REMEDY: Keep proper tension. Keep cutters sharp. Chain may need to be replaced.

CONDITION: Excessive heel wear on cutters and tie straps.
CAUSES: 1. Blunt top-plate filing.
2. Forcing dull chain to cut.
3. Forcing chain to cut frozen wood.
4. Low depth-gauge settings.
5. Lack of lubrication.
REMEDY: File cutters properly. Don't force dull chain to cut. Use oil freely.

CONDITION: Concave wear on bottom of cutters, connecting tie straps.
CAUSES: 1. Chain tension too tight.
2. Normal wear from undercutting (cutting with top of bar).
REMEDY: Adjust chain tension. Reduce the amount of cutting with top of bar.

A. Open bar groove.
B. Severe abrasion and wobbly chain on thin bar rails. **C.** Rails not flat. **D.** Wobbly chain, rails too thick. **E.** One rail too thin or soft.

CONDITION: Excess wear on bottom of all chain parts.
CAUSES: 1. Uneven filing, worn bar rails cause chain to wobble.
2. Excessive pressure, trying to make chain cut.
REMEDY: File chain properly. Recondition bar rails or replace bar. Replace chain if necessary.

CONDITION: Severe damage on either side of top and/or side plates.
CAUSE: Cutters hit abrasive material.
REMEDY: File cutters to remove all damage.

CONDITION: Edges burred and notch peened on tie straps.
CAUSE: Chain chatter as a result of loose chain tension and improper filing.
REMEDY: Correct chain tension. Refile chain properly. Replace sprocket if badly worn.

CONDITION: Peened notch in tie strap. Causes tight joints and broken drive links.
CAUSE: Chain run on badly worn spur sprocket or wrong pitch sprocket.
REMEDY: Replace worn sprocket. Chain may need to be replaced.

CONDITION: Broken tie straps opposite cutters.
CAUSE: Fatigue failure because of worn spur sprocket.
REMEDY: Replace sprocket. Replace broken tie straps. Chain may need replacement.

INCORRECT FILING

CONDITION: Back slope on side-plate cutting edge. Cutter won't feed into wood.
CAUSE: File held too high.
REMEDY: Refile cutters to recommended angle.

CONDITION: Feathered top plate causes rapid dulling.
CAUSE: File handle held too low.
REMEDY: Refile properly at recommended angle.

CONDITION: Hook in side-plate cutting edge. Cutters grab, cut rough.
CAUSE: File held too low, or file is too small.
REMEDY: Refile to recommended angle with right size file.

CONDITION: Blunt top-plate cutting angle. Chain won't feed into wood, won't cut.
CAUSE: File handle held too high.
REMEDY: Refile properly, at recommended angle.

CONDITION: Top-plate angle less than recommended. Causes slow cutting, excess wear on chain and bar.
CAUSE: File held at less than recommended angle.
REMEDY: Refile at correct angle.

CONDITION: Top-plate angle more than recommended. Side-plate cutting edge is thin and dulls rapidly.
CAUSE: File held at more than recommended angle.
REMEDY: Refile at correct angle.

DEPTH GAUGES

CONDITION: Uneven depth-gauge height. Chain won't cut straight.
CAUSE: Uneven filing.
REMEDY: Use correct depth-gauge jointer to lower gauges evenly.

CONDITION: Depth gauge is pointed, buries itself in wood.
CAUSE: Improperly filed depth gauge.
REMEDY: File cutters back so depth gauges can be set and re-shaped properly.

CONDITION: Blunt depth gauge causes rough cutting.
CAUSE: Improperly filed depth gauge.
REMEDY: Round off front corner to maintain original shape.

DRIVE LINKS

CONDITION: Scars on sides.
CAUSE: Loose chain jumping off bar.
REMEDY: Adjust chain tension. Replace bent drive links.

CONDITION: Rounded concave bottom.
CAUSE: Shallow groove on bar tip.
REMEDY: Regroove bar tip. Bar may need to be replaced.

CONDITION: Battered and broken bottom.
CAUSE: Chain jumped bar. Spur sprocket hit drive links.
REMEDY: Replace damaged drive links, sharpen tangs with round file. Remove burrs.

CONDITION: Sides worn round at bottom.
CAUSE: Chain wobbled in bar groove. Caused by uneven cutters or worn bar rails.
REMEDY: Rework bar rails and groove. Correct chain filing.

CONDITION: Front or back peened.
CAUSE: Improper sprocket fit. Prolonged chain chatter.
REMEDY: Replace sprocket. Adjust chain tension. Chain may be damaged beyond repair.

CONDITION: Straight bottom.
CAUSE: Shallow bar groove.
REMEDY: Regroove bar or replace. Re-shape drive-link tangs with round file to retain original shape.

CONDITION: Front point turned up.
CAUSE: Drive links bottoming in sprocket. Sprocket worn.
REMEDY: Replace sprocket. Sharpen tangs. Check for burrs.

CONDITION: Nicked bottom or back.
CAUSE: Cutting with loose chain or wrong-pitch sprocket.
REMEDY: Adjust chain tension. Install correct sprocket. File off burrs. Replace damaged drive links.

CHAPTER 9
USING YOUR CHAIN SAW

The season is upon us. We've gotten a Forest Service permit to remove a huge stand of beetle-killed Ponderosa pine. The trees are all standing dead and have been treated to prevent the spread of the beetles, so the wood is safe for us to store and use. It's still early in the season and no one else has even applied for a permit yet. Now's the time to put by as many cords of good wood as we have the time and energy to harvest. We'll work together, since it's much safer and easier for two people to get two supplies of wood than for one person to get one supply of wood.

GETTING ORGANIZED

First, let's organize a system for the daily maintenance of our chain saws and other supplies and equipment. We'll plan on using the tailgates of our pickup trucks as workbenches for servicing the saws and touching up the chains. The tools are in the cab, where they'll be out of the way and easy to get to. The fuel containers, chain-oil cans, and rags are up on one side of the truck's box so they won't be covered up with logs or create a fire hazard in the cab.

Last night, getting ready for a season's wood trip, we thoroughly cleaned and serviced and sharpened our saws and checked on all the other tools and supplies we'll need. The fuel is fresh and correctly mixed with two-cycle engine oil. Our saws have passed inspection and now start easily, run perfectly, and cut straight. We've got extra spark plugs, air filters, chain loops, and spare chain parts, so we shouldn't have to come back for anything once we get to the woods and start working. You brought along an extra bar and sprocket but I didn't, so I'll have to be extremely careful not to pinch my bar, or I may be out of business in no time.

Speaking of pinching the bar, maybe we should review some of the basics of woodcutting and general chain saw use before we actually head into the woods.

BUCKING

Lately we've been practicing out on the backyard woodpile, and we now have a real feel for our saws—how they handle and cut. And we've gotten used to cutting easy logs, in easy situations—like propped up on a sawbuck with one end free, so all we have to do is cut (but carefully, of course).

Now out there in the woods, we're going to be cutting all sizes and kinds of wood, under various conditions. How do we avoid limbs that snap back and logs that roll? We'd better take time for a look at some different kinds of woodcutting situations.

Our plastic wedges will be useful tools. In many cases, simply using a wedge will save a guide bar from being pinched in a cut. A pinched bar is often bent so badly that it makes continued cutting difficult or dangerous, so it is definitely to be avoided.

FIG. 9.1

When crosscutting on a hill, always *stand on the uphill side, because the logs will probably roll. Wedges are necessary to keep the cut open; use* only *soft plastic wedges.*

Out there on the woodpile, using a sawbuck, we've cut a lot of logs with no trouble. They weren't *huge* logs, though. Suppose we must cut a really thick log that's supported on one end. How do we keep the log from splitting or tearing when we cut through it?

The first thing to consider in any woodcutting problem is the stress factor. What is the nature and direction of the stress? If we analyze the stress conditions before we cut, we'll avoid many problems and some dangers.

The general rule is first to cut the side of the log where the wood is *compressed* by the stress, then cut the side on which the wood is *under tension* created by the same stress. For example, when a log is supported on only one end, the *compression* of the wood occurs on the underside of the log, while the wood in the upper portion of the log is *under tension*. On the other hand, if a log is supported at *both* ends, the compression occurs on the top side, while the tension occurs on the underside. Always stop to analyze the stress before cutting, and always cut the compression side first and then the tension side.

FIG. 9.2

Saw blade binding

When a log is supported under both ends, never allow the saw blade to get pinched in the saw cut by trying to cut through in one cut. Always cut on the compression side first and then on the tension side.

With our huge log supported on one end only, and our cut coming only on the free side of the support, we must minimize the amount of stress at the moment the cut becomes complete. A wedge won't help in this situation because it would increase the stress, rather than decrease it.

So let's start our cut from the underside of the log by cutting upward with the top side of the saw's cutting attachment (called *pulling chain*) until we've cut about a third of the way through. Then we can finish the cut from the top of the log, and the stress at the moment the cut is complete will be considerably less. The log will be unlikely to split and the cut end will simply fall free as soon as our top cut meets our bottom cut. Note that this procedure is made much more difficult, even impossible, if the saw won't cut straight because of a bent bar, an improperly sharpened chain, or unevenly filed bar rails.

FIG. 9.3

Two hints for crosscutting a felled tree that has a trunk thinner than the guide bar length, and which is supported at both ends

By the way, when cutting a log—however it is supported—be sure to stand on the uphill side and use a good stance with nothing underfoot to trip you or slow you down in case you have to move quickly. Keep your feet far enough apart to allow a firm, comfortable stance and balanced center of gravity, and keep both hands on the saw at all times.

Now suppose our large log is supported on *both* ends. The top side is the compression side and the bottom is under tension. To avoid splintered wood and a pinched bar in this situation, begin this time with an

FIG. 9.4

When crosscutting logs supported on one end, make two cuts in this sequence.

Stress

When logs, supported on one end, are thicker than the guide bar length, cut in this sequence.

When crosscutting logs supported at both ends, make two cuts in this sequence.

Stress

When logs, supported at both ends, are thicker than the guide bar length, cut in this sequence.

Stress

If cutoff section is likely to settle and bind against the blade, make cuts on an angle so the cut opens up.

Crosscutting techniques that prevent pinching and binding of the saw blade overcut into the top side of the log, again cutting only about one-third of the log's diameter. Then finish the cut from underneath, with an underbuck. Make both cuts at a slight angle to the line of the log so the bar isn't pinched in the kerf as the log settles. The top of the cut should angle slightly toward the end of the log that's being cut—that is, the short end. Another trick to avoid pinching the bar is to make the two cuts so they aren't directly opposite each other, but still close enough for the log to come apart when the cut is complete.

If you're going to buck a log that's lying fairly flat on the ground, so that its weight is supported by the ground for its entire length, there's obviously no way to underbuck it. In this case, start your cut on the top side and when you've cut a few inches into the log, use a wedge to keep the kerf open enough to avoid pinching the bar. Remember to work on the uphill side and avoid cutting into the dirt. When a log is flat on the ground, the stress occurs only as you saw. As you cut, compression tends to occur on the bottom side. This can cause the cut to close gradually as the stress increases. Thus the wedge helps to overcome the problem by keeping the cut fully open.

SEQUENCE BUCKING OF LARGE-DIAMETER LOGS

Now let's say we have two logs that are both larger in diameter than the length of the guide bar we're using. One log is supported on both ends, the other on only one end. In both cases, we'll have to make a number of cuts in sequence to avoid pinching the bar and to cut all the way through both logs successfully. The idea in sequence bucking of thick logs is to leave a break-off hinge of uncut wood in whichever third of the log is affected by the compression created by the stress. The exact placement of the hinge and the sequence of the cuts will be determined by the nature and direction of the stress.

Our first log is supported on both ends. Since the stress causes the compression to occur in the upper third of the log, that's where we'll want to leave our hinge. To buck this log, first make a one-third cut on the far side, as shown in Figure 9.4. Then overbuck from the top to leave a thin hinge in the upper third of the log. The third cut, on the close side of the log, brings the saw into position for the fourth cut, an underbuck. Finish with a fifth cut to take out the hinge. This can be done from any convenient angle. The log will then fall; watch your feet.

Our second log is supported on one end only, so we'll want to leave a hinge in the compressed lower third of the log to prevent splitting. Again, make your first cut on the far side of the log. Make the second cut an underbuck to create the hinge. The third cut is on the close side, the fourth is an overbuck, and the fifth takes out the hinge.

Much of the time, the logs you'll actually be bucking in the woods —in order to make them easy to handle—will be lying flat on the ground, more or less fully supported. If the diameter of a down log happens to be more than twice the length of your bar, the easiest way to cut it is to make a series of overbucks, then roll the log over and finish from the other side. Again, use wedges to keep the kerf from closing on your bar. Working in this manner, you can cut almost any size log with almost any size chain saw, although a very thick, tough log may well place great strain on the engine of a minisaw and would likely murder some of the cheap electrics now being sold in discount stores.

SAFETY ALWAYS

It's so easy to get carried away. There's all that wood to cut and the saw is sailing through it like crazy. Then it starts to get dull. You keep cutting. You push harder and harder. The last thing you want to do is take that break you've put off for two hours, although that would give you a chance to sharpen up. The next thing you know, you've gone and hurt yourself. Or maybe all you did was burn up your saw. Neither one is any fun, and neither one helps keep your house warm. Take it easy. Let the saw do the work. If it's sharp and in good running condition, you won't have to apply much force. Take frequent breaks to keep both you and your saw sharp. That way you won't have to learn how to split wood with one hand in a cast.

Remember to begin any cut as close to your saw's body as possible, using the bumper, or bumper spikes, as a pivot point. When you use this basic pivot motion you maintain maximum control and avoid the worst kickback and push-pull situations. You will also work easier and will not tire as quickly as the cutter who uses the tip of the bar for most of the cutting. Always take time to be sure your footing is solid and that you're not working in underbrush that may trip or stop you if you have to move quickly.

FELLING A SMALL TREE

Now let's practice felling one small tree. First, choose a tree that you're sure you want to cut down. Pick one that's fairly straight, or that leans slightly in the direction in which you want it to fall. It's very difficult to fell even a small tree against the direction of its lean. Also, we want a tree that we're sure will fall in a safe direction, away from power lines, buildings, parked or passing vehicles, and other obstructions.

Next, study the tree as you're walking toward it. Try to estimate its center of gravity, its direction of lean, and which side is most heavily weighted with branches. Now make sure that no one will come near the radius of the tree's height from any direction. Then clear a large area all around the tree. Remove any underbrush or fallen limbs that you might trip over if you have to move quickly. Underbrush or tall weeds can also cause kickback if they come in contact with your chain. Clear an escape route out from the tree. Your escape route should be back away from the anticipated direction of the fall and at an angle from it. Don't plan on running directly opposite to the direction of the fall, as the tree may well fall exactly opposite from the plan. Imagine a line extending from

FIG. 9.5

45°

Prepare the immediate cutting area by cleaning away undergrowth likely to interfere with the operator and saw, and by removing dead material that could cause a fire.

Prepare a path of safe retreat to the rear and at a 45° diagonal to the line of fall.

the expected direction of the fall, and then plan your escape route at a 45° angle to one side or the other of this line.

There are two basic cutting operations involved with felling any tree. These operations may be altered or complicated by the size or shape of the tree, the lay of the land, or the required direction of the fall; nonetheless, you should always use them when cutting down a standing tree. These are the *notch cut* and the *directional cut*.

The notch determines and controls the direction of the fall. The directional cut, also called the felling or back cut, is the final procedure that actually causes the tree to fall, if all goes as and when it should. The notch cut creates a notch by removing a wedge of wood from the tree on the side facing the desired direction of the fall. The felling cut, made from the opposite side, removes enough of the remaining wood to cause the tree to topple toward the notch, thus breaking the remaining hinge of uncut wood. The notch cut and the felling cut *must always* be made so as to leave an uncut hinge of wood that will break as the tree falls. NOTE: If the hinge of uncut wood is not left, that is, if you cut all the way through to the notch cut with your felling cut, the tree is likely to spin before falling, and the direction of its fall will be dangerously unpredictable. *Never* cut all the way through any standing tree with a single cut, no matter what the tree's size.

So first we make our notch. The basic notch for felling a small tree is made with two cuts. Make the upper of the two cuts first, to avoid pinching the bar. (It's not easy to dig a saw out of a cut with the tree's weight pressing down on it.)

FIG. 9.6

Direction of fall

Important: hinge thickness (about one-tenth of tree diameter)

Cut notch about 45°.

Cut a wedge into one-third of the tree's thickness.

Felling cut

Hinge

Notch

Fulcrum

Plan your escape route well, at a 45° angle.

Once the tree begins to fall, retreat quickly!

On a small tree, put the bumper of the saw to the log directly behind the hinge and make a fanlike felling cut.

Move to one side of the tree, facing the desired direction of the fall. Aim across the top of your saw, along your front handle or across the saw's falling sights (usually cast ribs in the saw's main housing). Aim at exactly the place where you want the tree to fall. This will correctly line up your guide bar with the trunk of the tree.

Now make the upper cut of the notch, sawing down at an angle so that the cut, when completed, will go about one-third of the way into the trunk. *Never* cut as far as halfway into a tree with any cut in the notching procedure. Doing so will make the fall uncontrollable. Study the accompanying illustrations to see how to cut the notch correctly.

Next, make the lower cut to complete the notch and remove the wedge of wood. With a small straight tree on level ground, make this second cut straight in, level with the ground, to meet the first. The hinge of uncut wood will be created when you make your felling cut.

Now go behind the tree to make your felling cut. This is another horizontal cut, *at least one inch* (more, for larger trees) above the second, or horizontal, notch cut. It's extremely important not to make the felling cut so as to meet the horizontal notch cut. It must be at least an inch or two higher in order to maintain control of the fall. It's also essential not to cut all the way through the felling hinge.

When your felling cut is deep enough, insert a plastic wedge into the cut, behind your bar but not touching it. If the tree is very small, it may be impossible to place a wedge into the cut without interfering with your saw. But use a wedge, if possible, to prevent the tree from settling back onto your bar and to help control the direction of the fall. Then keep an eye on the top of the tree and continue cutting until the tree begins to fall. Don't cut all the way through to your notch. When the tree begins to fall, remove your saw from the cut, leave the tool on the ground, and retreat quickly but carefully along your escape route—while glancing back over your shoulder to be sure the tree doesn't turn around and come in your direction. (That *can* happen and don't let anyone tell you it can't. It happens to Parp whenever he begins to get a little too sure of himself.) And remember that the butt of the tree can kick backward when the tree hits the ground. Also, unseen dead branches, called widow-makers, may fall straight down or fly in any direction, even from a small tree. Take no chances. Retreat quickly and without hesitation along your escape route while keeping track of what the tree is doing.

That's how you cut down a reasonably straight tree when the diameter of the tree is less than the length of your guide bar and the ground is fairly level. But when we get out there on a real woodin' trip, we'll also be cutting down bigger trees and trees that stand on uneven terrain. These situations require special techniques and specific sequences of cuts.

FELLING LARGE TREES

To cut a tree with a diameter larger than but not twice as large as the length of your saw's guide bar, use the following method. Exercise great caution, because the technique involves making a plunge cut that greatly increases the risk of severe kickback. For this reason, you should be quite experienced and comfortable with using your saw before attempting this procedure. This is definitely not for the novice cutter.

To notch a large tree, use two separate cuts to make each part of the notch. First, make one-half of the upper notch cut on one side of the tree, then move to the other side to complete the upper notch cut. Then do the same with the horizontal cut that completes the notch.

FIG. 9.7

The first step in felling a thicker tree is to make the directional cut by "pulling chain." Make sure that the angle is greater than 45°.

Sight line for felling precision

The decided direction of fall

Then change your position to finish the cut by "pulling chain" again.

Finish cutting initial wedge out, making sure the lower cut meets the upper one exactly.

Basic procedure for the first directional cut in felling a thick tree

After the notch is formed and you've removed the wedge of wood, make a *plunge cut* to one side of your planned felling cut. This plunge cut *must* be made from the rear of the tree on the side closest to the desired direction of the fall. Start the felling cut about an inch or two above the base of the notch. Keep your bar horizontal during this procedure. To minimize the danger of kickback, start the plunge cut with the underside of the tip of your bar and slowly cut inward. When the bar has cut a few inches into the tree, cautiously straighten the saw to begin boring straight inward with the tip of the bar, being careful to leave adequate wood for the hinge. Do not bore all the way through to your notch. In fact, your bar during this procedure should bore into the tree more or less parallel with the back of your notch, not toward it.

When your plunge cut is about halfway into the tree and you have formed about half of your felling hinge, proceed to complete the felling cut by sawing around the tree, toward your planned escape route. In other words, make a pivot with the tip of the bar up against the hinge. Insert a plastic wedge behind your bar as soon as you pass the halfway point—but not before, as that would tend to spin the tree away from your desired angle of fall. Be very careful to leave an adequate hinge of uncut wood between your felling cut and the previously formed directional notch. When your pivot is complete, you may remove as much of the hinge opposite from your present stand—that is, closest to where you began your plunge cut—as is necessary to cause the tree to begin to fall. Then get the hell out, fast, being sure to look over your shoulder at where the tree actually decided to go—which is hopefully not in your direction.

Incidentally, if you forgot to bring some plastic wedges, you can split one or two out of the wedge of wood you removed to make your notch.

To fell a tree having a diameter more than twice as great as the length of your guide bar, only one additional cut is necessary. This time, the additional cut is in the notching operation and, in effect, cuts the hinge in half (see Figure 9.9).

Make the notch, as before. Then make a plunge cut in the back center of the notch, thus segmenting the wood that will eventually become the felling hinge. Depending on the diameter of the tree, the plunge cut should be approximately twice the width of your guide bar.

Cutting a plunge at the back of the notch in this manner actually creates *two* hinges. Now from the other side of the tree, the felling side, make another plunge cut that meets the first, then pivot around the tree to make the felling cut. Place your plastic wedge as early as possible during this procedure, and be careful not to cut through the segment of wedge that faces the desired direction of fall.

FIG. 9.8-A

2. First in a series of fanlike cuts

Important hinge

First fulcrum

Direction of fall

3. Second fan cut

1. Initial notch cut

Second fulcrum

4. Final felling fan cut; retreat quickly!

To fell trees that have diameters exceeding the bar length, start with the notch cut, in about one-third of the tree's diameter; finish with about three fanlike cuts, changing fulcrums as little as possible.

FIG. 9.8-B

2. Second, speed up the engine and press the bar nose against the wood, then slowly pivot the engine while continuing to press the bar nose.

Never plunge the nose of the bar straight into the wood!

Making a plunge or boring cut

1. First, place the nose of the bar at an angle to the proposed bore.

FELLING ON A SLOPE

In the woods, you'll often want to cut a tree that stands on a slope. If you can drop the tree downhill, you can gain more control over the fall if you make both notch cuts at an angle. The first cut angles down, as before. The second angles upward, to meet the first. It's not easy to cut upward at an angle accurately, so don't try this procedure on larger trees until you've practiced it on smaller ones and feel comfortable with your ability.

The best policy regarding trees that must be felled uphill is to avoid them altogether. There are two reasons for this. First, it's more dangerous to fell a tree uphill onto a slope because it makes your escape more difficult and awkward if you must retreat downhill; also, the tree is more likely to kick back as it hits the ground. Second, if you're felling uphill, it's often because that's the direction in which you must move the wood after it's bucked. Carrying or skidding logs uphill is both more difficult and more dangerous.

Parp has avoided specifying how high up the trunk you should cut

FIG. 9.9

2. Plunge cut; use caution

3. First in a series of fanlike cuts

First fulcrum

4. Second fan cut

Direction of fall

1. Initial notch cut

Important hinge

Second fulcrum

5. Final felling fan cut; retreat quickly!

To fell big trees that have diameters exceeding twice the bar length, start by carefully making a plunge cut into the center of the tree, making sure to press the nose of the bar into the log until the guide bar is into the wood double its width *before making the boring cut. Finish with about three fanlike cuts, changing fulcrums as little as possible.*

FIG. 9.10

Provides control during a longer part of the fall

Lower cut should be made at an upward angle to obtain an open notch.

Preferable notching technique when felling on a slope

your trees. Most often, it's best to leave stumps that are as short as possible. That leaves the forest cleaner and easier for people to move through. But what's best for people is not necessarily what's best for the *forest*. Dead stumps provide shelter for small birds and animals, food for insects and for animals that eat insects and, of course, nourishment for the forest itself, for new plants and trees. Also, the closer you work to the ground, the more difficult it is to maintain control over the felling direction and the more dangerous it is for you, both during the cutting and during your escape. On the other hand, many forestry agencies demand that you cut close to the ground, often specifying a maximum stump height. Be sure to check with local authorities on this issue before cutting down any trees.

ORGANIZED FELLING

We're going out into the woods to fell a good number of trees. The trees are standing dead and are grouped pretty much together on the side of a slope facing the road but a good distance away.

We want to haul the trees no farther than is absolutely necessary, and we want to fell them so they'll be easy to limb and buck into loading-sized logs. We'll start out cutting trees at the edge closest to the road, and we'll use one or more of the trees as a workbench for limbing all the trees that come later.

For a workbench, fell a tree diagonally across the center of your start of operation. Then fell the next tree so that it falls across the workbench. This lifts the trunk up off the ground and makes limbing and bucking easier. Limb the whole tree, from trunk to top. It is convenient to mark the tree for bucking while you're limbing it. With the tree limbed, it's easy to roll or seesaw the tree across the workbench to one side. Then you can buck it into lengths to be rolled downhill to the road. This method quickly leads to piles of bucked logs, ready for loading.

When you follow an organized felling procedure like this, save the side trees for last; you can use your accumulated piles of timber for workbenches for these trees.

There is a variation on this procedure, suitable for smaller groups of trees. Plan your felling so that each tree forms a workbench for the next. Buck each tree where it falls so that bucked sections form piles, ready for loading.

Still another variation works if you're felling on a slope. In this case you use several workbenches that will also form "roads" for rolling subsequent trees to the truck. No trees are bucked until they are all rolled down to the road. Fell several thicker trees from those closest to the road. Drop them uphill, with their tops pointing into the trees to be cut. (Note that this is dangerous, in that some trees may slide back downhill.) Cut the tops off the trees and limb them clean. Then simply fell the subsequent trees across your "road," limb them, and roll them downhill to where they can be bucked and loaded. Be careful to stay on the uphill side of any log you're limbing. Remember that a trunk may start to roll before you've finished limbing. Also note that "the root always wins" when logs roll.

None of these operations should ever be attempted by a lone cutter.

FIG. 9.11

Choose a relatively thick "workbench" tree and fell it diagonally across the road approximately 5–10 meters in front of the group of trees to be felled. The work surface of this "bench" should stand 50–70 cm above the ground. Limb this tree but don't crosscut it.

FIG. 9.12

Fell tree No. 1 across the bench tree. Cut off the top and slash in the road.

FIG. 9.13

Limb tree No. 1 and mark crosscut points. Pull, roll, or seesaw the trunk into the timber zone. Crosscut on your way back to the root and finish off the lower limbing if necessary.

Fell the other trees in the group, following the same sequence of operations. Note how the diagonal bench helps balance the trunks by varying the felling direction.

FIG. 9.14

In certain cases it will be more advantageous to crosscut the first log while on your way to the top, as this provides better balance of the rest of the trunk.

Save the side trees until last. Use the piles of timber as a bench and proceed as usual. Finally, cut the original workbench in half and seesaw the two lengths to the timber zone.

FIG. 9.15

The timber zone method is preferred for thicker stands of trees with comparatively small numbers of branches.

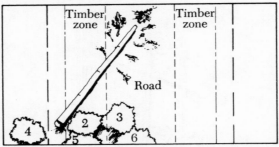

Plan and fell one group at a time. Place treetops and most of the slash in the road.

Crosscut tree No. 1 and turn the first two top logs, leaving the others in position to use as a workbench.

Fell tree No. 2, limb it, and mark the crosscut points. Crosscut a section to facilitate seesawing or rolling the trunk into the timber zone. Crosscut the rest and finish the lower limbing on the way back if necessary.

FIG. 9.16

FIG. 9.17

When felling trees on a slope, start by cutting three or four thickish "bench" trees perpendicular to the tractor road.

Continue felling the other trees in the group. Place the center of gravity somewhere on the woodpile.

Fell the remaining trees straight across the bench trees; limb and mark the crosscut points; then roll the trunks down to the road—but remember, never *walk along the lower side of the trunks, because they may start to roll before you have finished.*

Work evenly along both sides of the strake.

LIMBING

Of all the cutting operations, limbing is the one that holds the most unseen danger. The traditional North American method of limbing is to keep your guide bar on the opposite side of the tree trunk and to limb only one side of the tree at a time. In other words, you keep the tree trunk between you and your guide bar; you remove all the limbs on one side of the tree, the side opposite you, and then you reverse your position and do the other side. If you're working on your backyard woodpile, limbing one side at a time is the easiest and safest approach.

In the woods, this method has several disadvantages. In the first place, one side of the log or the other is always downhill. It's very dangerous to limb from the downhill side of a tree. The limbs tend to fall your way and, of course, when the tree rolls, it rolls right into you. Also, limbing one side and then the other is the slowest and least efficient limbing method.

In these situations, Parp recommends the Swedish Forestry Method of limbing, as outlined in this chapter. Actually, there are *two* of these methods: the *lever* method, and the *pendulum* method. Of the two, the lever method is the easiest and safest.

The "lever method" of limbing is so called because the saw's body is used as a lever for the necessary limbing movements. This method is most suitable on trees that have limbs of all sizes growing in a symmetrical pattern (called a *turn*).

Start limbing on the uphill side of the trunk end of the tree. Work toward the treetop so that the branches will be pointing away from you while you're working. Get a good stance with your feet wide apart. Stand close to the tree and get a firm hold on your saw. Be especially alert for kickback and keep your thumb curled around the handle of your saw. In limbing, work close to your saw. You won't be able to keep your elbow locked, anyway, and holding the saw close helps you maintain greater control. For all of these limbing methods, you move your feet only at certain specific times, *after* certain cuts. The idea is to complete a sequence of cuts, then move, then do another sequence of cuts, then move again, and so forth.

Suppose you have two groups or turns of three limbs each that are all safely within reach of your guide bar. Two are on your side of the trunk, two on the other side, and two straight up. The first one on the far side is number one. The closest straight-up limb is number two. The close limb on your side is number three. Number four is the second limb on your side, number five is the second straight up, and number six is the farthest limb on the far side of the trunk.

FIG. 9.18

The fundamental motion of the "lever method"

Branch two

Pushing chain

Branch one

Pushing chain

Place 10 cm feet in this stance for starting position.

Branch three

Pulling chain

Branch five

Pushing chain

Never move your feet with the saw on the *left-hand* side of the trunk.

Bring the saw forward to branch four by bending your knees, and your body weight will lift the saw automatically.

Branch six

Pulling chain

Branch four

Pushing chain

Do not limb on the left of the broken line, as the blade may reach your leg.

Move to the next starting position while resting the whole weight of the saw on top of the trunk.

When removing branches from a felled tree, use a systematic pattern. The "lever method" shown here can be used on most trees.

FIG. 9.19

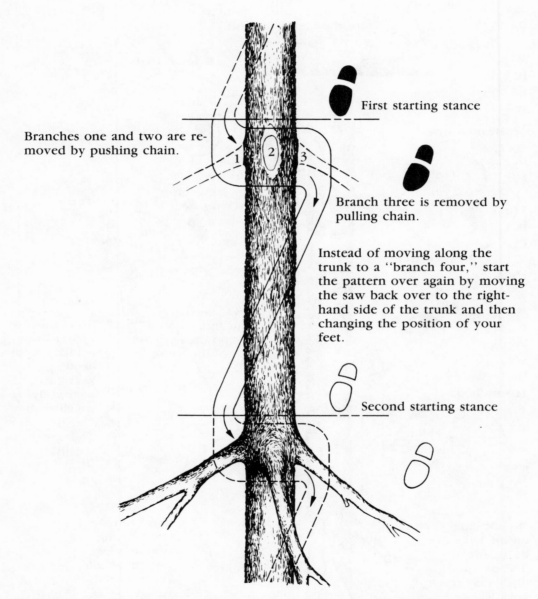

First starting stance

Branches one and two are removed by pushing chain.

Branch three is removed by pulling chain.

Instead of moving along the trunk to a "branch four," start the pattern over again by moving the saw back over to the right-hand side of the trunk and then changing the position of your feet.

Second starting stance

If the distance between branch turns is greater than 70 cm, the "lever method" pattern of movement must be changed.

You will cut all six limbs from one position, and you won't move your feet until after you've cut limb number six.

To start the sequence, stand your left leg out of reach of your guide bar and your right leg directly behind the rear handle of your saw.

Cut branch number one with the top of your guide bar, with your body weight on your right leg and your right leg leaning against the tree trunk for support. When branch number one falls, pull the saw toward you, using its body as a lever. Keep the weight of the saw on the tree. This will bring you into position to cut branch number two with the top of your guide bar.

With a slight swing and a shift of body weight to your left leg after cutting branch number two, you will automatically come into position to cut branch number three with the bottom of your guide bar.

When you move from that first turn of branches to the next, bring your body weight forward by bending your knees. At the same time, bring your saw across to your side of the trunk. Note that you do *not* change the position of your feet.

Branch number four actually begins the next turn of branches. For this, the saw is resting between the tree and your right leg. Hold the saw close with a firm grip. Most of the time, you cut branch number four with the top of your guide bar, but if it's a thick branch, you may have to finish with an overcut.

When the saw comes up from branch number four, you roll it over so its weight rests on the tree trunk. This puts you in position to cut branch number five with the top of your guide bar and allows your saw to continue its roll on the trunk to an upright position. This means that you have to operate the throttle with your thumb while cutting branch number five. During this turn, you bring your weight back evenly on both legs.

As the saw comes upright again, your finger once more moves to the throttle. You cut branch number six with the bottom of the guide bar, thus completing one entire sequence. You can now move to the next sequence with the entire weight of your saw resting on the tree trunk and the trunk between you and your guide bar.

Parp says this is the easiest and fastest method of limbing yet devised. With a little practice, anyone can master it—and in doing so, get to feel like a really expert woodsperson. And it's much easier than it might sound right now.

The "pendulum method" of limbing is another sequential system in which the saw describes a pendulous movement through groups of branches. This method is most suitable on trees with smaller branches, especially if they're dry and small like the lower limbs of spruce trees,

FIG. 9.20

The pendulum method of removing numerous and irregular branches

FIG. 9.21

Lever method

Pendulum method

Which method should you use? Both the lever and pendulum methods have their merits, even on the same tree. However, it should be observed that the lever method is the more laborsaving of the two.

or the limbs of trees growing in dense stands. It's also useful on trees with bunched branches, or branches that come in irregular turns.

Start by cutting a swath on your side of the tree. Cut to the extent of your comfortable reach. Then, with your saw resting on the tree, use the bottom of your guide bar to cut the second group of branches from the top of the trunk, back toward yourself. Swing the saw on its own weight so it comes into position for the last phase of the sequence. Shift your weight from your right leg onto your left. Use the top of your guide bar to complete the limbing sequence on the far side of the tree. This leaves the trunk between you and your guide bar and allows you to move safely to the next position. The final step is to transfer the saw from the trunk's left side to your side for the start of the next sequence.

There will be many times when you have to use both the lever method *and* the pendulum method on one tree.

LIMBING THICK BRANCHES

You'll often run into thick or complex branches that will temporarily stop your finely developed and speedy limbing methods. These branches can result in a pinched bar or a split tree unless they are cut properly. When you run into one of these problems, first analyze the stress factor. Cut or remove any branches that may obstruct your work. Then cut the sub-branches that induce the most stress. After that you can safely crosscut the main branch itself. If the main branch is very thick, undercut it first and finish it with a top cut to avoid splitting. If a branch is in a bind, start with a top cut and finish with an undercut. Be careful of limbs that may spring out at you or grab your saw.

FIG. 9.22

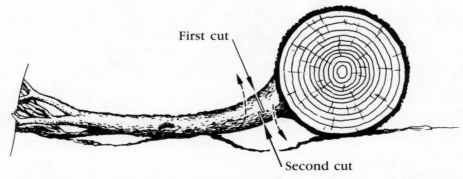

Branches in a bind should be top-cut, then undercut, if the tree's weight is on the branch.

FIG. 9.23

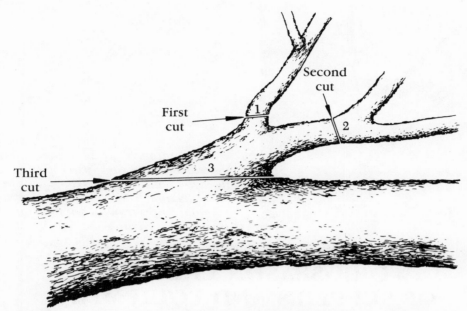

When limbing thick branches, avoid pinching and splitting by choosing the proper sequence of operations, paying extra attention to stresses and tension.

PRUNING

The only limbing procedure that isn't covered in these paragraphs is pruning. To remove a limb from a standing, living tree, always start with an undercut a few inches out from the trunk. Finish with a top cut a little farther out from the trunk. This way the limb won't split and break off near the trunk and tear the bark from the tree. When the limb is removed, undercut the stump off flush with the trunk and paint over the wound with pruning paint.

When you're cutting small brush, or clearing the underbrush around a tree you're going to fell, be sure to keep the guide bar close to the ground and cut at the thickest parts of the branches. If you cut higher up on the branch, the branches will whip toward you and the chain will catch in the work, causing push or pull or kickback.

Now we're ready to go into the woods and get those standing dead trees!

FIG. 9.24

When pruning, make an undercut near the trunk and finish with a top cut a little farther out from the trunk. This prevents the limb from splitting and breaking off near the trunk. Then flush out the stub near the trunk.

WORK-SEASON CHECKLIST OF SUPPLIES AND EQUIPMENT

1. Chain saw. Perform maintenance.
2. Owner's manual. Reread.
3. Extra chain.
4. Chain repair parts.
5. Chain breaker.
6. Rivet spinner.
7. Small machinist's hammer.
8. File guide.
9. Depth gauge or jointer.
10. Chain file.
11. Flat safety-edge file.
12. Flat file for bar.
13. Extra spark plug.
14. Spark plug wrench.
15. Screwdrivers.
16. One or two extra air filters.
17. Extra starter rope.
18. Wrench for bar nuts.
19. Grease gun for roller-nose or sprocket-nose bars.
20. Solvent or kerosene.
21. Fuel—fresh and ready-mixed with two-cycle engine oil.
22. Clean chain lubrication oil.
23. Toothbrush.
24. Rags.
25. Gloves.
26. Hard hat.
27. Ear protection.
28. Eye protection.
29. Safe work clothing.
30. Ax.
31. Plastic wedges for felling and bucking.
32. Sledge or heavy hammer.
33. Hatchet.
34. Felling lever.
35. Cant hook.
36. Logging tape.
37. Whistle.

CHAPTER 10
OTHER JOBS FOR YOUR CHAIN SAW

In addition to simply cutting firewood, a good chain saw can be used to perform many other practical tasks. It can be used as a power head to drive an ever-increasing variety of special tools—from ice drills to winches. And it can be an important source of extra income for those who keep their ears open and use a little imagination.

EARTH AUGERS

Accessory earth auger attachments are available for many medium-duty and professional-quality chain saws. These consist of large drills or augers that replace the bar and chain of your saw and are driven by the saw's power head. The best of these are often intended for use by two operators. If you expect to do extensive posthole digging or drilling for shallow wells, Parp recommends the two-person type of earth auger. If you're not going to be boring holes for a living or working in extremely tough and rocky ground, the single-operator model will probably do.

A strong chain saw power head equipped with an earth auger can quickly pay for itself if you hire out to dig postholes, soil percolation test holes, or foundation footings for your neighbors or for local government agencies.

HEDGE TRIMMERS

Even the smallest chain saw can be converted into a very efficient hedge trimmer by attaching a simple guide designed for that purpose. The cheapest and easiest hedge trimmer attachment is a model from Granberg that attaches directly to the bar of your chain saw with no drilling or customizing. This attachment is available to fit most saws.

Other hedge trimmer attachments are more complex and expensive. Stihl offers heavy-duty hedge trimmers designed for use on their 015 and 020 chain saw power heads. These trimmers are auxiliary attachments that *replace* the bar and chain, rather than simply convert it as does the Granberg model mentioned above. If you'll be using a hedge trimmer extensively for professional gardening or grounds keeping, the heavy-duty attachments are safer and stronger and will be worth the extra investment. Before you buy, however, be sure the attachment will work with your saw without reconfiguring.

CUTOFF SAW HEADS

You can convert your medium- or heavy-duty chain saw into a powerful circular saw with a cutoff saw attachment. These units tend to be quite expensive, but if you work construction, they can be well worth the investment. A cutoff saw is designed to cut concrete, steel, plumbing, or just about anything else that could not be cut with the normal woodcutting bar-and-chain attachment. They are widely used by rescue crews for freeing trapped victims in automobile accidents or collapsed buildings. Smaller, lighter models such as the Stihl TS-200AVE are available for home and light construction use. A cutoff saw head greatly expands the versatility of your chain saw.

GRASS TRIMMERS AND BRUSH CUTTERS

Many minisaws and lightweights can be converted into efficient grass trimmers with the addition of a grass trimming attachment. Similar attachments use solid blades instead of polyfilament lines and are designed for light to medium brush-cutting and light thinning. These attachments are usually of better quality and are designed for heavier cutting and trimming chores than are the inexpensive grass trimmers and brush cutters. So although the initial investment may be higher, the long-range value of a heavier attachment will undoubtedly be greater.

OTHER ACCESSORIES

Some of the other useful accessories that can be operated by the power head of your chain saw include wood drills, winches, pumps, and air brooms. The Fred A. Lewis Company of Medford, Oregon, makes an incredibly tough winch that can be attached to any fairly powerful chain saw head and then bolted to the tailgate of a pickup truck, or otherwise installed in a more or less permanent fashion. A good winch is very handy for moving large logs. Lewis also makes a fine heavy-duty power take-off, a universal adapter that works with any medium- or heavy-duty saw. This attachment allows drilling and digging of any size hole, either in the ground or in wood or logs, as for use in cabin construction.

Other companies offer smaller drills intended primarily or solely for wood drilling. Stihl's BT 309 is a good example, and Atom Industries produces similar heavy-duty wood drills to fit most full-size saws (see Appendix for address).

LUMBER MILLS AND ATTACHMENTS

Undoubtedly the best-known lumber-maker designed for chain saw use is the Granberg Alaskan Mill. Now available in many sizes and types, these mills range from simple ripping guides made to attach to your saw as is, on up to giant rigs that require two saw heads, or at least a helper handle, and a considerable amount of power for ripping huge logs into timbers and boards. Granberg Mills come as low-priced basic models that include only the absolutely necessary parts that clamp onto your saw to serve as ripping guides, or as complete Alaskan Mills that can rip logs up to 54″ in diameter. The complete mills come with a double-ended bar, an auxiliary oiler, a helper handle, a filing guide, and a loop of ripping chain. Bailey's is a good mail-order source for these outfits, in case you're way out there in the country somewhere—or even if you're not; it's often difficult to find good woods tools in the city, too.

One of the simplest and least expensive chain saw lumber-makers is the Haddon Lumber/Maker from Haddon Tools of McHenry, Illinois. It does a good job of turning medium-sized logs into rough lumber without a great deal of excess machinery to lug around. And to the best of Parp's knowledge, it will work with any chain saw on the market today.

CHAIN SAW CARVING

In the years since the original *Barnacle Parp's Chain Saw Guide* appeared, chain saw carving has grown up from a side attraction at logging festivals to become a widespread, popular hobby—especially in areas with a logging or timber tradition. Some of the carvings that turn up throughout the country are truly fantastic—so good that the art may be in danger of being included in the curricula of major universities. ("The Department of Chain Saw Wood Carving and Allied Arts," perhaps?) Be that as it may, chain saw carving has become so popular that special tools have been developed to make it easier.

Bailey's now offers a fine wood-carving package consisting of their own bar made especially for carving and a Poulan S25DA lightweight professional chain saw. The bar is pointed to reduce kickback and to increase control during the execution of all sorts of cutting techniques that the chain saw was never intended to do. The saw has a 2.3-cubic-inch engine and is light, fast, and powerful (it was originally designed for use primarily by tree surgeons and other professionals who require a light but very powerful and dependable saw). If you're serious about carving, Parp recommends this package.

Specially filed carving chain is also available from Bailey's. The heel of each cutter is ground off to reduce kickback and to make carving smoother. The rakers are ground at a slant to facilitate boring, and the cutters are ground at a 10° angle to produce the narrowest possible kerf and to minimize splitting. This chain really works and is much safer and easier to use for carving projects than is standard chain.

Please note that carving wood is an inherently dangerous business because of the greatly increased chance of severe kickback and because carvers frequently get too close to the wood. Eye and hand injuries are common, so please be sure to wear eye protection and good gloves. And try to avoid the temptation to get your face too close while concentrating on detailed carving.

SELLING FIREWOOD

If you have a good chain saw, a truck, and a nearby forest where commercial firewood cutting is allowed, you have everything you need, other than customers, to develop a firewood business. In most areas, a permit from the forest agency of that jurisdiction is required to gather firewood for resale in any quantity, so if you're planning to sell any of the wood you cut, be sure to find out if it's legal and if you need a permit. All national forests in the contiguous states require a resale permit for any commercial gathering at all.

It's best to go into the firewood business with a partner. This makes it safer and easier to gather and deliver quickly the large quantities of wood you'll need to do business. A partner is better than a paid employee because the employee will have to be paid a set wage, no matter how little your profit is. This does not necessarily mean that you should expect low profits. This seems to depend entirely on the area. In some parts of the Southwest, firewood prices have been low, despite the fact that wood is scarce and difficult to gather. On the other hand, firewood prices in the Northwest are sometimes high, although wood is plentiful and permits are easy to obtain.

If you plan to sell firewood, a practical addition to your tool collection is some kind of splitting device. You can split two or three cords a day by hand, but it's not easy, and the profits of the average firewood business do not justify that much labor.

The standard and traditional wood splitter is the hydraulic splitter, a large, heavy-duty machine usually transported by trailer. If you own a tractor, which is in itself a useful item for a firewood business, you can use the tractor's power take-off unit or hydraulic connections to power a good splitter.

There are numerous screw-type splitters available that are run by their own gasoline engines, by electric power, or by bolting them to the back wheel of a pickup truck. The screw-type splitter is still Parp's choice for an inexpensive, maintenance-free device that makes splitting a lot of wood a fast, safe, and relatively easy job.

The original and still best-known screw-type splitter was the Stickler, invented by Parp's neighbor, Mr. Arthur Stickler of Gunnison, Colorado. Unfortunately, the Stickler is no longer manufactured.

CHAPTER 11
INTRODUCTION TO BUILDING WITH A CHAIN SAW

By design, a good, well-tuned, well-sharpened, and well-maintained chain saw is a highly accurate and dependable tool that can be used by almost anyone to make almost anything that can be made of wood. Correctly sharpened and maintained, a good chain saw cuts a good straight line almost without guidance. In fact, a chain saw should never cut anything *but* a straight line.

Many noncarpenters, not especially talented at building things, have tried their hand at putting something together with wood and have given up because of one basic problem: the straight line. Even the most primitive construction demands reasonably straight lines. If you're not used to handling tools, you'll often find that last year's tree house is this year's doghouse and next year's bonfire.

PRACTICE CUTS

A good chain saw gives you a considerable advantage. The bar alone will help guide you through a cut on a straight line, but it does take some practice. Before you try building anything, get in a lot of practice cutting straight lines. The best way to do this is while you're bucking logs for firewood. Instead of just cutting the sections off, make every cut a practice cut for your future role as cabin builder. Make a conscious effort to make each cut as straight as possible until it becomes a habit. When you consistently get straight cuts on your firewood logs, you're ready to begin practicing the other cuts that are used in chain saw construction. When you can expertly perform all of these cuts on your firewood pieces, you can begin to think about trying them on some specially selected building logs. It does definitely take practice.

A *crosscut* is called a crosscut because you're cutting across the grain from one side of the log to the other. *Ripping* refers to cutting with the grain from one end of the log and parallel with the length of the log. It has a ripping effect on the wood.

After you've mastered crosscutting in a straight line, practice each of the following cuts, in turn, until they become easy for you.

PLUNGE CUT (BORING)

Parp has mentioned this cut before, and if you've cut down some large trees, you've probably already used it. But using this cut in construction is more exacting than it is in felling, and considerable practice is required to get it down pat so that you can consistently cut where you want to cut.

The plunge cut is basic to chain saw construction. It's used to make corner joints, cross joints, mortises, and many other kinds of joints and notches. The best way to practice is on a large upright log with one end buried securely in the ground. (Since all these practice cuts are made on future firewood pieces, there's little waste.)

Begin the cut with the lower part of the nose of the guide bar. Hold the body of the saw considerably lower than the nose of the bar. This helps prevent kickback and overcomes the tendency of the chain to crawl up the log. When the chain has cut about two inches into the log, steadily pivot the body of the saw up, cutting all the while, until the bar is parallel with the ground and perpendicular to the cut. You can then plunge, or press, the nose of the bar straight into the log. Don't press too hard and don't force the chain into the wood. Hold your saw firmly and let it do most of the work.

Be sure to begin any plunge cut with the saw held at an angle below the perpendicular, and then straighten it after the cut is established. And remember to keep the chain speed up.

END JOINT

This isn't as tricky as a plunge cut, but it does take practice and it's a good introduction to ripping. The product is a flat surface created by removing one-half or so of a portion of the end of a log. Two end joints can thus be joined to form a corner or a long section.

First, determine how long you want the joint to be. For practice, make it six inches or so. Begin by making a crosscut halfway through the log, straight down across the grain. Then turn the log so that the bottom of the crosscut is perpendicular with the ground. Stand on the opposite side of the log from the top of the crosscut. (These maneuvers will prevent the saw from binding in the rip that you're about to make and will make the practice safer and easier.) Be sure your log is supported well up off the ground, at least on the cutting end, so the chain doesn't hit. Now, with the guide bar at an angle, start a ripping cut at about the center of the bottom of your guide bar and in the middle of the log. You're going to pull the chain saw back and gradually straighten it out so that the guide bar will become perpendicular to the ground just before it reaches the bottom of the crosscut.

It may take a few tries and a little practice to get the ripping cut going without catching the chain. If the chain starts to bind inside the cut, leave your saw in the cut (if possible), turn it off, and insert a wedge in the top of the kerf where your chain first entered. Then finish the cut to meet the bottom of the crosscut. Practice until the technique becomes a habit and until you get an idea how the chain and the wood react to a ripping cut. Always try to rip logs so that the chain's cutters are approaching the cross fiber at the same angle you would use in chopping. Avoid cutting directly across the fibers or against them.

CROSS JOINT

Here you combine two crosscuts with a plunge cut to produce a flat notch or joint in the body of a log.

To do it, make three crosscuts halfway through a log and about three inches apart. Then make a plunge cut that you extend as necessary to meet the bottoms of both outside crosscuts. This is one of the easiest and best ways to joint logs together in the body. Practice on several logs, and concentrate on making the notch on one log fit the notch on another. When you can consistently make two logs fit together tightly, you've got it down.

SADDLE NOTCH

A saddle notch is formed by making two shallow cross joints opposite each other. Instead of coming to the middle of the log, each cross notch takes out about one-third of the log, leaving a center piece with two flat faces. This is the easiest and surest way of joining logs so that there is minimum space between them. Saddle notches are used in Lincoln Log sets.

ROUND NOTCH

This method of joining logs is superior to cross joining or saddle notching because the shape of the notch prevents water collection. It is also more difficult and must be fitted perfectly. The width of the notch is determined by the diameter of the log that will sit in the notch. Lay the top log across the bottom log at the place they are to be joined. Use chalk to mark the diameter of the top log onto the bottom log to indicate the width of the notch. Then move the top log off and use your chain saw to cut a V between the marks.

Now you need to clean and round the notch to fit your top log. Some

Boring

Corner joint

End joint

Mid joint

Cross joint

Joining logs

Round notch

Saddle notch

Tenon notch

Notching

people do this with the chain saw, but Parp says that an ax, a hatchet, and a wood knife ("slick") are far better. It's hard on a chain saw to use it for this kind of whittling—but, of course, that's what the wood-carvers do. If you do it with your saw, by all means take your time and don't ask your saw to cut any curves. It isn't meant to.

However you do it, you have to remove a little wood at a time until you've made a round notch that perfectly fits your top log. Check the fit of the notch frequently by laying the top log into it. Use chalk to mark high places when possible. A round notch is better construction than a cross joint, but it's also a lot harder to do.

RIPPING

After you've practiced all of the cuts and joints described above, you should learn to rip a log freehand. This means you're going to cut a log lengthwise to form four mill-end slabs and a timber. Mill-end slabs are the rounded or bark sides of a log that have been removed with a rip-ping cut. A timber is what's left after four slabs have been removed. Broken slabs make great kindling or kitchen wood, so you're still not going to be wasting anything by practicing. Whole slabs have hundreds of uses—from building a doghouse and toolshed to making siding for a timber or frame cabin. So when you get a solid, whole slab, you might think twice before cutting it up for firewood.

To rip slabs, draw a square on the small end of a supported log. You'll want the removed slabs to leave a square timber as large as possible, and you'll want the slabs to be about an inch thick in the middle, depending on the size of the log. Start a ripping cut at one of the sides of the chalk square and saw down the full length of the log. Have the thick side of the log between you and your guide bar, and turn the log for each successive slab. The chain will bind, and the bar will be pinched in the cut, so use plastic or homemade wooden wedges to open the kerf. Since your cutting line will be straight, each slab will be thicker on one end than on the other—but the timber produced should be square and uniform for its whole length. You should practice this until you can cut perfect slabs and timbers most of the time, freehand. And remember to start each ripping cut at the *small* end of the log.

BUILDING THINGS

To get a lot of really great ideas for easy things to build with a chain saw, write to Homelite for *Twenty-Two Weekend Projects* and to McCulloch for *101 Reasons to Own a Chain Saw*. Both publications are inexpensive. And there are books available at any public library on building projects of all kinds, many of which can be adapted for chain saw users.

There are many excellent standard works on the subject of cabin building. Among the best are those by Calvin Rutstrum, Bradford Angier, and Ben Hunt. Ben Hunt's *How to Build and Furnish a Cabin the Easy, Natural Way Using Only Hand Tools and the Materials Around You* (Macmillan, 1974) has a long title but is one of the classic works on this subject—and everything Mr. Hunt suggests is made easier with a chain saw. Finally, *The Foxfire Book* (Anchor Press/Doubleday, 1968) will answer your remaining questions and supply considerably more technical information.

The whole question of wood preservatives and protecting close-to-the-ground logs from decay or parasites is a problem. Creosote is the traditional treatment, but it's messy, toxic, and difficult to use. Penta and other popular preservatives contain dioxane, an extremely dangerous chemical that will kill wildlife, livestock, and pets. Dioxane is now recognized as a deadly poison that, if used, enters the food chain and becomes a threat to everything living in the area. Consequently, penta was recently banned by the Environmental Protection Agency. If you must use a preservative, use a zinc-naphthenate-based product, and follow the instructions carefully.

One of the best things to do with some of your practice logs is to make a sandbox or other useful structure that involves making log walls that aren't too high off the ground. This will give you more practice in fitting logs together, and you'll come to appreciate the difficulties of getting a tight fit.

A miniature log cabin for a doghouse or playhouse is another worthwhile project. As a rule, 8″ logs are the easiest to manage on a small project such as a playhouse, but you can do well with 6″ logs if you're careful. Make the walls in standard log cabin construction forms, using saddle notches. You can make a good floor and roof by ripping a log into planks for the floor and slabs for the roof.

Parp is especially fond of projects that use wood to best advantage. As nice as log cabins are, timber cabins can be better. If you're lucky enough to have a place to build such a structure, and trees to spare, you should consider ripping each log so that it supplies timbers for the walls, planks for the floor and interior, and mill-end slabs for siding or outbuildings. Be sure to save all the damaged or too-short pieces for building furniture.

You can elaborate the old bunk-bed project into a beautiful "sleeping fort" for kids by ripping boards for the frame and nailing the slabs vertically all around, leaving only an entrance. You can also do the same thing for a playhouse, using planks instead of round logs.

When you've gained considerable proficiency and confidence through a number of small building projects, you'll be ready to build a cabin. Not a house. A *cabin*.

TO BUILD A CABIN

You can make any kind of lumber with a chain saw. You can make slabs, timbers, beams, posts, planks, boards, crossties, and even laths. That's why you can build a cabin and waste no wood at all. You can also make skids so your mule can bring your stove or fireplace stones right to your brand-new doorstep. And you can throw the sawdust into your compost heap. Don't even leave the chips where they fall—rake them up and dry them out for kindling.

Now that you're an expert at ripping logs *freehand*, you're ready for the tools that make it delightfully easy. But don't get the idea you can skip the preliminaries.

TOOLS

A chain saw is a portable sawmill. All it needs is a little guidance to produce the most beautiful lumber in existence. You cannot buy boards at any lumberyard that look nearly as nice as those you can make yourself with a chain saw and a lumber-making attachment or mill rig.

There are a great many mill rigs available to fit all kinds and sizes of chain saws. Some of these—like Granberg's Alaskan Mill—are expensive and elaborate, and are essentially two-person tools. The Alaskan Mill is the best and most accurate mill rig available. The rig consists of braces and rollers that guide the saw through the wood, and is available in either one-person or two-person models. A complete two-person Alaskan Mill comes with a special 32″ bar, ripping chain, helper-handle, and auxiliary oiler. If you're going to have help in building a permanent cabin, an Alaskan Mill is a good investment.

Other mill rigs are far less elaborate and less expensive and are made to attach to your chain saw just as it is. The best and least expensive of these is the Haddon Lumber/Maker from Haddon Tool. Haddon's Lumber/Maker is a one-person tool that is incredibly easy to use. Although not as much of a production aid as an Alaskan Mill, the Lumber/Maker still enables any chain saw owner to produce beautiful lumber with very little effort. It consists of a brace, a roller, and a guide, and can be helpful in many other kinds of cutting jobs.

However you make your lumber, if you start a large building project such as a garage or a cabin, you should invest in a ripping chain for producing lumber. Most chain dealers carry ripping chain, or you can mail-order it from Bailey's or Zip Penn. Granberg, Carleton, and Oregon make the highest-quality ripping chain, and it's one of Granberg's specialities.

If you handle large logs or do a lot of ripping, you'll find that "log dogs" are like having another pair of arms. They're bracket-shaped iron braces with sharp, hooked ends that can be driven into logs, and they can be used anytime you need extra support. They're especially useful in long ripping projects and can be used with wedges (or instead of them) to keep the wood from binding your chain.

If you're building a cabin with a chain saw, the next best tool to have is *another* chain saw: a heavy-duty production model. A heavy-duty chain saw makes a good backup to your lighter, everyday saw. Heavy-duty, production-type saws have a great deal of lugging power, which will help you when ripping through long, tough logs. Also, these saws often have 1/2"-pitch chains. A 1/2"-pitch ripping chain and a long guide bar are ideal for making lumber with one of the larger mills. A large saw can also be a great help when you're sawing openings for doors or windows, or when you're trimming two logs for a better fit.

That brings up a cut that Parp didn't mention before. (Don't try this with a minisaw.) If you're putting round logs together, you can make them fit together tightly with this cut. Place the logs next to each other and block them from rolling, or secure them with log dogs. Then run the bar of your large saw between the two logs so that you're removing wood from both logs at once. This will shape the logs to fit perfectly when they're placed on top of each other. Please be careful, says Parp, because shaping the fit of logs or cutting between logs is the most dangerous procedure we've mentioned yet. And don't try this cut with logs that are already in or on a log wall; it's dangerous and will also make accurate notching impossible.

TO BUILD A HIDEOUT

Aside from the chain saw and mill-type attachments, several other tools, many of them very old and traditional, have particular uses in cabin building. It's not Parp's place or intention to cover the uses of these tools, but a quick review may be helpful. Any of the good books on cabin building can provide complete information on these tools and their uses. Among them are the *gimlet* for boring holes in logs, the *adze* for notching and shaping, the *gouge* for trimming, the *caliper* for measuring, the *scribe* for marking, the *plane* for finishing, the *level* and the *plumb line* for accuracy, the *froe* for splitting shingles, and the *drawknife* for peeling logs.

Many chain saws can be fitted to a debarking attachment, but this is quite expensive and a drawknife is not as difficult or as slow as it's often made out to be—it's still the best and fastest method of peeling logs by hand. If your cabin plans are elaborate and if you have no place to plug in an electric drill, you may want to get a drill attachment for your chain saw. You may also want a winch for moving logs, and an earth auger for digging postholes. Finally, a hammer is a really handy tool to have when you're building things with wood (especially if you use nails).

Let's look at producing specific pieces of lumber. We'll use the Haddon Lumber/Maker and a medium-duty chain saw, since this is the least expensive approach and doesn't require a helper. For ripping, the Lumber/Maker works by guiding a chain saw down a board that is fastened to the top of a log. Use a 2 X 4 or a 2 X 6 for a guide board.

To make a solid 4 X 4 timber and four good slabs, use a log that's 8" in diameter. Center a 2 X 4 on top of the log and nail it down firmly enough to take some pressure, but not so firmly that it's difficult to remove without splitting. Two or three nails should do it.

Following the instructions that come with the tool, attach the Lumber/Maker or a similar tool to your chain saw. Now set the instant portable sawmill—which is what you just put together—so that the roller rides on the guide board. Begin, as always, at the small end of the log. Now start your saw and pull it back, with one roller riding on the board, to cut the first slab. Then turn your rig around and go back the other way. On this second pass, you'll be cutting from the large end toward the small end.

When the first two slabs are off, remove the guide board and rotate the log so that a sawed side is up. Again, center and nail down your guide board. Now rip off the other two slabs. That's it for a 4 X 4 timber and four good mill-end slabs.

To make 6 X 6 timbers, simply adjust the Lumber/Maker (or whatever) according to the instructions and use a 2 X 6 as a guide board instead of a 2 X 4. A 2 X 6 works better anyway. You can make timbers of any size—from 4 X 4 to 12 X 12—by using the appropriate size of guide board and adjusting the tool accordingly. You can make guide boards of any size by adding strips of straight wood to your guide board stock. A good selection of various width guide boards comes in handy.

You can also make a cross jig to any size to help you cut lumber or logs to equal lengths. To make an eight-foot jig, cut a 2 X 6 to 95-1/2" long. This allows for the 1/2" distance between the guide board and the saw cut. Then nail 2 X 6 pieces of sufficient length at right angles across both ends. Use a square to be sure your endpieces are precise. The endpieces then form the guides that the Lumber/Maker moves on. You can, of course, make length jigs of any size as long as you allow the 1/2".

After the mill-end slabs are removed, a timber can be ripped into any size lumber. The boards that are produced this way are somewhat rough, of course, but are as beautiful as anything could be. (Parp sighs for the light of a kerosene lamp reflected by walls of handmade boards. Only the sun itself is so completely satisfying.)

To turn a 6 X 6 timber into three 2 X 6 planks, use a ruler to mark both ends of the timber into three equal parts. Use a 2 X 4 guide board and attach it to the timber so your chain saw is centered to cut at the first line. Saw off the first plank. Reset your guide board and chain saw to split the remaining two planks. It's that easy.

To learn a great deal more about making lumber with a mill or jig, write to Granberg, or order the booklet *The Chain Saw and the Lumber/Maker* from Haddon Tool.

One of the sturdiest designs for log cabin construction is the cross-and-filler type suggested by Jesse Haddon. This method produces a solid timber cabin with all the advantages of squared timbers and all the beauty of round logs.

To make a cross-and-filler cabin, cut the slabs off three sides of each of the logs to be used. Cut the logs to equal thicknesses and to lengths that fit your plan. The opening between each pair of the cross logs is filled with two filler logs that fit tightly between the cross logs. Lay the logs so that the bark side is out and you have flat sides facing up, down, and in. You alter the position of each course of logs so that filler sits on cross and cross sits on filler. Jesse says a winch helps pull the cross logs tight against the fillers. You can, of course, use any kind of hoist or hand winch, or even a Handyman Jack with chains or ropes attached. When the walls are up, you can saw in the doors and windows, using your Lumber/Maker and guide boards nailed to the timbers. Always make the right-hand cut first, since the guide board for the right-hand cut will be nailed to the timbers you're removing. The left-hand guide board will be clear of the moving timbers, which will come out easily as the left-hand cut is made. Be careful.

MAKING PLANS

The primary purpose of this chapter is to show how the modern chain saw affects the process of building a cabin. The great Alaskan Mill and the little Lumber/Maker are both inventors' dreams, but they would never have appeared if the chain saw weren't around. A chain saw, a lumber-making tool, a supply of fuel, and everything else you need can be packed or pulled into even the most remote areas. Any remote area that grows trees will provide all you need to build a cabin.

And it had probably better be a remote area.

When Parp was honored to serve as zoning officer for a certain county, he encouraged the use of outhouses and hand-dug wells. He made sure the outhouses were well made and well kept, but he encouraged their use. Parp was able to do this because of a liberal-minded and sparse populace and the absence of a building code.

Most of the cabins Parp has loved would fail any inspection, though not on reasonable grounds. The point is, you can't build just anything you want, anyway you wish, anyplace you like, anymore.

If you have a piece of ground far from any zoning officer (or if you have a good security system), you can build a very serviceable cabin for hunting, fishing, hiking, or hiding out. And you can build it by yourself, with no waste, a minimum of effort and experience, and only slight damage to the area around you. It just takes time.

Some time ago, the Oregon Saw Chain people generously began distributing free copies of a fine cabin plan, loved by Parp. The cabin we're going to build here is similar to the Oregon plan, but changed somewhat and simplified a lot by Parp. (Copies of the original may be obtained through your local Oregon dealer.)

Now, let's be realistic. Parp has never seen anything that will give you a good idea of just how long it takes to build a plain and simple cabin, step-by-step. Let's keep track of how long the average malnourished back-to-the-lander from Detroit via Berkeley spends on each step of building a cabin in the wilderness, all alone. We'll start out by not even counting the time it takes to find and acquire the land.

Before you build even the most informal cabin, you have to consider the hazards of the proposed site. It's not Parp's place to describe all of the hazards to a dwelling, but a few lesser-known, although obvious, ones deserve mention.

If you find a nice flat shelf in mountainous terrain where aspen grow in a clump surrounded by pines or hardwoods, don't build there. Aspen and its relatives are the first trees to grow after an area has been hit by an avalanche, a rock slide, or a flood. Also watch for avalanche paths. They look like funnels going up between mountains. If you see the results of an old rock slide piled above your proposed site, be sure to build well out of its path; it may decide to move down. And any low, flat area between hills and near a body of moving water is a floodplain area. The incidence of flooding is presently increasing and is likely to go on doing so. That's because many flood areas are hundred-year floodplains. They look like great building sites with their level deposits of rich earth, but in any given year there is a one-percent chance of flooding. We've just been lucky for a hundred years. Parp suggests you look into this in more detail at your library, or through your state land control office. Plan on at least a week of hiking and searching for the site.

So you have your land, and you've chosen your building site. One year, in September, you go out and cut your building logs. Select cedar, pine, fir, or spruce, in that order. Here's what you need to build a 10' X 12' one-room cabin with a plain pitched roof and a practical overhang:

1. Two solid logs 10" in diameter and over 12 feet long for foundation logs.
2. Three solid logs 10" in diameter and over 10 feet long for foundation cross-members.
3. Six more 10" logs about 12 feet long to rip into floor planks.
4. Eight logs 8" in diameter for uprights.
5. Two 6" logs, 12 feet long, for top plates.
6. Four logs about 6" in diameter and 14 feet long for rafters and porch overhang.
7. Fifteen 3" or 4" poles or logs, 14 feet long for purlins.
8. Five assorted logs ranging from 6" to 12" for miscellaneous lumber, slabs, doorsteps, door planks, etc.
9. Fifteen cedar bolts or other stock for splitting shakes. You can make do with green aspen and other woods. Experiment.

What with searching for the trees, spreading the cutting, moving the logs to your building site, plus countless other hassles and delays, it's done in a month, maybe—if you're lucky and if you work like a bear. Fortunately, you have a chain saw.

Now you carefully peel and stack all the logs in drying stacks with plenty of air between each log. Allow another two weeks or so for this task. It's now late October or early November, and it's time to go away until the end of next August. Spend the spring and summer of the drying year putting by a pile of firewood the size of your proposed cabin and packing in the rest of your tools, spikes and nails, a small potbelly stove or a shepherd's stove, stovepipe, chimney jack and rain cap, hardware for your door, and a window. Also clear your building area. If you work hard, you'll get it all done in time: You have ten months.

CONSTRUCTION

No cabin will stand up straight for very long if it isn't set on a foundation that reaches to bedrock or below the frost line, whichever comes first. Dig six deep foundation holes, each 12" X 12". Pack the earth down in the bottom of the holes, and then use a wooden form and pour concrete footings. This is the easiest and best foundation for a simple cabin. Digging, mixing, and pouring: Allow one week.

Use the best, most solid, well-dried and peeled 10" logs as foundation logs. Take advantage of each log's roundness and roll it into place. Since these large logs are to be lifted only a few inches above the ground, one person can do it. Use end joints to join the four outside logs and

A good foundation

Haddon's cross-and-filler log construction

Cross-member logs

Filler log

cross joints for the middle log. The joints are, of course, 10″ wide and 5″ deep. All log joints rest on the concrete footings. Secure the joints with 60d spikes, using two spikes at each joint. If you don't want to plunge-cut the cross joints, use your chain saw to make three cuts 5″ apart and 5″ deep. Then add a few more cuts between them. That makes it easy to split out the notch with an ax.

After two days of getting the foundation logs notched, settled, and secured, you're ready to put in your floor.

Use a Lumber/Maker or Alaskan Mill to rip floor planks from the chosen 10″ logs. Or you can do it freehand, maybe. Make the planks 2″ thick and let the slabs be good and thick; you'll be using them for siding. Spike your floor planks onto your foundation logs. Rip your planks from logs in the round, rather than from squared timbers, and alternate the beveled, outside edges of the planks so they fit tightly together. They'll take a heavy load that way. When the floor is finished, use your chain saw to trim the ends flush with the foundation logs. Be careful not to hit any spikes with your chain. Plan on a day and a half for the floor.

For corner posts and uprights, use the 8″ logs with slabs removed from two opposite sides only. Face one bark-side out. Spike each post to the floor with four 60d spikes. Brace the posts until you add the top plates. The height of your cabin and the pitch of your roof depend on the height of the uprights. The tallest go in back, of course. Count on three or four hours to complete this step.

Top plates join the corner posts. Rip slabs from two sides of the two 6″ logs that are 12 feet long. Lay these top plates across the upright posts with flat surfaces up and down. Again, secure them with 60d spikes. This will take one hour.

Now set four log rafters, 14 feet long and 5″ in diameter, across the top plates with their butts toward the high side of the pitched roof. Cut and shape 1″ notches to fit the top plates. You can now see what your cabin is going to look like. Allow three hours.

Now you need 15 logs, each 14 feet long and 3″ in diameter. These are the purlins that go on top of the rafters at 11″ intervals. Use a timber spiked across the purlins to align the ends. Notch the purlins individually, as you put them up, in order to get them as level as possible. This is the base for the shake roof. Figure on four hours.

Next, place horizontal framing members across the window wall in 1″ X 3″ notches cut into the corner posts. Spike the butted ends of the members in place with 40d nails driven through the posts from the outside. Now make permanent cross braces between the upright posts. Cut the ends of the braces at angles to fit the floor and the uprights. Spike the base of each cross brace to the floor planks and the tops to the

Notch each purlin individually as you put it up to keep it as level as possible.

Slab siding with battens; cut the window hole after the siding is put up.

94"

Windowsill

With a wood mallet and a shake froe, split 25" bolts of cedar; lay shakes across the purlins to form the roof.

69"

69"

13-1/4'

48"

Horizontal framing members

Notch out corner posts for horizontal members.

One of three diagonal braces

80"-long front post

One of three 9"-diameter cross-members. Half-lap notches fit into foundation logs.

10"-diameter foundation logs notched in three places each

Concrete footing with roofing felt covering the top

Front step set in two notched logs

Log patio

Cut all members with a chain saw; some can be sawn with the aid of a "ripping" attachment.

Floor boards

Slabs for siding

Corner posts

Horizontal members

Battens

Top plate and middle posts

To build an inexpensive weekend cabin with a chain saw and a few simple tools, follow the basic techniques outlined in this illustration.

upright posts. All this will take about three hours.

Before you lay your shake roof, decide where you want your stove. Center rear is best, with two or three feet of air space behind the stove. Use a wooden frame of 1 X 6 boards to attach the chimney jack to the purlins. When you lay the shakes, fit them tightly to the sides of the frame. Install the chimney pipe with one length of pipe extending through the chimney jack. Then use tar to seal the shingles and the fittings of the frame and the chimney jack. Keep the tar away from the chimney itself. There should be six inches of clean jack tin all around the chimney. Set your stove on an asbestos pad.

Split your own roofing shakes from cedar bolts 2 feet long and finish your roof. All that work and installing the stove will come to five days. Use slabs for siding, nailed vertically into the cross framing with 30d nails: Another day. Cut a window opening after the siding is on. (Cut it to fit any window you're using or going to make.) Fasten the window sash with nails driven into the horizontal framing members. Then caulk it: one hour.

Panel the interior with ripped boards: one day. Make your doorstep from a 12"-diameter log 4 feet long and ripped in half. Set the doorstep in notched blocks. Make a door with 10" planks and use slabs for cross braces. Spend another day or two for finishing and cleaning up. Altogether, one year, one week, and 27 hours or so. A cabin in fact.

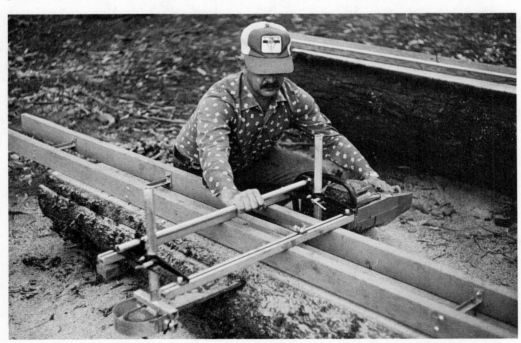

CHAPTER 12

HOW IT WORKS AND WHY IT DOESN'T

THE ENGINE

All of the currently manufactured gasoline chain saws are powered by small, one-cylinder engines known as *two-cycle* or *two-stroke* engines. All of these engines are air-cooled, and all are lubricated by mixing the lubricating oil with the fuel. And all modern chain saw engines have at their heart a specially designed carburetor which is known as the *all-position* carburetor.

The words "two-stroke" or "two-cycle" do not mean that the engine has two cycles. Those words mean that all of the functions or phases of the engine's operation are completed during one upward and one downward stroke of the piston. Each function or phase must occur in the right way at the right time. If even one part is impaired in any way or is out of time, the engine will not perform properly and usually will not work at all. Thus, in order to understand why a particular chain saw engine isn't working properly, you need to be familiar with all the functions necessary to the saw's operation. Once you are familiar with these functions, it becomes much easier to isolate and determine a cause of trouble. Such a procedure is universally known as troubleshooting.

When you learn the functions of a chain saw's engine and when you learn to troubleshoot accurately, it becomes possible to decide whether the problem is one that you can repair yourself, or whether you need to take your saw to a professional. If you can learn to troubleshoot your chain saw, you will save many trips to the mechanic, much downtime, and a lot of money. Most mechanical difficulties with chain saws are elementary, easy to isolate, and easy to repair.

The most common problem that prevents a chain saw from starting is a turned-off ignition switch. You may think that's ridiculous. It isn't. When you know this basic truth, you know that the first thing to do when your chain saw won't start is to check the ignition switch. Then you turn it on. Then you start your chain saw. Many, many people take turned-off chain saws to mechanics. The point is, if you approach all mechanical difficulties logically, you will usually be able to discover and correct the problem yourself. Logically means "in order"; that is, you check the first thing first. The first thing to check when your engine won't start is the ignition switch. The second thing is the fuel supply. But before we go any further, let's look at the functions of a two-stroke chain saw engine.

HOW IT WORKS

It's a way of trapping fire. That's what an engine is. It's a way of trapping fire and then changing the energy of the fire, which is chemical energy, into mechanical or turning energy. The turning energy is then transferred to the chain in a simple and direct manner.

A chain saw gets its fire by burning a highly combustible vaporized mixture of gasoline and air, with a little oil thrown in to keep the moving parts lubricated. This vaporized fuel mixture is burned in the upper portion of a special tubelike trap. The tube is called a *cylinder*, and the upper portion—where the burning occurs—is called a *combustion chamber* (see Figure 12.1). This trap is solid all around to contain the energy from the fire. But the energy has to go someplace, and since we want to use that energy, we fit the trap with a movable plug called a *piston*. The piston fits tight enough to hold the fuel vapor in, but loose enough to move when the vapor burns. Thus, when the vapor burns, the ener-

FIG. 12.1

Spark plug

Compressed fuel vapors burning

Cylinder

Piston

Connecting rod turns on piston wrist pin

Connecting rod

Crank assembly

Crankshaft

Crank assembly, connecting rod, and piston inside the crankcase of a chain saw engine gy from the fire moves the piston, which changes the chemical energy to mechanical energy. The piston has almost the same diameter as the cylinder. In order to make it fit as tight as possible and still work, the piston has a ring fitted into a slot near its top. This ring, called a *piston ring*, fits very snugly against the walls of the cylinder. It helps seal the sides of the trap.

In order to burn vaporized fuel mixture in the trap, we need some way to force the vapors into the trap. We also need some way to vaporize the fuel and to hold it under pressure in a waiting room near the trap. We'll look more at the *carburetor* in a while, but for now it's sufficient to imagine it as a storage chamber or waiting room where fuel is vaporized and held under pressure. Now we need a door that opens and closes when we want it to.

Many chain saws are designed so that the piston itself is the only door between the waiting room, or carburetor, and the trap, or combustion chamber. Others are designed with a small door made of spring steel, called a *reed valve*. In either case, the door opens at exactly the right time, and the pressurized fuel vapor rushes in to fill the combustion chamber. When that happens, the piston moves up in the cylinder to compress the fuel vapor. When the piston has squeezed the fuel vapor into a much smaller area, it's time to start the fire. We start the fire by making an electric spark that jumps from one electrode of the spark plug to the other. Since the spark plug is screwed very tightly into the top of the combustion chamber, the spark starts a fire in the vaporized fuel. The fuel vapor burns very quickly, and the resulting explosion forces the piston down again.

But now we need another door, since we have to get rid of the useless burned gases. Most of the energy from the fire is used to push the piston down, but some of it remains as burned fuel vapor. This burned vapor is called *exhaust*, and the door through which it is expelled is called the *exhaust port*. If we don't get all the burned vapor out of the combustion chamber, there won't be room for the new fuel vapor. The pressure behind the fresh, incoming fuel vapor will help, since it will tend to chase out the thinner exhaust vapor.

Once again, the piston itself can be used as a door. We'll just put a small hole (or often three holes) in one side of the combustion chamber. We'll position it so that it becomes uncovered or opened when the piston moves down. But it also has to be positioned so that the fresh, incoming fuel vapor won't escape with the exhausted vapor. Many chain saw engines have a piston that is domed so that when the exhaust port is uncovered, the new fresh vapor is deflected upward into the combustion chamber.

Now let's start over from the beginning. We have a supply of vaporized fuel-oil mixture standing by under pressure. This mixture is forced or drawn into the cylinder when the piston opens the door or valve. When the piston moves up, it compresses the fuel mixture and reduces it in volume. Then the compressed mixture is ignited by a timed electric spark from the spark plug. The burning fuel vapor expands instantly, exerting great force on the piston and pushing it down.

The piston is connected by a *connecting rod* to a crank assembly on a *crankshaft*. When the piston goes down, the connecting rod turns the crank, and the crank turns the crankshaft. So the power from the chemical energy of the burning fuel is transformed into the mechanical energy of the turning crankshaft. At this time, the piston also uncovers the other door, and the burned gases are exhausted from the cylinder so that a new cycle can begin. This sequence of events, in order, is *intake*, *compression*, *ignition*, *power*, and *exhaust*. Note that each of these events must occur at the proper time in every cycle in order for the engine to work. Whenever a chain saw engine fails to work, the trouble can always be traced to one or more of these events.

In a chain saw engine, the full cycle of all five events must occur while the piston is moving from its bottom position to its top position and back again. The upward movement of the piston is known as the *compression stroke*, and its downward movement is called the *power stroke*. Thus we say that all five events occur within two strokes of the piston: the upward stroke and the downward stroke. That's why it's called a two-stroke or two-cycle engine. (Actually, the more accurate term is "two-stroke engine.")

Compressed fuel vapor is burned each time the piston nears the top of its compression stroke. Each downward stroke is a power stroke and has behind it the force of the expansion caused by the burning fuel vapor.

In order to force the fresh fuel vapor into the combustion chamber, the pressure of the incoming fuel vapor has to be somewhat higher than the lowest pressure existing in the cylinder. Chain saw engines are designed so that the crankcase itself is the last storage area for the incoming fuel vapor. The piston and the cylinder together act as a pump to increase the pressure of the fuel vapor in the crankcase so that it rushes into the combustion chamber when the valve port is opened. In this way, the crankcase is used as a scavenging pump—which is the reason most chain saw engines are referred to as two-stroke, *crankcase-scavenged* engines.

Figure 12.2 is a simplified drawing of the phases of a reed valve two-stroke engine. At the beginning of the intake phase, the piston is at its lowest point. It has passed the intake port to allow the vaporized fuel

Reed valve

Rotary valve

Reed valve open

Reed valve closed

Intake and compression

Power and exhaust

FIG. 12.3
Rotary valve chain saw engine

FIG. 12.2
Phases of a reed valve chain saw engine

mixture to enter the combustion chamber. When the piston moved down during the preceding exhaust phase, it slightly increased the pressure in the crankcase, helping to force the vaporized fuel from the crankcase up through the intake port. The piston has just finished delivering power to the crankshaft, and the burned gases from the last cycle have just finished escaping through the exhaust port. In the intake phase, then, the piston will now start upward on the compression stroke. While it travels upward, it will close off both the intake port and the exhaust port; it will also cause the pressure in the crankcase to drop considerably lower than the atmospheric pressure outside. That pressure drop will cause the reed valve to be pushed open by still another incoming charge of vaporized fuel from the carburetor. When the piston comes back down again in the power and exhaust phase, its return will increase the pressure in the crankcase, close the reed valve, and force the new fuel vapor up through the intake port into the combustion chamber just after the exhaust leaves through the exhaust port. And so it goes, several thousand times per minute.

You can now see why it's so important to keep a chain saw's exhaust ports open and free of carbon deposits. You can also see that the reed valve must open and close properly and that the carburetor must do its part by vaporizing the fuel mixture. And, of course, the spark plug has to fire, and fire exactly when it's supposed to. You can also see how all those exterior things that you are familiar with—spark plug, muffler, fuel tank—are related to less familiar parts and events that occur inside the engine. The process of troubleshooting always begins outside and goes inside until the trouble is identified.

Many chain saw engines use a three-port system instead of a reed valve. A *piston-ported* engine, as this type is called, utilizes the skirt of the piston itself as a slide valve. Figure 12.4 shows a piston-ported chain saw engine. Many of the most dependable chain saws incorporate this efficient design.

In a piston-ported chain saw engine, there is no reed valve. Instead, there's a third port at one side of the cylinder, leading from the carburetor. When the piston goes up on its intake and compression stroke, it creates a low-pressure area in the crankcase. It also uncovers the third port, allowing the vaporized fuel mixture to flow into the crankcase to fill the low-pressure area. When the piston goes down on its power stroke, it blocks the fuel port and increases the pressure in the crankcase. The increased pressure in the crankcase forces the vaporized fuel mixture up into the cylinder. When the piston is down, the exhaust ports

Inlet from
carburetor

Exhaust
port

Inlet
port

Intake and compression

Power and exhaust

FIG. 12.4

Phases of a piston-ported chain saw engine

are uncovered to allow the exhausted gases from the last cycle to escape. When the piston goes up to compress the fresh charge of fuel, it closes off both the exhaust ports and the intake ports, allowing no escape for the fresh fuel, which is then compressed until ignition occurs.

Now that we have a general overview of the principles of a two-stroke chain saw engine, let's take a look at how some of the particular needs of such an engine are met.

THE FUEL SYSTEM

In order for an engine to burn fuel, it must have a constant supply of fuel mixed with air in a vaporized form. That's why we have the carburetor. If you create a strong flow of air across the top of a container of liquid, the airflow will pull small amounts of the liquid up and into itself. If you make the opening to the container of liquid rather small, you can condense and control the amount of liquid that is mixed with the air. In the case of a gasoline chain saw engine, the liquid is gasoline, and the container is the fuel tank. The place at which the fuel is mixed with air is the carburetor.

Carburetor design is based on the *venturi* principle. The venturi principle says that if a gas flowing through a passage encounters a sudden decrease in the diameter of the passage, as shown in Figure 12.5, it will increase in speed and decrease in pressure as it squeezes through the narrower passage.

In a chain saw, the upward movement of the piston creates a low-pressure area in the crankcase, as we have seen. This low-pressure area then creates a flow of air into the crankcase. The flow of air is regulated by a *throttle*—which consists, simply, of a plate that opens and closes and determines the effective size of the air passage and, therefore, the amount of airflow. Since the airflow is created by low pressure in the crankcase, there's no need to mount the gas tank above the engine, as is the case with some small engines. Besides, since the chain saw must operate in any position, a gravity-feed fuel system would not be suitable.

One of the most common fuel-system failures in chain saws is the result of a leak, or loss of vacuum pressure in the carburetor, the crankcase, or the point at which they meet. Another common failure occurs when dirt clogs the tiny passageways in the carburetor or the fuel line. Carburetors very seldom "break."

In Figure 12.5 you see a representation of a fuel line from the fuel tank to the venturi in the air horn, where it ends in a fuel jet. As the airflow is sucked through the air horn by the vacuum in the crankcase, it passes through the venturi, where it undergoes an increase in speed and a subsequent decrease in pressure. Since there is less atmospheric

FIG. 12.5

The venturi principle applied:

I.　*Atmosphere exerts pressure on fuel at 1, and into air passage at 2.*

II.　*Upward movement of piston creates low-pressure area in crankcase at 3, opening reed valve and pulling air into air passage at 2.*

III.　*At venturi, air speed increases while air pressure decreases. Air pressure at venturi is now less than air pressure on fuel, at 1.*

IV.　*Low air pressure and high air speed in venturi pull droplets of fuel up through fuel line at 4. Droplets mix with air stream and become vaporized.*

V.　*Continued low pressure in crankcase pulls vaporized air-fuel mixture past open throttle plate and into crankcase.*

pressure at the jet, the airflow across it draws fuel from the jet in the form of little drops that are then carried into the crankcase with the air.

Most of the mixture burned in a chain saw engine is air. Although the percentage of fuel mixed and burned with the air is very small, the amount is critical. If there is too much fuel, the engine will flood and fail to run. If there is too little fuel, the engine will run lean and over-heat, or it will be starved and not run at all. The exactly correct mixture of air and fuel for different engine speeds must be precisely controlled by metering mechanisms in the carburetor. The mixture that engines burn at idle is about 11 pounds of air to each pound of fuel.

In an automobile engine, a simple float is used to regulate the amount of fuel that's in the carburetor at a given time. The fuel level raises the float until the float moves a mechanism that cuts off the flow of fuel. Again, this design will not work on a chain saw because the engine must operate in all positions. All modern chain saws utilize an all-position carburetor. This kind of carburetor has no float.

In a chain saw's all-position carburetor, the flow of fuel into the carburetor is controlled by fitting the inlet valve to a spring-loaded diaphragm. The pressure of the spring is offset by the vacuum at the fuel jets in the venturi of the carburetor. Also, a pulsating diaphragm is operated by the changes in crankcase vacuum and acts as a fuel pump.

In a chain saw, this fuel pump is usually integral to the carburetor, although it is not technically a part of it. That is, the fuel pump and the carburetor may be parts of the same assembly, superficially, but they are not the same. The typical fuel pump consists of a flexible diaphragm that moves up and down in response to changes in pressure in the crankcase. As the diaphragm moves, it opens and closes passages between the fuel tank and the carburetor. Again, it's the engine's crankcase itself that provides the vacuum and the changes in pressure that are the basic source of mechanical energy for various aspects of the fuel system.

Figure 12.6 is a simplified drawing of a chain saw fuel pump. You can see that the changing pressure in the crankcase causes the diaphragm to move up and down. When the low pressure pulls the diaphragm up, a suction is created under the diaphragm. This suction opens the inlet valve. Fuel then flows through the inlet valve and into the fuel chamber. At this time, the suction is also pulling on the outlet valve to keep it closed. When the pressure in the crankcase pushes the diaphragm down, the inlet valve will close and the pressure in the fuel chamber will push open the outlet valve.

An engine's fuel mixture requirements are different at different engine speeds. At low speed, the vacuum in the crankcase is low and so the airflow doesn't do a thorough job of vaporizing the fuel droplets.

Low pressure from crankcase

From fuel tank

Inlet valve open

Outlet valve closed

Diaphragm up

Fuel chamber

High pressure from crankcase

Inlet valve closed

Diaphragm down

Outlet valve open

To carburetor

FIG. 12.6
Chain saw diaphragm fuel pump

At high speed, the air flowing in the venturi becomes stretched and thin, but the fuel doesn't stretch accordingly. Thus the engine requires a richer mix of fuel and air at both idle and high speeds. That's why all chain saw carburetors have high-speed and low-speed mixture control *jets*, along with screws that adjust needles affecting these jets. Even if the high-speed mixture screw is "fixed," as it is on many smaller chain saws, it's still there to perform its function.

The high-speed screw controls a jet located in the venturi at the point of lowest pressure. The idle-speed screw controls three jets located in the air horn below the venturi, near the throttle valve.

Almost all currently produced chain saws are equipped with either a Walbro carburetor or a Tillotson carburetor. Figure 12.7 is a schematic drawing of a typical Walbro carburetor, at the time of starting, with all parts and functions labeled. Figures 12.8, 12.9, and 12.10 show this same carburetor at each of the three principal operating phases. With these illustrations as a guide, you can see exactly how the external adjustments affect the carburetor at different phases of operation. Figure 12.11 is a schematic drawing of a typical Tillotson carburetor. Although constructed somewhat differently, the Tillotson performs very much like the Walbro at each of the different phases of operation.

Parp says that it's not so important that we understand exactly how each part of the inside of a carburetor works; as long as we understand the basic principle and function of the carburetor and how it fits into the whole picture of the fuel system and the engine, we'll be able to locate most problems related to the carburetor. Modern carburetors are so developed that with a proper rebuilding kit, attention to the instructions, and reasonable care, almost anyone can rebuild a carburetor. Almost anytime that an internal malfunction occurs in a carburetor, the best solution is to rebuild the entire carburetor, step-by-step. Again, it's not very difficult, and it's usually easier and more practical for most chain saw users than attempting to isolate and repair a single carburetor problem. Besides, when one thing goes wrong inside a carburetor, you can usually assume that the whole thing needs to be cleaned or rebuilt. (Nevertheless, specific individual carburetor service steps are covered in Chapter 13.)

FUEL TANK VENTS

A small but essential part of any fuel or flow system is a *vent*. As the fuel level in a fuel tank goes down, air must be allowed to enter the tank to replace the used fuel. Otherwise, a vacuum would develop, and no fuel would flow. (NOTE: This is also true of the chain-oil tank.)

Many chain saws have the simplest of all vent systems. It's essentially

4 Outlet check valve — 3 Fuel pump
2 Inlet valve
1 Fuel inlet
5 Engine impulse
16 Choke valve
6 Throttle valve
7 Third idle hole
8 Second idle hole
15 Nozzle
9 Primary idle hole
10 Inlet needle valve
14 Metering chamber
11 Metering lever
13 Metering diaphragm
12 Metering lever spring

FIG. 12.7

Starting phase of typical Walbro chain saw carburetor

1. Fuel inlet: fuel drawn from tank
2. Inlet valve: opens on demand from fuel pump
3. Fuel pump: responds to engine impulse force
4. Outlet check valve: forced open by pump pressure
5. Engine impulse: actuates fuel-pump diaphragm
6. Throttle valve: regulates engine speed as it exposes primary, second, and third idle holes, then nozzle for dual delivery
7. Third idle hole: increases fuel flow at part throttle
8. Second idle hole: allows additional fuel flow on acceleration
9. Primary idle hole: only fuel source to engine at idle position
10. Inlet needle valve: lifts off seal to allow fuel entry
11. Metering lever: lifts inlet needle off seat
12. Metering lever spring: transmits force to metering lever
13. Metering diaphragm: drawn up by vacuum to activate metering lever
14. Metering chamber: fuel reservoir, feeds to idle and nozzle holes
15. Nozzle: increases fuel discharge for high speeds
16. Choke valve: closes air passage at starting position

FIG. 12.8

Throttle stop lever

Idle speed screw

Fuel inlet

Throttle valve

Secondary idle hole

Third idle hole

Primary idle hole

Main nozzle

Idle port

Nozzle check-valve

Inlet needle valve

Idle needle

Metering lever spring

Metering diaphragm chamber

Metering lever   Idle adjusting orifice   Metering diaphragm

Walbro carburetor at idle phase

FIG. 12.9

Throttle valve

Fuel inlet

Third idle hole

Venturi

Secondary idle hole

Main nozzle

Primary idle hole

Metering diaphragm chamber

Main fuel take-off

Walbro carburetor at part-throttle phase

FIG. 12.10

Fuel inlet

Crankcase pulse

Venturi

Throttle valve

Main nozzle

High-speed needle

Idle needle

Walbro carburetor at high-speed phase

FIG. 12.11

Impulse fitting

Pump diaphragm

Fuel intake fitting

Fuel screen

Choke plate

Throttle plate

Main nozzle (valve jet)

Secondary idle discharge port

Primary idle discharge port

Main adjustment screw

Idle adjustment screw

Inlet needle

Metering diaphragm

Atmospheric vent

Operation of a Tillotson HU chain saw carburetor

a hole in the tank cap. Since dirt could easily get through the hole and into the fuel, some method of filtering the incoming air is always employed. In the simpler systems, there is merely a filter screen or piece of fiber. These caps should be replaced often, since they are more likely to become clogged.

Other cap-vent systems are more elaborate. A common design has a valve that is opened when a vacuum develops in the fuel tank. When the tank is tilted, the pressure of the fuel closes the valve.

All fuel-tank vent systems should be checked and cleaned regularly. A clogged vent can silence a chain saw instantly, while a partially clogged vent can make it stammer.

FUEL LINE PICK-UP FILTER

Fuel flows from the fuel tank to the carburetor through a fuel pick-up line that is weighted on one end so that it sits on the bottom of the tank. The weight moves when you tilt your chain saw, so that the end of the fuel pick-up line is always at the lowest part of the fuel tank.

Water is heavier than gasoline. That's why water tends to collect at the bottom of your vehicle's fuel pump. In a chain saw's fuel tank, any water—even the smallest amount—will sink to the lowest part of the fuel tank, right where the end of your fuel pick-up sits. That's why water can clog your fuel filter and fuel pick-up line. Your fuel filter can look clean and be as clogged by water as if it were full of mud.

Parp is mumbling about how moisture condenses in partially filled fuel tanks while a saw is stored for long periods of time—more than two months. That's one of the many reasons that stale fuel is bad for a chain saw—whether it's stored in the saw's fuel tank or in a gasoline can; it turns into varnish.

IGNITION SYSTEM

Now we need a way to create that spark in the combustion chamber that will fire the vaporized fuel mixture after it's compressed by the piston.

All commonly available chain saws utilize a flywheel and magneto ignition system. The *flywheel* is a heavy wheel mounted on the crankshaft at the side of the engine opposite the sprocket and drive mechanism. Part of the flywheel's purpose is to add its weight as momentum to the turning crankshaft to help keep the engine turning smoothly. The flywheel in a chain saw is also fitted with permanent magnets. This is true of both conventional magneto systems and electronic, or breakerless, ignition systems.

The flywheel and the crankshaft are held together by a small piece of relatively soft metal called a *half-moon key*. This key fits into a slot in the crankshaft that corresponds to a slot in the flywheel. Note that one very common problem with all small-engine machines is a sheared, damaged, or partially sheared half-moon key.

When you pull the starter rope on your chain saw, you spin the flywheel. And because the flywheel is firmly attached to the crankshaft, you also turn the crankshaft. When the crankshaft turns, the crank moves the piston up and down. We have already seen how the piston, moving in the cylinder, creates pressure changes in the crankcase and how the pulsations of those pressure changes provide the impulses that activate the fuel system. Thus, spinning the flywheel with the starter rope causes the piston to move and the fuel mixture to flow. It also simultaneously creates the energy that causes the flow of electricity resulting in the spark at the spark plug which fires the compressed fuel mixture. When you pull the starter rope on your chain saw, you are providing the initial energy that turns the engine, moves the fuel, and creates the fire. After the engine starts, it does all this for itself, and the expansion of the burning fuel mixture replaces your arm as the energy source.

The other part of a flywheel and magneto ignition system is the *magneto*. A magneto is a coil of wires that are tightly wound and held by a cylinder-shaped container. It generates alternating current that converts magnetic energy from the magnets in the flywheel to electrical energy flowing to the spark plug. The word "magneto" is short for magnetoelectric machine.

If you think back to your grade school days, you might remember doing an electromagnetic experiment in science class. If you're like Parp, you didn't understand it then, you won't now, and you don't give a hoot. And nobody knows anything about electricity anyway, because it's clearly magic or else how could pictures come through the air? Right?

OK. Say it's magic. It's nevertheless true that if you move a wire across the lines of a magnetic field, you can produce electricity in the wire. If the wire is part of a complete circuit, you can make electrical current flow through the circuit. If you wind another wire into a coil around the wire in the circuit and then move the coiled wire through the magnetic field, the voltage of the current you produce is multiplied by the number of turns in the coiled wire.

And another thing about the relationship between magnetism and electricity: Just as you can use magnetism to induce an electrical current, a flow of electricity also creates magnetism. Whenever an electrical current is flowing in a conductor, a magnetic field exists around the conductor. If the conductor is a tightly wound coil of wires, the magnetic forces merge to create a single magnetic field that's stronger than the field surrounding a lone wire.

The strength and direction of the force of a magnetic field present around a conductor are determined by the strength and direction of the electrical current *in* the conductor. If you change the current, you also change the magnetic field. If you stop the current completely, the magnetic forces collapse. If you stop the current in a coil of wire, the magnetic forces collapse across the turns of the coil and induce a new current.

Electricity flows only in a complete circuit, and a current of electricity also takes the path of least resistance to complete its circuit. In other words, electricity is "alive" only when it can travel from one place to another and return by a different road. And it always takes the easiest road.

Now what we want to do is use the ideas we've just reviewed, plus a few others, to produce the spark that starts the fire in our fire trap—the combustion chamber.

We have a flywheel with permanent magnets cast into it, as shown in Figure 12.12. If we move those magnets past a coil of wire, we'll create potential electrical pressure, or voltage, in the coil. We can use the potential voltage thus produced to create the spark. Note that the flywheel and the coil must pass at exactly the correct distance from one another. Actually, the flywheel passes closest to a laminated core of soft iron plates called the *armature core*. Soft iron is an excellent conduc-

FIG. 12.12

The schematic view of the flywheel magneto ignition system (breaker point system) tor of magnetic forces, so it's used to transfer the magnetic forces from the flywheel magnets to the magneto coil. It also concentrates the strength of the magnets. The distance between the flywheel magnets and the armature core at their closest points is known as the *armature air gap*. (*Magneto edge gap* is a different matter that we needn't bother our heads about now.)

A magneto coil actually consists of *two* coils, or windings, of wire. The inner winding is called the *primary winding*, and the outer winding is called the *secondary winding*. The primary winding consists of about 200 turns of rather thick copper wire, and the secondary winding consists of about 10,000 turns of very thin wire.

In a chain saw's magneto system, the primary winding is connected to an electric switching mechanism called *breaker points*. The points open and close to break or complete the electrical circuit. They are caused to open and close by a simple mechanism: a lobe on the crankshaft. One of the points is fixed in a certain position, and the other can be moved by the lobe on the crankshaft. Each time the crankshaft turns, the lobe pushes the movable point away from the fixed one. At that instant, the points are open and the circuit is broken. When the lobe passes its point of contact with the movable point, a steel spring brings it back into contact with the fixed point, and the circuit is complete again.

The magneto's primary winding and the points are also connected to an overload device called a *condenser*. The condenser absorbs the flow of current at high voltage when the spark plug fires, preventing the current from arcing across the breaker points before it's supposed to. If that happened, it would "short out" the circuit to the spark plug and prevent the spark.

When you pull the starter rope and spin the flywheel, its magnets pass the armature core and the magneto coil. The armature transfers the concentrated magnetic forces to the magneto coil. The magneto coil converts the magnetism to electrical energy. When the crankshaft lobe—also moved by the spinning flywheel—moves past the movable breaker point, the points close, and the electricity flows through the points to ground.

Now this is the tricky part. When the points are opened, the flow of current in this primary circuit is interrupted. Since the flow of current caused a strong electromagnetic field to surround the primary winding of thick wire, the interruption causes this field to collapse across the secondary winding of thin wire. This compresses the current and tremendously increases the voltage. It increases it so much that, if it weren't for the condenser, it would leap across the breaker points even though they are open. The electrical pressure increases from about 300 or 400 volts to about 15,000 or 20,000 volts. This is caused by the far greater number of turns in the secondary winding. And, of course, the current always moves to the secondary winding when the primary circuit is interrupted, because it is the path of least resistance.

Since this high-voltage current is blocked by the condenser from jumping across the open points, it travels along its secondary lead to the spark plug. Here there is no condenser to stop it, and the gap is small and easy to jump. The current jumps across the gap, and we have our spark. Since the spark plug is screwed into the cylinder head, the electrode that's connected to the threads forms an electrical ground, and the circuit is complete.

We now have fuel to burn, a place to trap the fire, a way to use the energy from the trapped fire, and a spark to start the fire. We have an engine. If any of the systems of the engine hesitate or fail, the engine will run poorly (or not at all).

ELECTRONIC (BREAKERLESS) IGNITIONS

The number of new chain saws that are equipped with breakerless ignition systems increases each year. As recently as the late 1970's, these systems were considered too expensive for installation on relatively inexpensive machines such as chain saws. But the production of these systems increased so greatly and the production methods became so efficient that the considerable advantages of these systems quickly outweighed their higher costs. Of all gasoline-powered small-engine machines, chain saws have the most to gain from the breakerless ignition.

Changing or adjusting the breaker points in chain saws has always been a simple job, but one that many owners were reluctant to attempt. The flywheel nut usually has to be removed, a formidable obstacle in itself, and the flywheel has to be separated from the crankshaft. Parp believes that anyone with a little confidence can successfully change or adjust the points in any chain saw, but many users lack the confidence. And most manufacturers, dealers, and mechanics have contributed to the difficulties by making the job seem mysterious and specialized.

The breakerless ignition has no points to adjust and no moving parts to wear out. It can be permanently sealed against moisture and dirt, the two culprits most responsible for ignition failure. The breakerless ignition also greatly increases the efficiency of any engine at all speeds and significantly reduces its polluting emissions—a worthy advance. It's also virtually maintenance-free.

In the breakerless ignition, the points and condenser are replaced by various transistorized circuits that may include the use of a capacitor, a gate-controlled switch and trigger, and diodes, thyristors, or rectifiers. Most chain saw users have no need for a technical explanation of how electronic ignitions function, but we'll go through some of the elements as nontechnically as possible.

A *capacitor* is an electrical storage device and safety or overload control that's designed to discharge stored voltage through a coil to create the high-voltage current that provides the spark. A capacitor is not always used in electronic ignitions. Essentially, it replaces the condenser, and then some.

A *gate-controlled switch* is an electronic switch with no moving or mechanical parts. It's opened and closed by changes in current direction. A positive current direction closes the gate, or turns the switch on. A negative current turns it off. The trigger is actually an electrical current that activates the gate-controlled switch.

Diodes, *thyristors*, and *rectifiers* are electronic devices that allow current to flow in only one direction. They are called *semiconductors*. When current is traveling in one direction, they conduct and the current flows. When the current reverses, they refuse to do anything.

All of these devices are very small and may be incorporated into a single unit called the *trigger plate*. That's why these ignitions are often called *solid state circuits*. Solid state circuits employ semiconductors as control devices, or switches.

Magnetic induction supplies the potential voltage for breakerless systems, just as it does for conventional systems (see Figure 12.13). When

FIG. 12.13

The schematic view of the ignition system of the 015 L Electronic Ignition

the flywheel turns, magnetic forces cut across the windings of the magneto coil and produce a negative current in the primary windings. In a typical system, a diode then allows the current to flow. Remember that this diode is a one-way device. When it is conducting, the situation is similar to a conventional system at the moment when the breaker points are closed and current is flowing in the primary windings of thick wire.

As the flywheel turns, it reverses the direction of the magnetic forces. This, of course, reverses the direction of the current in the primary windings, and the diode sits down on the job. Again, a condenserlike safety device prevents the current from proceeding before it's supposed to. At this time, the gate-controlled switch is turned on by a positive voltage, and a current flows in the primary windings. The gate-controlled switch is then immediately opened, or turned off, by a negative current in the coil, induced by the trigger. This interrupts the current at its maximum voltage, and its electromagnetic field collapses across the secondary windings, creating the high voltage that provides the spark.

POWER

We don't want the chain on our chain saw to move when the engine is running at idle. We do want it to move when we increase the speed of the engine by depressing the throttle control that opens the throttle plate and allows more fuel to flow. To insure that the chain moves when we want it to and stops when it should, all chain saws utilize a *centrifugal clutch*.

Since the crankshaft is a turning mechanism, it possesses centrifugal force. Centrifugal force is another of those ideas you probably discussed and experimented with in grade school science class. You have also experienced it, in considerable strength, when riding a Ferris wheel or some other amusement park ride. As your body spins on the wheel, you feel a force pushing you out away from the center of the wheel. That force is *centrifugal force*. The word "centrifugal" is an adjective that describes moving or being moved away from a center or axis. Anything spinning on an axis has a tendency to move away from the axis.

A centrifugal clutch (see Figure 12.14) consists of a drum casing with a hub that fits over the drive side of the crankshaft. The hub fits over a bearing assembly so that the crankshaft can turn in the hub without turning the drum. Inside the drum, clutch shoes are attached by springs, and the entire friction assembly is held to the crankshaft by retaining washers, or by a half-moon key similar to the flywheel key. At rest or at idle, the springs keep the clutch shoes from touching the inside walls of the clutch drum. When the engine idles, the drum stays still and the shoes turn inside it with the crankshaft. When you speed the engine,

FIG. 12.14
The centrifugal clutch

At idle speed, the clutch shoes rotate freely in the drum.

When engine speed increases, the shoes are thrown outward by centrifugal force and press so hard against the drum that both the drum and the chain start to move.

the crankshaft turns faster and the centrifugal force on the clutch shoes is increased. At speeds above idle, the centrifugal force pushes the shoes outward, against the inside of the clutch drum. This causes the drum to turn, and since the sprocket is attached to the clutch drum, the sprocket turns also. The sprocket turns the chain.

Note that if the engine is operating at only a moderate speed, the shoes are not pushed very tightly against the walls of the drum. This situation results in friction between the shoes and the drum. That's why a clutch wears so rapidly if you cut wood at less than maximum engine speed.

Clutch bearings are another common cause of trouble. If water gets into these bearings, they become rusted. When that occurs, the bearing assembly must be replaced.

CHAIN LUBRICATION SYSTEMS

Now that we have the chain moving, we need some way to keep it lubricated and some kind of mechanism that will allow us to adjust the chain tension when necessary. A discussion of these matters will complete our brief overview of the general mechanics of a chain saw.

The most common chain lubrication system is still the *hand-operated oil pump.* Such an assembly has very few parts and is quite simple in operation. A typical thumb-push oil pump consists of a push rod that moves a plunger inside a very small, simple, cast-unit pump. A pump plunger spring presses against the pump plunger and exerts the pressure that moves the push-button back out after you remove your thumb. When the spring pushes the plunger and the push-button out, a vacuum is created inside the pump. This pulls the oil from the oil tank through an intake check valve. When you push the button, the plunger forces the oil through a discharge check valve and into the oil line that leads to the oil discharge hole near the mounting area of the guide bar. The oil squirts through oil holes in the guide bar and onto the chain. A bent push rod is the most common problem occurring with manual oilers.

Automatic oiling systems are somewhat more complicated, and there is quite a lot of variation in design. In general, there are two different kinds of drive mechanisms and two methods of attaching the pump assembly to the chain drive mechanism.

If the pump is driven directly by the crankshaft, as it is with many chain saws, the pump is operating anytime the engine is running. This often means that the pump is using oil even when the engine is at idle and the chain isn't turning. A small amount of oil may be wasted with this system.

Some chain saws (Stihl, some Homelite models, and others) have automatic oil pumps that are driven by the sprocket, the clutch drum, or the sprocket shaft. With this system, the pump delivers oil only when the clutch is engaged and the chain is turning. If the chain isn't moving, no oil is pumped.

Automatic chain lubrication pumps are driven either by a worm gear or by an eccentric. The worm gear may be part of either the crankshaft or the sprocket shaft. An eccentric, when used, is a part of the crankshaft. Let's look at the eccentric system first (see Figure 12.15-A).

An *eccentric* is a disc or wheel that has its axis of revolution displaced from its center (that is, it turns lopsided), so that it's capable of impart-

FIG. 12.15–A

This is the eccentric type of chain-oiling system. Fig. 12.15–B on the next page shows another type.

ing reciprocating motion. That way, it can push something away and then allow it to return. It's easy to produce a crankshaft that has an eccentric portion.

As the crankshaft turns, the large side of the eccentric pushes the plunger away. When the plunger is all the way back, it opens the inlet channel, and the pump distribution cylinder fills with oil. When the eccentric turns away, a spring pushes the plunger forward, and the oil in the pump cylinder is forced out through a check valve. When the plunger moves back, the check valve closes to prevent oil from being sucked backward into the pump.

Not all of the oil that enters the distribution cylinder is pumped to the chain. Some of it returns to be pumped again. At one end of a typical eccentric oil-pump system there is a set screw that moves the distribution plunger and changes the relationship between the amount of oil going to the chain and the amount being returned. This set screw can be used to adjust the amount of oil flowing to the chain.

Most automatic oiling systems are driven by a *worm gear* located either on the crankshaft or on the sprocket shaft. In a typical system, the worm gear turns and causes the pump plunger to rotate. A reduction system is used to reduce the rotation speed of the pump to considerably less than that of the crankshaft. As shown in Figure 12.15-B, one end of the pump plunger is beveled. A spring pushes this end against a curved sup-

FIG. 12.15–B   *This is a worm gear chain-oiling system.*

port that is located eccentrically in relation to the pump plunger. The entire support assembly may be moved by adjusting the set screw that controls its position. This changes the eccentricity of the support and alters the amount of oil delivered to the chain.

As the plunger turns, the eccentric support pushes it back and forth. As the plunger moves back and forth, it opens and closes the inlet and outlet channels and so pumps oil to the chain.

Some oil pumps are located behind the flywheel of the chain saw. Others are located in a recess in the crankcase on the drive side of the saw. All are hidden and covered to protect them from dirt, impact, and chain saw owners.

Most recent automatic oil pumps are adjustable, but many are difficult to adjust. There's a reason for this. As you can see, it's easy to damage an oil pump by putting too much pressure on the set screw or by turning the adjustment mechanism too far. Most oiling systems are designed so that they need to be adjusted only if you dramatically change the size of the guide bar used. If you're just going to do some heavy cutting for a short while, you shouldn't need to adjust your oiler. Parp prefers to have a manual oiler in addition to an adjustable automatic oiling system. That way, the chain is always oiled by the automatic system, and you can add more oil during heavy cutting sessions by using the manual oiler freely. For the average user, though, any of today's quality automatic systems will supply sufficient lubrication under almost all conditions, without additional manual oil.

CHAIN ADJUSTMENT MECHANISM

All chain adjustment mechanisms are similar. They consist of a chain adjustment screw and a nut that moves on the screw. The screw is installed in a cast housing, usually on the bar mounting pad but sometimes built into the clutch cover.

When you turn the screw, the adjusting nut moves. On one side, the nut has a pin, usually a square pin, that fits into a square hole at the tail of the bar. When you turn the screw, the nut moves on the screw, and the pin moves the bar. If you exert excessive pressure on the adjusting screw, all of that pressure is concentrated by the adjusting nut. Since all of that pressure is on one small part of the screw, the screw can bend or the threads can strip, especially if the adjusting nut is not in position in the hole in the guide bar. When you clamp down the guide bar mounting nuts, you can bend the adjustment screw or even punch a hole in the crankcase or tank casting. That's about all that can happen to this mechanism, but it happens often enough. Take the time to make sure that everything is aligned correctly before you tighten the mounting nuts.

TROUBLESHOOTING

Even if you never want to try any mechanical repairs on your own chain saw, learning to troubleshoot can save you a great deal of time and money. Parp believes that anyone can learn to perform most of the services and repairs that a chain saw usually needs. It's certainly true that anyone can learn to troubleshoot accurately enough to determine at least the likely cause of most problems. In any case, if you try to determine your own problems before you go to a mechanic, you'll discover many instances of insufficient fuel, turned-off switches, fouled spark plugs, and loose nuts, bolts, and screws.

Troubleshooting is a logical process that always begins with the easiest tests and the most obvious functions and then proceeds to the most complicated or difficult only after all others have been exhausted. In other words, as we said before, troubleshooting is a diagnostic process that begins outside, with the symptoms, and goes inside until the cause is discovered.

Parp is nudging me to suggest, before we go any further, that if your saw is under warranty when a problem develops, you should see your dealer before you do anything yourself (unless your saw is simply out of fuel or you forgot to turn the ignition switch on). Any real problems in a new saw should go straight to the dealer. All chain saw warranties become void if an unauthorized person, mechanic or not, attempts any repairs other than those called for by normal owner maintenance. And if you added STP to your fuel tank, forget it.

A great majority of apparent chain saw engine failures are not true engine failures. Almost anytime a chain saw fails to start or fails to continue to run, the failure is caused by a problem or problems in either the ignition system or the fuel system. If your year-old chain saw suddenly refuses to operate at high speeds, or runs poorly at any speed, you should not assume that your piston rings are worn or that the crankshaft is bent. These are relatively uncommon troubles that should occur only after many, many hours of hard use, if at all. It's much more likely, for example, that the carburetor needs to be adjusted or repaired or that the fuel line is split. Before you tear into the heart of the engine, exhaust all the easier and more external possibilities.

Without exception, the first thing you should do is to take a good look around the entire exterior of your saw. It's a detective process: You don't know, often, what you're looking for, but you do have a pretty good idea how things should look. Many times, you'll discover that the high-tension wire (spark plug cable) is loose, that the carburetor is loose (though this problem may not always be visible), or that fuel is leaking from a defective gasket. Troubleshooting should always start with a visual inspection.

By the way, the only reliable check of chain saw engine compression is to pull the starter rope or spin the flywheel by hand to determine if the resistance to engine turning is normal, as caused by the compression in the combustion chamber. Chain saws often continue to run, and run well, even after a considerable loss of compression, depending on the cause. Any other compression test on a chain saw can be very misleading and is usually a complete waste of time. Manufacturers' shop manuals sometimes specify a compression test and a compression range, but even these should be viewed as arbitrary and inconclusive.

In the Appendix, you'll find a group of troubleshooting charts. Before you follow these very far, you should become familiar with a typical and logical process of troubleshooting. We'll begin where the first simple chart ends.

If your chain saw refuses to start and you are certain that the problem is not covered by that chart, proceed as follows.

First, pull the starter rope several times. Does the engine turn over? If it doesn't, the problem is your starter, and there's no question about it. If the engine does start, the simple chain saw starter is probably working, and you should go on.

Next, remove the spark plug. If the fuel system is delivering fuel to the cylinder and to the compression chamber, and if the spark plug is cold, you'll be able to smell gasoline on the spark plug. If the plug is quite dry but still smells rather strongly of gasoline, the problem is probably not in the fuel system. If the spark plug is dry and odorless, the fuel system is probably not delivering fuel. If the spark plug is wet or fouled or oily, the problem is likely to be in either the fuel system or the ignition system.

You still don't know whether the problem is in the fuel system or in the ignition system. If the spark plug is wet, it's either because the fuel system is delivering too much fuel to the cylinder, or because the ignition system is failing to provide the spark necessary to burn the fuel.

The easiest next step, and the most logical, is to determine whether or not the ignition system is delivering a spark. This was covered for other reasons in Chapter 5, but we'll repeat it here for the sake of convenience and to explain some minor differences.

Find a well-shaded place. Disconnect the spark plug cable and leave the spark plug screwed in. If your cable has a boot or cap that fits over the spark plug terminal, insert a metal rod, a nail, or a paper clip in the boot so that it projects from the boot. Hold the metal piece or the spark plug wire so that the end of it is about 1/8″ from the top of the spark plug. Be sure to hold the cable by the rubber insulation and to keep your hand back from the end of the metal. Pull the starter rope briskly. Each time you pull the rope, a spark should jump from the cable end to the spark plug terminal several times. You may not be able to see the spark if you're outside in broad daylight, but you'll be able to hear it. In moderate shade, you should be able to see the spark as it jumps.

If you see several strong blue to white sparks each time you pull the starter rope, the ignition system is good at least as far as the spark plug—and if the spark plug is good, then the ignition system is probably good all the way through. In that case, the problem is most likely to be in the fuel system.

If you get no spark at all or if the spark seems weak, you have a problem in the ignition system. More than likely, it's the magneto.

If the spark plug was dry when you removed it for the first test, leave the plug screwed in and the cable disconnected while you pull the starter rope several more times. Then immediately remove the spark plug. If it still isn't wet with gasoline, the problem is probably in the fuel system. To make sure, pour a very small amount—about half a teaspoon—of fresh, correctly mixed fuel straight down into the spark plug hole. This will fill the cylinder with fuel. Then immediately replace the spark plug, connect the cable, and pull the starter rope. If the engine starts and runs briefly, you can be certain that the problem is in the fuel system.

Now if you determined that the problem is in the *ignition* system, you should replace the spark plug—unless it's quite new and you know for certain that it has been firing up until the time of failure. And even then it's worth trying a new plug. You should always keep new plugs around for exactly this reason. You may have a defective spark plug, or the plug may be fouled in such a way that you can't visibly detect the fouling. If you replace the plug and the engine runs, your problem is solved. If you replace the plug and the saw still doesn't run, you know that the ignition failure is probably someplace between the magnets in the flywheel and the end of the spark plug cable. The culprit is probably that magneto.

If you determined that the problem is in the fuel system, you should now double-check the fuel. If you have any doubts, discard the fuel and replace it with a fresh, correct mixture. While you're at it, check the vent in the fuel tank cap. A clogged fuel cap vent can prevent fuel from reaching the cylinder. If that doesn't do it, check the air filter. Even if it looks spotless, clean it with gasoline, blow it out, and allow it to air dry. Do the same with the fuel line filter. Even a small amount of water in the fuel filter will block the line, and no fuel will reach the cylinder.

While the air and fuel filters are drying, smell the carburetor. If you detect a heavy gasoline smell, your problem is probably there. Unless you find a disconnected or broken fuel line, you will probably have to remove, clean, and rebuild the carburetor. It's not a difficult job, and you really should be able to do it yourself (see Chapter 13).

If the ignition failure was not the fault of a turned-off ignition switch, fouled spark plug, or loose spark plug cable connection, carefully examine as much of the spark plug cable as you can see. If you find any breaks or cracks in the insulation, that may well be your problem. If not, as Parp said before, it's probably the magneto. It could be that a simple servicing of gaps, timing, and so forth will correct the problem, or it could be that you'll have to replace the magneto. Of course, it could also be the points, if you've let your maintenance slip; or it could be the ignition switch. Consult the next troubleshooting chart, the next chapter, *The Chain Saw Service Manual* (put out by Intertec Publishing Corporation), and your favorite good-luck charm.

If you have cleaned or replaced the air and fuel filters and your saw *still* doesn't start, readjust the carburetor as discussed in Chapter 6, and try again. If that doesn't do it, squirt a small amount of fuel mix into the combustion chamber, through the spark plug hole. If you have a spark and fuel and if all of the parts are together, the saw should run. And if that doesn't do it, you've at least eliminated a lot of possibilities.

Parp cautions that much of the material in this chapter and many of the suggested procedures assume that you have treated your saw properly and performed all the maintenance and service procedures recommended in your owner's manual and in Chapters 5 and 6. If you haven't done these things, you may miss some obvious problems (such as excessive carboning of exhaust ports) and erroneously conclude that your fuel system has a major malfunction. You can't follow a logical process by leaving out Step One. Step One is to follow all the steps of a sound maintenance and service schedule.

Most of the Appendix consists of troubleshooting charts. These charts can't be a cure-all for every chain saw difficulty, or anywhere near it. In fact, many of the repairs or procedures referred to are within the capabilities of only a well-trained mechanic, whether professional or not. But these charts should nevertheless help you decide what your problems are likely to be and whether you should try to fix your saw yourself, take it to a mechanic, or junk it.

We'll start with the cutting attachment, but we'll concentrate on the mechanical aspects of the drive, clutch, and adjustment mechanism. Parp has detailed the saw chain itself in Chapter 8 and in the "Saw Chain Troubleshooting Guide." In the charts in the Appendix, Parp has tried to list the troubles and causes in the order of their likelihood.

CHAPTER 13
SOME REPAIRS

In this chapter, Parp intends to bridge the gap between your owner's manual and the more technical repair guides such as shop service manuals and Intertec's *The Chain Saw Service Manual*.

Parp thinks back to his first experiences with chain saw mechanics and remembers that gap clearly. *The Chain Saw Service Manual*, like its companion volume, *Small Engines Service Manual*, is chiefly for professional mechanics, professional users, or others who are already reasonably familiar with service and repair procedures. As such, *The Chain Saw Service Manual* is a useful aid for which Intertec deserves full credit.

The Chain Saw Service Manual offers detailed information on virtually every recent chain saw and some that aren't so recent. Included are extremely detailed drawings, diagrams, and specifications of every engine, part, and function of the saws covered. A mechanic can refer to these drawings and specifications to discover the exact order of assembly and disassembly. But it doesn't tell you, for example, that you'll probably need a spanner wrench in order to remove the clutch, or that you need some way to protect the piston head and limit the turning of the crankshaft when you remove a clutch nut or flywheel nut.

There are several excellent and specialized books on the subject of small engine repair. The best of these, says Parp, is Paul Weissler's *Small Gas Engines*, a *Popular Science* book from Harper and Row. Parp differs considerably regarding some of Mr. Weissler's comments on chain saws, but not regarding repair procedures for the engines themselves. Parp suggests that a combination of your owner's manual, a shop manual for your saw, *The Chain Saw Service Manual*, this book, and Mr. Weissler's *Small Gas Engines* would be an excellent library of resource material with which to begin a study of chain saw mechanics. Begin, Parp says, because books and mechanics don't mix readily. What you really need is some gumption, a collection of tools, a chain saw that doesn't work, and a diminishing wood supply with winter coming on about 50 miles west of Nowhere. That will make a mechanic out of you.

In other words, hands-on experience is the only real teacher. There are, however, many easy repairs you can make now with a minimum of tools. Once you get started, you'll be reluctant to surrender your saw to that guy in town who calls himself a mechanic.

Guide bar

Saw chain

Handle bar

Bumper spike

Starter
handle

Fuel
filler cap

Rewind
starter

Flywheel

Fuel tank

Grip

Annular
buffer

Spark plug

Throttle trigger

Chain-
sprocket cover

Clutch

Oil quantity
control knob

Oil pump

Crankshaft

Worm gear

Chain
sprocket

Connecting rod

Cylinder

Muffler

Piston

THREE TIPS

Here are three tips worth mentioning. First, always keep your work in order. Lay down your parts exactly as they come off. Draw pictures to remind yourself of particular assemblies. If you remove bolts and screws that are different sizes, be sure you put them back where they belong. If necessary, draw a picture of the assembly and label the parts or punch the bolts and screws through the picture in the correct places.

The second tip is never to use a tool that doesn't fit the job, and to be exceedingly cautious about substituting for recommended tools or procedures.

The third tip is to watch out for one tragedy that is common to all beginning mechanics, especially if they begin on chain saws: Many chain saw parts are made of soft metals such as aluminum, brass, and magnesium; threads cut into these metals are exceedingly easy to damage. Be cautious about applying force or pressure to a wrench or screwdriver. Damaged threads can be repaired with a Heli-Coil thread repair kit (the source address is in the Appendix).

ANOTHER LIST OF TOOLS

To begin basic maintenance, service, and repair operations on a chain saw, you should have a fairly good collection of hand tools. Here is a list of the most basic tools you'll need. Some special tools will be mentioned in the course of discussing repair procedures. If you read each section before attempting the procedure, you'll know which tools you'll need.

- Small machine hammer
- Slip-joint pliers
- Set of ignition or small low-profile combination wrenches
- Set of combination wrenches through 1"
- 1/4"- and 3/8"-drive socket sets with extensions
- Set of deep-well sockets
- Spark plug sockets
- Set of long allen-head wrenches (professional quality)
- Small and large Vise Grips
- Assorted slot-type screwdrivers
- Small, medium, and large Phillips screwdrivers
- Plastic feeler gauge set
- Test light (this you can make)
- Small, medium, and large needle-nose pliers

- Center punches
- Offset screwdriver
- Wooden mallet
- Tap and die set, or a Heli-Coil thread-repair kit
- Impact driver set and bits (same drive size as your socket set)

Other than noted exceptions, the repair instructions in this chapter apply specifically to the Stihl 031 AV, a popular midrange lightweight chain saw. This allows Parp to be more particular than if he were discussing several saws at once. Most of these instructions can be readily applied to any other chain saw, especially if you have a shop manual for that particular saw, or *The Chain Saw Service Manual* as a guide.

The first, the most important, and the most basic maintenance procedures for chain saws are those covered in Chapters 5 through 8 of this book. If you follow those procedures conscientiously, as well as any others recommended in your owner's manual, you'll avoid or postpone many of the repairs mentioned in this chapter.

CLUTCH AND SPROCKET

The entire drive mechanism is a relatively simple assembly. As long as you keep the saw's parts in order and take precautions to protect the piston head, you should have no trouble.

Because of the turning direction of the crankshaft, chain saw clutch assemblies have left-handed threads to keep them from loosening when the chain is turning. That means you have to turn them clockwise to get them off. Since this is the direction in which the crankshaft turns, you need some way to stop it. When you turn the clutch, and hence the crankshaft, you move the piston up and down. Therefore, one way to stop the crankshaft from turning is to stop the piston from going up and down. We're already up against two of those specialized shop tools that Parp mentioned earlier.

The first is a *crankshaft locking nut*. This tool is supplied with all Stihl chain saws and so isn't really just for the pros. But most chain saw manufacturers don't supply a crankshaft locking nut or screw, or even a reasonable substitute. Check your owner's manual to be sure. You can make a passable substitute with a clean lightweight rag or towel. This is risky, since you may well leave bits of thread in the cylinder, but it will do in an emergency. Another method is to use a short length of starter rope with a knot that will slip through the spark plug hole.

The second special tool is a *clutch wrench*. Again, Stihl and a few other manufacturers supply a clutch wrench with every chain saw, but most do not. There is no totally satisfactory substitute. The problem is that the face of the clutch is flat, and the disassembly points differ widely in size and shape from saw to saw. You can and should obtain a clutch wrench from your dealer or the distributor of your chain saw. There are adjustable spanner wrenches available that are designed to fit many small engine clutches. These are inexpensive tools and have other uses as well.

If the clutch shoes are just dirty or oily, you won't need to replace them. Just remove them and wash them in gasoline. When dry, roughen the clutch shoes with emery cloth.

If the clutch shoes are worn, replace the complete set. Likewise, if the springs or spring hooks are stretched or fatigued, replace them all. Otherwise, you'll be doing the whole job over again immediately.

Whenever you remove the clutch, check the bearings. Most bearings consist of needles in a needle cage. If they're rusted, they'll need to be replaced. Always grease new or used bearings with a high-quality waterproof grease before installing. Also put a small amount of oil onto the crankshaft behind the clutch drum.

First, remove the guide bar nuts, the sprocket cover, the guide bar, and the saw chain. Then remove the starter assembly from the other side of the chain saw. Otherwise, you might damage the starter when you reassemble the clutch and tighten the clutch retaining nut. Do not disassemble the starter, but simply remove the entire housing and assembly from the saw.

After the starter assembly is removed, remove the spark plug. Then screw in the crankshaft locking nut by hand. Insert a clutch wrench between the clutch shoes and turn the clutch clockwise, gently, until the piston stops against the crankshaft locking nut. Then use a socket and breaker bar or combination wrench to loosen the clutch retaining nut. Remember that this nut has left-hand threads and so is removed by turning it clockwise. Use a spanner wrench or clutch wrench to hold the clutch still while removing the nut.

On both sides of the clutch of a Stihl 031 you will find clutch retaining washers. (These details differ with other saws.) On this model, the washers hold the clutch shoes in position on the clutch assembly. These washers are slightly arched and each has a rim on one side. They must be replaced exactly as you found them.

Remove the first washer and note its correct position. Then insert the clutch wrench and unscrew the clutch assembly by turning it clockwise. Remove the second retaining washer. Remove the chain sprocket, needle cage or bearing, and the clutch cover plate. On this model, a drive pin extends from the cover plate to a hole in the chain sprocket. This pin drives the automatic oil pump when the clutch is engaged.

Cover plate
Needle cage
Chain sprocket, 3/8″ (9.32 mm), 7 teeth
Chain sprocket, .325″ (8.25 mm), 8 teeth
Washer
Clutch shoe
Clutch spring
Washer
Clutch carrier
Gasket
Pump housing
Washer
Helical spring
Pump piston
Spur gear
Spur gear
Helical spring
Bolt
Control bolt
Rubber ring
Cylinder-head screw
Nut
Guard plate
Cover   Pin
Cylinder-head screw
Notched pin
Outer guide plate
Hex head screw
Chain-sprocket cover
Spiked bumper
Retaining nut
Hexagonal nut

Oil pump, chain sprocket, clutch, and chain-sprocket cover (Stihl 031 AV)

Before you disassemble the clutch any further, take a good look at the clutch shoes and other parts of the assembly. If you decide that the problem is here for sure, remove the damaged parts of the clutch. Remember that springs and shoes must be replaced as a set. If the clutch drum is scored or burned, you'll have to replace it. Be sure to examine the sprocket, too, now that you can see it easily—but Parp assumes that you've already eliminated the sprocket as the cause of your trouble. If you do see signs of moderate to excessive wear, you should replace the sprocket. Replace the needle bearings if they are burned, rusted, or damaged.

The cover plate should be in good condition, and you should be able to reuse it. If it's bent, however, you must replace it.

There are very few parts to worry about in a chain saw clutch, and these clutches are usually quite strong. Many clutches outlive the chain saws they come with. If you replace clutch parts more than once in a chain saw's life, something is wrong. Most likely you're not cutting at full engine speed, or you're not sharpening your chain often enough.

To reassemble the clutch, place the clutch cover plate so that the oiler drive pin extends into the hole in the small spur gear of the oil pump.

A dirty or improperly operating clutch must be disassembled as follows:

Remove the starter cover with the rewind starter. Unscrew the spark plug, and screw the crankshaft locking screw into the spark plug hole by hand. Then remove the chain-sprocket cover.

Clutch carrier

Hexagonal nut

Chain-sprocket drum

Place the clutch wrench between the clutch shoes and turn it clockwise until the piston bottoms at the crankshaft locking nut.

While holding the clutch with the wrench, loosen and unscrew the hexagonal nut, using a combination wrench.

Clutch carrier

Clutch shoe

Spring

Replace the damaged parts of the clutch; the *whole set* of clutch shoes and springs should be replaced if damaged. If they're simply dirty, wash all parts in clean gasoline and then dry them with compressed air. Roughen the surfaces of the clutch liners with emery cloth.

Remove the front washer and unscrew the clutch with the clutch wrench by turning it *clockwise*.

Then remove the second retaining washer from the crankshaft, then the chain sprocket, the needle cage, and the cover plate.

Replacing the clutch

Crankshaft locking nut

Tighten the new clutch with a torque wrench to 3.5 kgm (25.32 ft. lb.).

Then put the second retaining washer onto the crankshaft and screw on the hexagonal nut. Tighten nut to 4 kgm (28.94 ft. lb.).

Then replace the greased needle cage or bearing, the chain sprocket, and the inside clutch retaining washer. On other saws, a half-moon key may be used to attach the friction assembly to the crankshaft. Be sure this key goes back in its exact original position. Half-moon keys frequently have nearly invisible differences from end to end that make them work in one position only. A retaining washer must be replaced so that it's pressed against the clutch assembly under tension.

Now screw the clutch back onto the crankshaft so that the counter-sunk side of the clutch carrier thread goes toward the chain sprocket. Then use your clutch wrench to turn the clutch until the piston is again resting against the crankshaft locking nut. Tighten the clutch to about 25 ft./lbs. Then replace the outside retaining washer and the clutch retaining nut. If possible, use a torque wrench to tighten the clutch retaining nut to the torque recommended by your manufacturer. In the case of our example, it's 28.94 foot-pounds.

Now remove the cylinder plug or crankshaft locking screw and replace the spark plug. Put the starter in place—but before you tighten it, pull the starter rope until the starter pawls engage the rope rotor. You'll have to remember to do this every time you remove the starter housing from your saw. Now you can replace the guide bar, chain, and sprocket cover.

AUTOMATIC OIL PUMP

Again, we'll stick with the Stihl 031 as an example. The 031 has an automatic oil pump driven by a worm gear that's driven by the chain sprocket. The worm gear is driven by the chain sprocket via a drive pin and two spur gears.

You have determined that your problem is in the oil pump. You have already cleaned the guide-bar oil outlet holes and the guide bar groove. You have also already cleaned the oil pick-up body and checked the oil pick-up hose. When you check the hose, by the way, don't bend, twist, or pull it; to replace it, you often have to disassemble the crankcase.

Every automatic oil pump is designed with close limits between the maximum and the minimum oil flow. On our example, the maximum oil flow is 0.61 cubic inches per minute. The minimum is 0.244 cubic inches per minute. The minimum setting is used for guide bars of 14″ or 15″, and higher settings are used with larger bars. To make this adjustment on this saw, use a screwdriver to turn the set screw on the control bolt. It will travel only a quarter of a turn at the most. Do not exert force.

Our sample oil pump is located in a recess in the crankcase and is protected by a cover plate. To remove it, first remove the clutch and chain sprocket as described in the previous section. If the pump drive pin on

To disassemble the oil pump, take off the clutch and the chain sprocket. Remove the four screws of the pump cover and pull the small spur gear off the crankshaft. Then unscrew the three cylinder-head screws, one of which is accessible only through the bore in the big spur gear.

Pump cover screw hole

Crankshaft

Pump cover screw hole

The individual parts of the oil pump

the clutch cover plate is broken or sheared, you must install a new cover plate. Like most parts, this will be available only from your dealer, the saw's manufacturer, or the manufacturer's distributor in your area.

The pump cover is secured to the crankcase by four screws. Remove the screws, take off the cover, and pull the small spur gear off the crankshaft. You are now looking at the large spur gear on the oil pump. It has a hole in it. When you turn it, you will see (one at a time) two or three screws. These hold the pump in place. Turn the spur gear so that you can insert a screwdriver through the hole and remove each of the screws. You can now remove the pump.

You will probably not need to replace any pump parts. If your pump is not delivering oil, you can bet that the problem is dirt and clogging. To clean it and inspect its parts, pry off the retaining ring that holds the two segments of the pump together. On many saws, a round pin holds the pump control bolt. Simply pull the pin from the pump housing with pliers. Then remove the control bolt with its O-ring and bushing. Remove the pump plunger with its spring and washer. Then carefully remove the worm gear, the spur gear, and the ring washer.

Clean all pump parts thoroughly and blow out the pump passages. If you find any defective or worn parts, replace them. If you find a handful of shavings, replace the pump. If you replace only the pump plunger, install the washer and spring in the pump before inserting the pump plunger and bushing. Reassemble the pump and reinstall it in the exact reverse order of disassembly. Be sure to replace all ring gaskets and washers.

CARBURETOR

Parp suspects that the day of the nonrebuildable, throwaway carburetor isn't far away. Now everything in Parp revolts at the idea of another conquest for the throwaway culture, but he can also understand how and why it may happen—he just hopes he's wrong. And there is hope that the present kit system of repair is so efficient and so well established that it will prevail.

These kits are so good and so well developed that it's now an understatement to say that you don't have to understand your carburetor in order to rebuild it. All you need is the kit, a small screwdriver, small needle-nosed pliers, a 1/4"-drive socket set, a set of low-profile combination wrenches, some solvent, a soft toothbrush, and—possibly—some nonhardening sealant such as Permatex Number Two or Form-a-Gasket. A source of compressed air can be a great help in cleaning out the carburetor passages.

There is no point at all in reviewing the directions for rebuilding a chain saw carburetor. All the directions you'll ever need come with the kit. Just be sure you get the correct kit, and buy only the brand that was made for your carburetor by the original manufacturer of your carburetor. Parp says that all substitute kits made by other companies are grossly inferior.

In almost all cases, the best approach to any genuine carburetor problem is to buy a rebuilding kit and rebuild the entire carburetor following the easy instructions, step-by-step. Just a few tips are in order.

Never touch a carburetor with slip-joint pliers. Never tighten any "screws" on a carburetor unless you know what you're doing; you may damage the needles. Handle a carburetor carefully. Keep all the parts in order, laid out on a flat surface as you remove them. Lay out the new replacement pieces from the kit with the old parts that they replace. That way you'll get it back together in order. Take note that every single mistake that Parp has seen made by carburetor rebuilders was the result of mixed-up parts or replacing a part upside down or backward.

With linkage, fuel-line connections, and throttle connections, look very closely at the correct assembly before you take it apart. If anything sticks or seems stubborn, don't force it. Look carefully to see if anything is blocking the approach you're taking. Many parts can be removed or loosened only when in a certain position. Again, disassembly problems of the carburetor itself will be covered in the kit instructions—but the kit won't mention the linkage of your particular saw, or the fuel-line fittings. Most fittings simply pull off, but be careful not to twist or split lines or bend linkage.

Identifying the jet screws and the throttle screw is not difficult. The throttle screw, or idle-speed screw, is the one that doesn't go into the body of the carburetor. It rests against a mechanism that moves the linkage that moves the throttle plate. It's usually a large screw, and the saw housing above it is usually labeled T or I. The jet screws are near each other. The larger one is the high-speed adjustment and the smaller one is the low-speed adjustment. If you remove your carburetor only to replace the gasket between the carburetor and the crankcase, don't touch the jet screws. If you're rebuilding your carburetor, pay particular attention to the kit's instructions regarding these needle screws.

Since you've got the kit, Parp suggests that you remove all parts that you can replace with new ones. It's the only way to clean the carburetor thoroughly, and it's the only way to be sure you've done a complete job in replacing all the worn or damaged parts. Clogging, wear, and damage, for example, are often hard to detect in filter screens, and a leaking welsh plug is nearly always impossible to detect. A welsh plug leak usually makes the carburetor difficult or impossible to adjust, or causes it to lose adjustment quickly.

Our Stihl 031 AV is equipped with a Tillotson HU carburetor, a model that is used on a great many other saws and is very similar to most other contemporary chain saw carburetors. Its main difference from the Til-

Carburetor box, air filter, muffler, and carburetor heating (Stihl 031 AV)

lotson HS carburetor is its smaller size. Also, the HU is choked by a choke plate in the air box near the air filter rather than by a choke plate in the air horn of the carburetor itself. It's sometimes pictured in the air horn only for convenience.

The fuel pump is an integral diaphragm fuel pump, as discussed in Chapter 12. The fuel pump is a unit that operates independently from the rest of the carburetor.

An impulse hose connects the impulse chamber of the fuel pump with the crankcase. The impulse operation of a diaphragm fuel pump is discussed in Chapter 5. When pumping, the diaphragm pulls fuel from the fuel pick-up in the fuel tank, through the fuel line, and through the inlet and outlet valves of the fuel pump to the needle valve of the carburetor. The inlet needle of the needle valve is linked with the metering diaphragm by an inlet control lever. Under the metering diaphragm is a chamber that is vented to atmospheric pressure by a hole in the metering diaphragm cover. The metering diaphragm is activated by alternating pressure pulsations from the crankcase. When the diaphragm moves upward, it unseats the inlet needle and allows fuel to flow into the diaphragm chamber. The carburetor and the crankcase are connected by an elbow connector.

Carburetor (Tillotson) (Stihl 031 AV)

Carburetor (Walbro)

To remove the carburetor, take off the air box cover, the oil filter retainers, and the air filter. Remove the retaining washers from the throttle shaft and unhook the throttle rod. Then disconnect the fuel line from the tank-vent fitting and unscrew the nuts from the carburetor studs. Now you can carefully pull the carburetor away from the saw.

To disassemble the elbow connector, loosen the two screws at the top of the handle bar. Remove the collar screws at the handle frame and the three screws that hold the carburetor box to the handle frame. Push back the handle frame and pull the impulse hose from the fitting at the bottom of the cylinder. Then you can push the elbow connector out of the carburetor box and remove the hose clip and the elbow. All of these details will differ on other saws, but the basic procedure is similar. Remember to keep all the parts in order and draw pictures or write yourself notes to help remember how and when you did what. Reassembly is usually done in exactly the reverse order of disassembly.

If you have a carburetor kit, you are now ready to rebuild your saw's carburetor. Just be sure to clean it thoroughly and use a toothbrush to scrub the air horn with solvent. Don't soak the entire carburetor in solvent if it has unremoved plastic or nylon parts, as most carburetors do; instead, use a canned carburetor cleaner such as Gumout. Squirt the Gumout into all openings and passages and use a toothbrush to clean whatever you can reach. This is a passable but incomplete approach.

INDIVIDUAL CARBURETOR REPAIRS

This section is included primarily as emergency reference material. If you're 50 miles west of Nowhere and can't wait for the dogsled to bring a carburetor kit, you might need to try one or more individual repairs. To do that, you will at least need gasket material from which to cut gaskets. Good luck. If you have an old carburetor around for spare parts, that may sometimes help, but most carburetor troubles are caused by dirt. If you can clean the culprit and replace the gasket between the carburetor and the crankcase, you may be back to cutting wood soon. Obviously, anyone 50 miles west of Nowhere should have a couple of axes and a large bow saw with an extra blade.

If the problem is corrosion caused by stale fuel or improper storage, you should be able to get away with cleaning your carburetor and replacing it as is, without disassembling it further than is necessary for cleaning.

If corrosion is the problem, pay special attention to the choke and throttle plates and shafts. Move the shafts to see if the plates move freely. Clean the shafts with solvent or Gumout as well as you can. If they come clean this way, leave them on the saw. If not, remove the lock screw in the center of the plate, then remove the plate and the shaft. You can then clean these parts thoroughly and reinstall them.

To disassemble the carburetor, remove the four screws that hold the pump diaphragm cover to the carburetor body. You'll find that the diaphragm is stuck to a gasket that must be peeled off. Separate these parts carefully.

When you remove the diaphragm and gasket, you will find a filter screen. Clean the screen and the diaphragm carefully. The diaphragm has valve flaps—the inlet and outlet valves. If these valve flaps are damaged, you'll have to replace the diaphragm (even if it means waiting for the dogsled). Lay out these parts in order as you remove them.

Four screws hold the metering diaphragm cover. Remove these screws and remove the metering diaphragm and gasket. Again, the diaphragm and gasket will stick together, so separate them carefully. It is possible, in an emergency, to replace these gaskets with Form-a-Gasket or some other nonhardening sealer, but be very careful not to use too much sealant or get it on the diaphragms. You may also cut new gaskets from any suitable gasket material. Since blown gaskets are, other than dirt, the most common carburetor failure, you may be able to correct all your problems by cleaning the carburetor without taking it all the way apart, and then replacing the gaskets with homemade ones. A rebuilding kit is, again, a better approach when one is available.

The pivoting device of the inlet control lever is fastened to the carburetor body. The inlet needle is linked to the dovetailed guide of the inlet control lever. To remove the inlet needle, remove the screw and take out the inlet control lever together with the inlet needle. Be sure to remove the small spring, as well. Note that there's a rubber tip on the inlet needle, or a rubber fitting that the needle presses into. You can now replace any defective parts, if you have replacements, and you can completely clean the metering sections and inlet control parts. Check the tapered end of the adjustment screws. If they're bent or damaged, they'll have to be replaced. You can pry out filter screens with the awl blade of a Swiss Army knife, which is also a fine tool for removing welsh plugs. If you don't have a carburetor kit, don't remove any welsh plugs. Just paint over them with the nail hardener some people use on their fingernails. Don't remove any jets unless you have to. These will come clean while still in the carburetor.

When we reassemble the Tillotson HU carburetor, we must be sure that the inlet needle is correctly linked to the guide in the inlet control lever. The dovetailed end of the inlet control lever must not be bent. Install the inlet control lever so that the longer end of the lever is flush with the floor of the diaphragm chamber. The rest of the reassembly process is straightforward—or straightbackward, actually—and you should have no trouble as long as you kept your parts in order, or can visualize the reassembly process from this section or from the drawings. For carburetor *adjustment* procedures, see Chapter 5. The normal settings for a Tillotson HU are as follows: H or high-speed screw: out 1 turn from light bottom; L or low-speed screw—out 1-1/8 to 1-1/4 turns from light bottom. In reassembly, note that the H screw is shorter than the L screw.

If you tore the gasket between the carburetor and the crankcase, don't reach for your ax. Just apply a thin but adequate coat of Form-a-Gasket to the area and tighten the parts firmly to set the seal. Happens to everybody.

FUEL LINE

Fuel is drawn from the tank into the fuel line pick-up in the tank, through the fuel line and into the carburetor. All of these parts have to be cleaned now and then, as Parp said before. You should certainly do this anytime you clean or rebuild the carburetor.

On the Stihl 031, disconnect the fuel line from the fuel tank vent and pull the whole thing out of the vent. Then clean it all in gasoline, including the tank and cap. When you reassemble the parts, just be sure to put the pick-up back together and get the fuel line straight.

To install a new fuel line in this model, just cut it to match the old line and fit it to the pick-up assembly with the insert. Installing a new fuel line on most other chain saws involves a few more problems, so let's use the Poulan 4200 as an example.

To remove this fuel line, just pull it out through the fuel tank filler hole. The new line must be 7-3/4″ long, including a section on one end cut at a 45° angle for purposes of installation only.

Remove the fuel filter from the old fuel line and install it on the square end of the new fuel line. Then insert a stiff wire through the hole in the bottom of the air box so that it comes out through the fuel filler hole. Slide the new fuel line onto the wire, angled end first, and use the wire as a guide to push the point of the angle out through the air box hole. Use needle-nose pliers with one tip inserted into the fuel line, the other grasping from the outside. Pull about 2″ of the fuel line into the air box. Remove the wire. Then carefully cut off the angled end of the line just below the angle. Cut it square. At this time somewhat less than 2″ of line is showing in the air box. Again use your needle-nose pliers to pull more fuel line into the box to a total length of 3-5/8″. Route the fuel line to the carburetor over the choke control rod.

Obviously, the details will vary. But these examples demonstrate correct procedures that will apply to all other chain saws, as well as solutions to most of the problems that you'll ever run into with fuel lines. If you watch for the problems mentioned here, you'll have no trouble seeing how Parp's suggestions apply to your saw. You might have to route the fuel line under the choke rod instead of over it, but you'll know which it is because you'll notice how the original was installed.

REED VALVE

A reed-valve job is fairly easy with the better chain saws, so we'll use a good one for our example. Our model this time is the Poulan 4200; the Stihl 031 has a piston-ported engine and so does not incorporate a reed valve. Poulan builds an excellent and very popular chain saw. They also build many saws for other companies who affix their own brand names, so it seems likely that this simple procedure will apply to many chain saws owned by readers of this book.

A reed-valve job is actually an item of full-system service, rather than a true engine problem. Therefore, we start with the carburetor once again.

The Poulan 4200 has a single nut right on top of its top cover. When you remove the nut and the top cover, you have access to the air cleaner, carburetor, insulator block, reed-valve assembly, and cylinder.

Remove the two nuts holding the air filter and lift it off. Disconnect the fuel line and remove the cotter pin that holds the choke rod to the choke shaft. Then remove the carburetor studs and the carburetor. Disconnect the spark plug wire and lift out the air baffle that sits against the cylinder fins behind the carburetor. If the spring clips on this baffle are fatigued or broken, the baffle should be replaced with a new one. Be sure to replace this baffle when you reassemble your saw: It's an essential part of the Poulan cooling system.

Now lift up the insulator block that the carburetor was sitting on. The reed-valve assembly is immediately under the insulator block. Remove the two screws holding the reed-valve assembly.

When you have the reed-valve assembly removed, check the reed-tip gap. If the gap is larger than .010, replace the reed. Also replace any bent, broken, warped, or cracked reeds. If the assembly is cracked elsewhere, a situation which is not likely, it will have to be replaced.

Reassemble in the reverse order of disassembly. For other saws, the entire process is very similar. The reed valve, when used, is always between the carburetor and the crankcase. The only complication you might encounter is a torn gasket, which you can replace or repair with Form-a-Gasket. If you find that you must disassemble the two halves of an engine block in order to replace a gasket, forget it. Use the Form-a-Gasket.

REWIND STARTER

We discussed starter rope and spring replacement in Chapter 5, and that's most of what can happen to a starter. There are just a few other things we should mention now.

If your spring and rope are in good condition, but the rope is hard to pull and then goes back only partway or very slowly, the mechanism is probably clogged with dirt or the spring may be frozen.

The spring, of course, doesn't really "freeze," but at very low temperatures the oil on the spring can thicken enough to stick the coils together. Remove the screws in the starter housing and move the starter assembly away from the saw. Then apply kerosene to the spring coils. Do not slip the kerosene in through the sawdust guard.

If the starter is clogged with dirt or resin, as often happens, you should remove the spring (in one piece) and wash all parts in kerosene. Then oil the spring and reassemble the parts.

If you find that the starter pawls on the flywheel are damaged, they must be replaced. This is extremely rare. Note that you must use identi-

Fan housing, pick-up body, fuel filler cap, starter cover with rewind starter (Stihl 031 AV)

cal replacement pawls. If you can see a problem with the pawls, you can also see how they come off. The screws may be held in place with Loctite, and you may have to use your impact tool. Be careful not to break the flywheel. Use the hammer lightly. Draw a picture of the correct assembly of the pawls.

When you replace the pawls, use Loctite (readily available at auto supply and hardware stores) and be sure the new pawls can move freely and don't pinch.

IGNITION SERVICE

Why didn't Parp call it a tune-up? Because, in a chain saw, a tune-up amounts to a complete overhaul of all systems. Or, for many people, it consists of replacing the spark plug and breaker points. The first approach is too much for most of us, and is beyond the scope of this book in any case. The second notion of a tune-up is often a little worse than doing nothing at all.

Complete ignition service consists of a thorough cleaning, a check for damaged, worn, or frayed parts or wires, a renewal of nonpermanent ignition parts whether they appear worn or not, and a check of all adjustments and required gaps. The adjustments include spark plug gap, armature air gap, ignition timing, and magneto edge gap. The parts to replace are the breaker points and the condenser for sure, the magneto coil if necessary, and probably the spark plug. The parts to check are all leads, wires, cables, and connections, the flywheel magnets, and the coil.

If you do all of these jobs plus clean and adjust or rebuild the carburetor, remove carbon from and clean all cooling and exhaust-system parts, lubricate moving parts, and service the cutting attachment, you could call it a tune-up—but only if your engine is mechanically in good condition. You can't tune a chain saw that has worn piston rings. That's why Parp didn't call it a tune-up, and that's why we're going to discuss only ignition service in this section.

Although Parp believes that the fuel system causes most chain saw problems, he also knows that professional mechanics see more ignition problems than anything else. That's because the owner is more likely to be intimidated by the ignition system than by the fuel system, and so the owner is more likely to correct fuel system problems at home. When the ignition fails, most owners head straight for the mechanic.

Parp doesn't wish to discourage you from that approach to ignition problems. It's very often the best approach. Ignition work is more likely to be fussy and to require special tools than most other aspects of chain saw repair.

Chain saw manufacturers supply their authorized repair people with special shop service tool kits. Many of the tools in these kits are related to ignition service. At the very least they include a flywheel puller and an ignition timing device. They also often include an ohmmeter, and other testing devices and tools. Few chain saw owners have these tools or have access to them, but we can get around this in most cases. For that reason, Parp will be deviating from recommended procedures occasionally.

THE SPARK PLUG

Always begin any ignition system service with the spark plug. If necessary, use the combination tool that came with your saw to remove the spark plug. If possible, use a spark plug socket and breaker bar. Avoid

Ignition armature, set of points, flywheel, and oil filter cap (Stihl 031 AV)

those cheap spark plug "wrenches" with the rod handle—the kind sold in discount department stores. They can damage your hands and anything else that gets in the way. If you have any doubt about the spark plug, replace it. Always try to replace a spark plug with exactly the same kind of spark plug, preferably from the same manufacturer. In all cases use a quality, name-brand spark plug. And Parp says that those charts that tell you that plug 901 from Brand Z is the same as, or is replaceable with, plug 817 from Our Brand X, are often stretching it a bit in commercial interest. Stick with the plug your manufacturer put in the saw, or be very sure any replacement is acceptable.

Good spark plugs are so well made and so inexpensive that a complete discussion of them would be a waste of paper, even if it were possible. Just remember that you won't always be able to visually detect a spark plug problem. A slight film of oil on the insulator can short out the spark plug and take the high-tension current straight to ground, or weaken it considerably. But before you throw it away, that old spark plug can tell you quite a lot.

Since chain saw engines are lubricated by mixing oil with the fuel, moderate oil fouling of the plug, after a time, is normal. This fouling will cause a used chain saw plug to be somewhat darker than a normal automobile spark plug after normal use. Most automobile spark plugs have light tan or gray electrode deposits after service in a clean engine. Normal electrode deposits on a chain saw spark plug are thin and dark gray to black, but flaky and not thick. If the deposits seem thick and oily, you may be using too much oil in your fuel mix, or the wrong kind of oil. If the deposits are thick, sooty carbon, you may have an exhaust problem—probably caused by carbon-clogged exhaust ports or a dirty muffler. If the deposits are thick, flaky carbon, something like graphite, your fuel mixture is too rich. A rich mixture can be caused by an incorrect carburetor adjustment, worn carburetor parts, a choke that sticks, or a dirty air filter. If the deposits are light-colored and flaky, your engine is running too lean. A carburetor problem or an air leak may be the culprit. If the deposits are light and the electrodes appear blistered, melted, or burned, your engine is running too hot. This may be caused by an air leak, incorrect timing, a dirty air filter, the wrong spark plug, clogged sawdust guards or cooling fins, a missing air baffle, a dirty exhaust system, or a broken flywheel—and you ought to find out which.

(Parp says that if you're 50 miles west of Nowhere and have only one spark plug, you might think about moving to the city.)

The spark plug wire or high-tension wire of many chain saws is a permanent part of the magneto coil. If this is the case in your saw, the entire unit must be replaced if a part becomes defective. You may be able to patch a high-tension wire temporarily with black vinyl electrical tape if the only problem is frayed insulation—but this should be considered an emergency repair that won't hold up long.

If the high-tension wire throws sparks or is cracked or oil-soaked, or if it feels limp in the middle, you must replace it. If the saw is quite new and you're getting no spark, always suspect the high-tension wire first. If you check everything else in the ignition system and can't find your problem, replace the wire.

In the case of the Stihl 031, the high-tension wire is not a part of the magneto coil and may be removed by disconnecting it at the spark plug and unscrewing the wood screw that holds the other end onto the armature. But first, we have to get in there.

REACHING THE IGNITION PARTS

The ignition parts of a chain saw are located near the flywheel, as we've seen. The flywheel is always under the starter housing on the side of the saw opposite the chain. The parts you have to remove to reach the flywheel and other ignition parts vary from saw to saw. In all cases, however, you have to remove the starter housing and the starter. You *don't* have to disassemble the starter, and never should except when it needs repair. You should also always disconnect the high-tension wire at the spark plug before working inside the ignition system.

Reaching the ignition system of the Stihl 031 is a typical example. Remove the two screws that hold the front handle to the handle frame. Remove the air box cover and the air filter. Pry the retaining washer from the throttle shaft and unhook the throttle rod. Unscrew the handle frame and the three screws that hold the carburetor box to the handle frame. When you fold back the handle frame, you'll see the fuel line and its fitting to the fuel tank. Disconnect the fuel line. Then remove the four screws that hold the fan housing and tank housing to the rest of the saw. On our example, one of these screws is beneath the chain-sprocket cover on the other side of the saw. Now pull back on the engine assembly (including starter housing, tank housing, and handle frame) until you can reach the ignition switch wire. This wire is actually a ground lead to the ignition switch; when the switch is OFF, it's actually grounding out the primary windings of the ignition coil.

All of the above details vary greatly from saw to saw, as Parp just said. It's easier to reach the ignition systems of some saws and harder with others. With many, you simply remove the starter housing. Always watch for fuel-line and ignition connections when going into an ignition system. If you realize that the above disassembly procedure allows you to reach almost all parts of the engine, it will seem more worthwhile.

Our example has a Bosch ignition system with the armature core and ignition coil positioned outside the flywheel. If you have to replace only the high-tension lead, you've gone far enough. Simply unscrew the wire at the coil, remove it, and install the new one.

Your new high-tension wire must be exactly the same length as the old one. In this case, it's 4.6″ long, not including the boot. To attach the boot, use a small amount of Vaseline (or oil) to lubricate the end of the wire. Insert the wire into the boot and pull it through with pliers. Use a new spring connector if possible, but you can probably reuse the old one. Press the hook of the spring connector all the way into the exact center of the end of the wire. Then push the wire with the spring connector into position in the boot. Position the wire away from any sharp edges and reassemble the saw.

MAGNETO EDGE GAP

To check the ignition system further, turn the flywheel (which is still mounted on the crankshaft) past the magneto coil. The coil and the flywheel must not touch at any time. Turn the flywheel enough to be sure. If they touch at all, the magneto is damaged and must be replaced. If they don't touch and the magneto looks intact and seems tight and has an obvious gap, it's probably good. If it's loose, tighten it down and check again for contact with the flywheel. Note that the gap between the flywheel and the magneto doesn't have to be precise as long as it's within recommended specifications. In the case of our example, it can be anywhere between .14″ and .3″. That's a lot of room for aging. This gap is measured (with a feeler gauge) between the trailing edge of the north pole of the magnet and the inner edge of the left-hand leg of the armature when they are at their closest point. Do not change this setting if it's within the specifications, since any change will affect the ignition timing.

If you find cracks or damage in the magneto coil and you don't have a replacement, you *may* be able to patch it with black vinyl electrical tape. No other kind of tape will do. The same also goes, in an emergency, for any frayed insulation or stripped wires, as mentioned above. Broken wires can be spliced in an emergency and covered with tape. Don't be surprised if it doesn't work, though, since the damage is likely to be more extreme than it appears.

ARMATURE AIR GAP

To check the armature air gap, measure the distance between the pole shoes of the armature and the flywheel. The Stihl 031 calls for a gap between .012″ and .2″. This gap is somewhat more critical than the magneto edge gap, since it determines how close the magnets pass to the armature. To adjust it, loosen the armature screws in the slotted poles and carefully and gradually move the armature to the correct gap. Be sure the armature ground lead is connected.

REMOVING THE FLYWHEEL

Now we're up against that flywheel that causes so much trouble and concern. And it certainly can be a hassle. If you don't *have* to remove it, by all means leave it alone. But a lot of the worry about pulling a flywheel is needless. All you need is the right tool, or a good substitute.

Removing the flywheel is an easier job on most chain saws than it is on most other engines. Most chain saw crankshafts are not as tapered as the crankshafts of other machines. This means that when you remove the flywheel nut, the flywheel will be relatively easy to remove. The problem is the nut.

Once again, we need some way to protect the piston and hold the entire cranking assembly and the flywheel while we remove the flywheel nut. In most cases, we'll need a way to deliver a considerable shock to the flywheel nut in order to loosen it. Again, we can be glad we're working on a chain saw, since the flywheel nuts of many chain saws are easier to loosen than the same parts on other machines.

Without a doubt, the best way to crack a tough flywheel nut is with a power impact wrench. Unfortunately, few of us own or can borrow one of these expensive tools. If you do have access to an electric or air impact wrench, it will loosen the flywheel nut with so much shock that you don't even have to worry about the flywheel turning. It doesn't have time to turn.

The next best choice is the hand impact tool mentioned in our basic tool list. Parp says this tool is close to essential for anyone who works on small engines. It consists of a driver that you hit with a hammer, and different bits that usually include slot-type or Phillips-type screwdriver heads. The bits fit into an adapter that you attach to the drive mechanism of the driver. These tools are available with either 1/4", 3/8", or 1/2" drive, and ordinary sockets can be fitted over the drive itself without the adapter. When you hit the head of the impact tool with a hammer, the drive mechanism turns the bit or socket just a little. This small turn, combined with the shock from the hammer blow, will loosen almost any tough screw, bolt, or nut. An impact wrench is a handy addition to any tool kit. Parp's set cost $10. Sometimes you can find them at larger auto parts stores or small-engine repair shops, but they are always easy to mail-order from J.C. Whitney or U.S. General Supply (addresses are in the Appendix).

If you use a hand impact tool with a socket, or if you substitute by hitting the end of a breaker bar with a hammer, you should use a flywheel holder or flywheel wrench to anchor the flywheel. Sometimes you can hold the flywheel with blocks of wood jammed between the work surface and the fins on either side. Parp doesn't recommend using a screwdriver or bar between the flywheel fins; flywheels are incredibly easy to break. Better than that is a flywheel holder, your socket set, and a hammer. Flywheel holders are inexpensive and can be obtained through your chain saw dealer, or from any repair station or distributor. You do have to remove the flywheel to get to and replace breaker points, so it's a problem you'll have to deal with eventually—and the right tools make it a lot easier.

With the Stihl 031, we do have a tapered crankshaft that holds the flywheel very firmly. So, even after the nut is removed, we still face a problem in removing the flywheel. You can remove most chain saw flywheels by using a pair of screwdrivers as levers. Stihl, like most other manufacturers, makes a special tool for this job—a flywheel puller. Here's the complete process for the 031:

First, remove the spark plug and screw in the crankshaft locking screw. Then remove the flywheel nut. Screw the flywheel puller onto the crankshaft by hand. Turn the flywheel clockwise until the piston bottoms against the crankshaft locking screw. Then screw in the thrust bolt of the flywheel puller and tighten it with a socket wrench until the flywheel pops loose from the taper. If it doesn't pop when you turn in the thrust bolt, whack the head of the thrust bolt with a hammer (but not too hard). You can then remove the flywheel puller and lift off the flywheel.

Before you remove the flywheel, check it for slop. Use Vise Grips to hold the crankshaft still, being careful not to damage the crankshaft or threads. Don't tighten down hard—just enough to hold it steady. Then try to turn the flywheel either way. If it moves at all with the crankshaft still, the flywheel half-moon key is probably damaged. A damaged half-moon key is a common ignition problem that can cause all sorts of bad chain saw behavior. You should always make this test *before* you remove the flywheel, but *after* it's loose from the crankshaft taper. Damage to the key is not always obvious or visible.

If the flywheel is damaged or the magnets are dead, it must be replaced. To check the magnets of a flywheel, hold a screwdriver with the tip about an inch from the magnets. The magnets should pull the screwdriver. If they still don't pull it from a distance of 1/2", the magnets are dead.

The flywheel and the crankshaft on the ignition side must be grease-free and immaculate. If you find oil in this area, or on the breaker assembly or other ignition parts, you have a defective seal. That means you need an engine overhaul.

BREAKER POINT GAP

Here we run into a peculiarity of the Stihl 031 that doesn't apply to most chain saws, but which we have already worked around. To set and check the points of the 031, you don't have to remove the flywheel. Flywheel removal was covered before this because you normally must remove the flywheel just to see the points. So, for the 031, we'll back up to before the flywheel came off.

Inside the mounted flywheel of our 031, we find two seals, each with one countersunk screw. Loosen these screws just two turns and pry out the seals with a screwdriver. Underneath you'll see the breaker points. You can then check the gap with a feeler gauge. When the points are pushed all the way open by the lobe on the crankshaft, the gap should be between .014" and .016". If the gap is incorrect, simply loosen the two screws in the breaker-point assembly and move the base of the assembly until the gap is correct. Then tighten the screws and check the gap again. It may take a few tries to get it right.

With most chain saws, you'll take the flywheel off to check the points. You'll see the points assembly and the condenser right under the flywheel; they're often covered by a plastic case. You can easily remove the case.

As we saw in Chapter 12, the points are opened by a lobe on the crankshaft, and pulled closed by a spring. The gap must be checked when it's all the way open. In order to check the points, you must know what gap is specified by your saw's manufacturer. Use a feeler gauge to check the gap. Be sure to insert the feeler gauge straight in: if it's at an angle, you won't get an accurate reading. The gap is correct if the right feeler gauge just barely touches both points.

To adjust the gap, loosen the screw in the slotted hole of the fixed point. Loosen it just enough to enable you to move the fixed point by pushing on it with a screwdriver, but not enough to allow it to move by itself. Turn the crankshaft so that the lobe is pushing the movable point all the way open. Then move the fixed point with a screwdriver until the gap is correct. Again, this may take several tries and three hands, but you'll get it eventually. When it's right, tighten the screw in the slotted hole of the fixed point. Tighten it firmly but take care not to strip the threads.

If the breaker points are burned, pitted, or not aligned properly, you should replace them.

REPLACING THE POINTS AND CONDENSER

Parp says always to replace the condenser when you install new points. Since the points and condenser are usually purchased together as a kit, it costs no more and can save another trip to the inside of your saw's ignition system.

If you've gotten this far, you can probably see exactly what you have to do to remove and replace the breaker-point assembly and the condenser: Loosen the screws carefully, remove the old parts, and install the new ones.

Some tips are in order. Be very careful not to drop any screws into your saw. Also, remember that the flywheel has magnets in it. If you're missing a screw, look there first. And look there last, too, to be sure you're not installing any shrapnel with your flywheel.

Be sure to disconnect all wires before you start pulling out parts. The movable point of the breaker assembly will be connected to the magneto and the condenser with two separate wires. Sometimes you have to lift the condenser from its seat or retainer in order to reach the connections, and it may fit very tightly.

Be careful to remember what goes where and what connects to what. Parp says you should draw a detailed picture for yourself. You can also use different colors of fingernail polish to mark connections.

Be sure the new points are properly aligned and will make good contact. If necessary, bend the fixed point until the points face each other squarely.

When you install the points, lightly tighten the fixed-point screw so that you can adjust the points as above. The correct installation of the condenser should be obvious, but do be sure to get the new one in exactly the way the old one came out. Sometimes you have to force a condenser to seat it in its sleeve or retainer or whatever.

IGNITION TIMING

We haven't mentioned this before, but ignition (the spark) is always timed to occur slightly before the piston reaches the top of its stroke. Ignition timing is usually stated as a certain distance before *top dead center*. Top dead center is a term that describes the piston at the top of its upward stroke. You will often see it abbreviated as TDC, and BTDC means *before top dead center*.

Many chain saw engines have timing marks that make ignition timing easy, as with the 031. You will often find one timing mark on the flywheel. If you find that, then there is another one someplace, or there is a specified reference that serves as the other timing mark. Some companies use the leading edge of the magneto coil as one reference. Some engine manufacturers place timing marks on the coil and the breaker housing.

The correct timing of the 031 is .092″ BTDC. That means that the spark must occur when the piston is .092″ below the top of its upward stroke.

But we probably won't need that information, since we have two obvious timing marks. To set timing by ignition marks, turn the crankshaft until the marks are aligned. Now find the thinnest blade in your feeler gauge. You need to determine if the points have just begun to open. When the timing marks are lined up, there should be just the slightest gap between the points. If the gap was correct when you measured it at its maximum (points all the way open), and if it now is just barely open with the timing marks aligned, the ignition is correctly timed.

If the point gap was correct when fully open, but the points are not open at all when the timing marks are aligned, or they are open more than just slightly, you need to adjust the breaker plate. Loosen the breaker-plate bolts and turn the breaker plate until your thinnest feeler gauge just barely fits between the points. Be careful not to move the points. Anytime you move, adjust, or replace breaker points, the ignition timing must be checked and set. When the gap is as small as you can set it, tighten the breaker-plate bolts.

By adjusting the breaker plate so that the points are just barely open when the timing marks are aligned, you insure that the spark occurs at the right time—just when the breaker points break the primary circuit to induce the spark.

If the ignition system doesn't have timing marks, the process is different. You can get around the problem by making your own timing marks while the saw is still new, or while the timing is still correct. Use a sharp tool to scratch a line in the flywheel and another right across from it on the engine. It doesn't matter where you put the marks as long as they're across from each other, and as long as the second mark is on a permanent part of the engine. If you install a new flywheel, it will go on the same way the old one did, so you can use the engine mark as a reference for putting a mark on the new flywheel.

If the timing is already disturbed and you have no timing marks, you must use a special tool called a *timing dial*. These tools are made only for two-stroke engines and are used to measure the distance of the piston from top dead center. You screw the tool into the spark plug hole and set the dial to the correct BTDC setting. Then you move the piston up against the movable part of the tool. When the piston is at the correct distance BTDC, you loosen the contact plate and move it until the points are just barely open. Then tighten the plate and the timing is set. The only other method is to use a machinist's ruler to measure the distance of the piston from the top of the cylinder. This is difficult in any case, and impossible on many chain saws.

Whenever you remove the flywheel, check the flywheel key for damage. Also check its fit in the flywheel and the crankshaft. If one slot or the other is damaged, which isn't likely, that part must be replaced. Either part is an expensive hassle, but at least you can replace the flywheel yourself. Replacing a crankshaft involves overhauling the engine.

Always end any ignition work by rechecking all gaps and connections. Watch for any loose screws you might have dropped, and blow away the ashes and seeds and stems and stuff.

PISTON RINGS, CYLINDER, AND CYLINDER GASKET

Parp isn't going to cover any repairs that require disassembling the crankcase or removing the crankshaft. Those repairs are advanced, and you should tackle them only if you're experienced at two-stroke overhaul.

There are several reasons. Many of the repairs require special tools, and those tools often require expert handling. You might have a problem that seems elementary at first—like defective crankshaft seals. To replace crankshaft seals you need a cylinder-pin punch, a heat gun, a seal-mounting sleeve that fits only your saw, and a bearing driver—not to mention a pressure-testing device . . . and that doesn't name them all. You also need to check the crankshaft itself and, if it's bent, you need a machine to straighten it. If you are capable of such repairs and have suitable tools, you will certainly be able to accomplish whatever you need to do by combining your experience with *The Chain Saw Service Manual* and your saw's shop manual. If you're interested in becoming this proficient, collect the tools and find an experienced mechanic or (even better) a good trade school or community college course on small-engine mechanics. With a little learning time, some tools, and determination, anyone can become an expert chain saw mechanic.

There are circumstances under which you may decide to replace the piston rings without overhauling your chain saw. Let's say you live 50 miles west of Nowhere and last year you bought two used chain saws of the same model and year. You got them both for $20, and neither works very well. One of them has a busted crankcase from a falling tree, and the other one is tired. You don't have the tools or experience to replace the busted crankcase, but you hope to rejuvenate the tired saw. You've got a carburetor kit, gasket material, new ignition parts and piston rings, and your hand tools. You can use the parts from the dead saw—such as clutch parts, sprocket, rewind starter, flywheel, or what-have-you—and you can follow the procedures in this book (or the instructions with the carburetor kit) to do a pretty good job of fixing up the tired saw. You also have decided that your saw has no compression, which is the reason you picked up the piston rings. You're just hoping you don't find something like a terribly scored cylinder when you get inside.

You'll need some long allen-head wrenches, two pieces of smooth softwood measuring 1" X 1" X 6", and the piston-ring compressor that you purchased with the new rings. We're not going to remove the piston from the crank assembly, so we won't need a heat tool or any of the special piston tools.

Remove the housings and parts necessary to strip the engine, as for ignition service. Strip the cylinder of the muffler, and so on. Clean the outside of the cylinder thoroughly and look for defects. Be sure the rest of the saw and your work area are also clean. Insert the correct size longreach allen wrench down through the holes in the top of the cylinder. There are four allen-head screws at the bottoms of the holes. When the screws are loose, carefully and slowly pull the entire cylinder up off the piston. If you're going to install a new cylinder, you must also install the new piston assembly that you had to buy with it, and you'll be going it without Parp. The cylinder is off now, and the piston is resting against the crankcase. Put the two pieces of wood between the piston and the crankcase for a piston support. (You can also make a piston support from one piece of wood with a slot cut to fit around the connecting rod.)

Now examine the inside of the cylinder. If it's heavily scored, new rings probably won't improve performance much. You might be able to replace it with the cylinder from the dead saw. If the scores (there are bound to be some) are light, try washing the inside of the cylinder with solvent and a soft cloth. Do not use a toothbrush. If the scores are moderate and you must reuse the cylinder, you can take a desperate gamble and use an automotive body cleaner. Be sure to wash the cylinder in solvent afterward.

Now remove the old rings and clean all exposed parts with solvent, being very careful not to get dirt or dirty solvent into the crankcase. Pay special attention to the piston head and the inside top of the cylinder. Then install the new rings the same way the old ones came off.

Whenever you remove the cylinder, you must replace the cylinder gasket. Often, this is the only reason for removing the cylinder in the first place. It's impossible to reinstall a used gasket correctly; you must use a *new* gasket of gasket material, not Form-a-Gasket. Put the new gasket on the cylinder using a very thin coat of gasket sealer. Then install the cylinder over the piston, using the ring compressor to hold the rings. Be careful not to damage the inside of the cylinder. Remove the piston support after the cylinder is past the piston rings. Apply a very light coat of gasket sealer to the crankcase gasket seat. Move the cylinder into place. Then replace the allen-head screws lightly, and turn the engine over to make sure everything is free and aligned before torquing down the cylinder mounting screws.

CHAPTER 14
SOFT WORDS FOR TENDERFEET AND SENSITIVE SOULS

It's the end of winter now, and the end of Parp's tussle with this book, the second time around. Now there'll be time for the forest where the living trees are waking in the spring and whispering of their own lives, separate and free. Somewhere in the Sierra Mountains the oldest being on earth, a bristlecone pine, knows the peace and solitude of growing where nothing else can live.

Millions of other trees have, this year, stopped the kind of growth that we call life. Mostly, that makes no immediate difference. They will stand a long time in the wind and rain. Their return to the forest floor is imperceptibly slow. Long before they are actually down, they will begin relinquishing their precious elements to other beings, to insects and mushrooms, birds and animals.

One of the animals, *Homo sapiens*, will greatly speed the disintegration process for a few thousand of the standing dead in an attempt to keep warm through another winter. But even in the age of the chain saw, most of the dead trees will still be left to dry and fall by themselves, and then to rot and provide homes and food for other creatures. All of this is good and natural, including this particular human involvement, and it doesn't matter what tools the individual human uses. The individual is providing for natural needs and a natural life.

Other humans, using chain saws, work in groups to provide housing for people who live far from the forests. Even this can be done decently, and the use of forest products becomes, in one way, more efficient every year. Every year, we use more of the wood we cut for a greater variety of products. Most of those products are unnecessary, but at least we don't throw the wood away immediately.

It's not Parp's place to preach on forestry or logging methods, as many will jump to agree, but we are still clear-cutting in many forests, scalping the earth, leveling millions of acres of living, sentient creatures—*and we do not have to do that*. There the human animal is being not good or natural, and it must stop. The large timbering companies and their friends in government offer all sorts of excuses for clear-cutting, and even maintain that it's better for the forests than selective cutting. *Parp says that's a lie.* And a spirit moves in the trees to which all the guilty parties—governments, corporations, individuals—will answer. That's good enough for Parp, and he trusts to it.

We have come so far from ourselves. We accept, at conception, the elemental gift of the great trees that have gone before. But we don't return that gift to the mushrooms and insects that start the chain of giving over again. We have to learn to do intentionally all the things we no longer do naturally.

This is a book about a tool that either can take us further away from ourselves by increasing each individual's circle of destruction, or can help bring some of us back, close enough to relearn the language of the trees, by making a more natural life easier and more possible for an animal that has forgotten how to live and die. Parp offers this book and these words to those who make the second choice.

Many myths and notions surround working in the woods, especially with an ax and chain saw. Great shoulders roll and tense with the exertion of cutting trees and chopping wood. Many people, themselves dwarfed by the trees, would have us believe that you have to be big and tough and male (whatever that is) to be a woodsperson. Parp has news for those folks, yes, indeed.

It is manifest that neither testicles nor large wrists contribute anything whatsoever to a person's love and understanding of the natural world. And testicles (or the lack thereof) do not in any way affect one's ability to do good work with a chain saw or any other kind of tool, as we all know.

Whatever kind of human one is, we must all share the same woods on the same planet. In order to avoid destroying it all, we must give up our toughness and our insistence on unimportant differences. A college education is also not conducive to a natural understanding. Many of us who went "back to the land" in the early seventies have learned that lesson thoroughly in the years since. And we have certainly made our own contributions to the communities and regions that became our homes. If you're a logger living near a group of "hippies" (whatever that is), look closely at what they're trying to do. And if you're a new homesteader living near a group of loggers, watch one of them alone in the woods sometime. You'll see a pure love of this planet, similar to your own, as that rugged face turns up toward the trees and the sky. We are all the same.

So if that logger happens by when you're out there cutting wood, stop and talk awhile. If you get unwanted or bad advice, or the silly, macho kind of teasing that still turns up now and then, remember that it's *your* saw and *your* wood and *your* way. Besides, you use a good clean oil on your bar and chain and that logger uses old tractor drippings. *You* are the expert.

You should consider that working with a chain saw is poor exercise that may add some strength to your arms but will do nothing else for your physical good. Parp suggests that you devote some time to regular meditation and good clean yoga after any chain saw session. It's the best cure, though a fine walk in the woods is just as good.

Sleeping under the trees on a warm afternoon is another ideal way to counter the negative effects of running a gasoline-powered engine. And sitting by a river dipping your toes is good, too. Whenever you work in the woods, remember this: The natural woodsperson takes long and frequent breaks. It's the only way to remember what you are, where you fit, and why you're there. For safety's sake, you should work with a partner whenever you can. For nature's sake, you should take your breaks in solitude.

So, Parp says as we're heading into the woods in different directions, please be careful. And don't forget your whistle.

APPENDIX

We wish to express our appreciation to the following individuals for their cooperation in providing information, material, and photographs used in the completion of this book:

Rhys V. Campbell and Jeff Crow, Oregon Saw Chain Div., Omark Industries, Inc.; Jackson D'Armond, Stihl, Inc.; Erik Granberg, Granberg/Firmont, Inc.; John D. Hall, Bell Industries, Inc.; Steve Moore, Homelite Div., Textron, Inc.; Scotty Schaefer, Schaefer Motor Co., Inc.; Jim Shipman, Jim's Small Engine Shop; David Tilton, Jr., Tilton Equipment Co.

—*The Editors*

To obtain information on industry regulations pertaining to chain saws, write to:

Portable Power Equipment Manufacturers Association
4270 Montgomery Lane
Suite 514
Bethesda, MD 20814

Consumer Product Safety Commission
5401 Westbard Avenue
Bethesda, MD 20816

To call the Consumer Hot Line, dial 800-638-8326 (800-492-8363 in Maryland).

ADDRESSES OF CHAIN SAW MANUFACTURERS

ALLIS CHALMERS CORPORATION
P.O. Box 512
Milwaukee, WI 53201

DOLMAR NORTH AMERICAN
947 West Foothill Boulevard
Monrovia, CA 91016

JOHN DEERE & COMPANY
John Deere Road
Moline, IL 61265

ECHO CHAIN SAWS
3150 MacArthur Boulevard
Northbrook, IL 60062

**HOMELITE DIVISION OF
TEXTRON, INC.**
14401 Carowinds Boulevard
Charlotte, NC 28217

HUSQVARNA
224 Thorndale Avenue
Bensenville, IL 60106

JOBU CHAIN SAWS
Elkem-Spigerverket a/s
1441 Drobak
Norway

JONSERED CHAIN SAWS
Tilton Equipment Company
4612 North Chatsworth
St. Paul, MN 55112

McCULLOCH CORPORATION
5401 Beethoven Street
Los Angeles, CA 90009

McCULLOCH MITE-E-LITE, INC.
P.O. Box 92180
Los Angeles, CA 90009

OLEO-MAC® (OLYMPYK)
Tilton Equipment Company
4612 North Chatsworth Street
St. Paul, MN 55112

PIONEER/PARTNER
Division of Techfor, Inc.
224 Thorndale Avenue
Bensenville, IL 60106

POULAN CHAIN SAWS
Beaird-Poulan Division
Emerson Electric Company
5020 Flournoy-Lucas Road
Shreveport, LA 71109

SACHS DOLMAR
708 Florence Street
Atlanta, TX 75551

SHINDAIWA
11975 S.W. Herman Road
Sherwood, OR 97140

SOLO, INC.
P.O. Box 5030
Newport News, VA 23605

STIHL, INCORPORATED
Dept. TR
536 Viking Drive
Virginia Beach, VA 23452

TANAKA CHAIN SAWS
7509 South 228th Street
Kent, WA 98032

OTHER ADDRESSES OF INTEREST

ATOM INDUSTRIES
15 Reynolds Street
Balmain, N.S.W.
Australia 2041
Manufacturer of chain saw drill attachments.

BAILEY'S WESTERN DIVISION
P.O. Box 550, Highway 101
Laytonville, CA 95454
1-800-358-1661 or 707-984-6133

266

BAILEY'S SOUTHERN DIVISION
P.O. Box 9088
1520 South Highland Avenue
Jackson, TN 38314
1-800-356-1300

Mail-order suppliers of saw chain, tools, and accessories. They also have an effective logger's job service.

BELL INDUSTRIES
Saw and Machine Division
3590-T West 3rd Avenue
P.O. Box 2510
Eugene, OR 97402

Manufacturer of home and shop electric saw chain grinders, carb-cutter attachments, and chain saw related machines.

CARLTON COMPANY
3901 S.E. Naef Road
Milwaukie, OR 97268

Manufacturer of saw chain.

DIDIER MANUFACTURING DIVISION
P.O. Box 23045
7777 North 73rd Street
Milwaukee, WI 53223

Manufacturer of hydraulic wood-splitting machines.

GRANBERG INDUSTRIES, INC.
244 South 24th Street
Richmond, CA 94804

Manufacturer of chain saw tools, accessories, ripping chain, Alaskan Mill, Break-N-Mend and File-N-Joint.

HADDON TOOL
4719 West Elm Street, Route 120
McHenry, IL 60050

Manufacturer of chain saw accessories and Lumber/Maker attachment.

HELI-COIL PRODUCTS
Division of Mite Corporation
1564 Shelter Rock Lane
Danbury, CT 06810

Manufacturer of thread repair kits. A chain saw mechanic's must.

J.C. WHITNEY & CO.
P.O. Box 8410
Chicago, Illinois 60680

KOLVE SAWCHAIN COMPANY
P.O. Box 1270
Gresham, OR 97030
Manufacturer of saw chain.

FRED A. LEWIS COMPANY
40 Belknap Road
Medford, OR 97501
Manufacturer of chain saw winch attachments.

OREGON SAW CHAIN DIVISION
Omark Industries
4909 S.E. International Way
Portland, OR 97222
Manufacturer of saw chain, tools, and accessories.

PIQUA ENGINEERING, INC.
234 First Street
Piqua, OH 45356
Manufacturer of hydraulic wood-splitting machines.

SANDVIK, INCORPORATED
1702 Nevins Road
Fair Lawn, NJ 07410
Manufacturer of forestry tools, guide bars, and chain saw tools and accessories.

SPENCER PRODUCTION COMPANY
P.O. Box 224
Pullman, WA 99163
Manufacturer of logger's tape, felling and bucking wedges, and chain saw and logger accessories.

U.S. GENERAL SUPPLY
100 Commercial Street
Plainview, NY 11803

WALBRO CORPORATION
Cass City, MI 48726
Manufacturer of chain saw carburetors.

ZIP PENN, INC.
P.O. Box 179
Erie, PA 16512
Mail-order supplier of saw chain, tools, and accessories.

SAW CHAIN CONVERSION CHART

Pitch	Gauge	Canad	Carlton	Homelite	Laser	McCulloch	Oregon
1/2	058	5, 80	D2E; D2S		5	PM 508	9AC
1/2	063	6, 90	D3E; D3S	50-C-63	6	PM 503	10AC
3/4	122	100			34	PM 752	11BC
.325	050	45					20AP
3/8	050	747				SM 370	22
3/8	058	737				SM378	23
1/4	050	41		25-C-50		SM 250	25
.404	058	767				SM 408	26
.404	063	757				SM 403	27
.404	050	777					28
.354	058	354A	J2C			PM 358	45C
.404	050	10	B1C; E; S	40-C-50	10		50C
.404	050					SPR 400	50L
.404	050					SPS 400	50AL
.404	058	3, 30	B2C; E; S		3	PM 408	51AC
.404	058					SPR 408	51L
.404	058					SPS 408	51AL
.404	063	4, 40	B3C; E; S	40-C-63	4	PM 403	52AC
.404	063					SPR 403	52L
.404	063					SPS 403	52AL
3/8	050	9, 95	A1C; E; S	38-C-50	9	PM 370	72D
3/8	050						72DP
3/8	050					SPR 370G	72LP
3/8	058	7, 75	A2C; E; S	38-C-58	7	PM 378	73D
3/8	058						73DP
3/8	058					SPR 378G	73LP
3/8	063	8, 85	A3C; E; S		8	PM 373	75D
3/8	063					SPR 373G	75LP
3/8	050			37-N-50		MM 3 0	91
3/8	050			37-C-50		MP 3703	91S
3/8	050						91TS
.315	050						
7/16	058		C-2		1		61, 68
7/16	063		C-3		2		62, 69

Pioneer	Poulan	Remington	Sabre	Skil	Stihl	Windsor	Zip Penn
		58PF	15-150			DH58, 58D	5
	P10	53PF	25-250	D58	3832	CH63, 63C	6
			75			FH122, 122F	34
			325		3862	50J	11
	P22		747		3857		
			737		3858		
	P25		16		3856	KH50, 50K	41
			767		3822		
	P27		757		3860		
			777				
			357A			GH58	
			34-340			BH50, 50B	10
404R58T		48PF	14-140		3822	BH50, 58B	3
404R63T	P52	43PF	24-240	C58	3860	BH63, 63B	4
					3846		
38R50T	P72	30PF	18	B58	3857	AH50, 50A	9
					3873		
38R58T		38PF	48		3881	AH58, 58A	7
							8
			28		3868	AH63, 63A	
	P100						19
	P101		350				
						50H	
D6EH		78PF	17			58C	1
D6EJ		73PF	27			63C	2

TROUBLESHOOTING GUIDE

Probable cause

Ignition System Possible Cause

Trouble

Trouble	Defective spark plug	Spark plug gap too large	Burned breaker points	Breaker point gap incorrect	Breaker mechanism loose or other contact failure	Bad condenser	Connections loose or wire grounding	Flash-over at ON/OFF switch	Coil failure	Incorrect ignition timing	Short-circuited spark plug	Breaker points oily
1. No spark when engine is turned over	X	X	X	X	X	X	X	X	X			X
2. Engine misfires under load, lacks power	X	X	X	X	X	X	X	X	X	X		
3. Engine stalls at high speed				X	X	X	X	X	X		X	
4. Breaker points burned						X					X	
5. Engine overheats	X		X	X					X	X		
6. Excessive fuel consumption	X			X	X				X	X	X	X
7. Fuel reaches carburetor, but not engine												
8. Fuel does not reach carburetor												
9. Engine lacks power, apt to race												
10. Exhaust smoke (fuel mixture too rich), engine lacks power												
11. Engine stalls when idling, operates normally at full throttle												
12. Clutch slips at operating speed												
13. Clutch engaged at idling speed												
14. Automatic oil pump does not work												
15. Oil pump delivers too much oil												
16. Poor oil pump feeding												
17. Does not respond to accelerator												
18. Oil system leaks												
19. Oil leakage at bar												
Remedy	Replace spark plug (original spare part)	Set gap to .020" (0.5 mm)	Replace breaker points	Set gap to 0.012"–0.016" (0.3–0.4 mm)	Adjust or replace	Replace condenser	Adjust or replace	Clean, adjust, or replace	Replace ignition or generator coil	See owner's manual	Replace spark plug (original spare part)	Clean or replace breaker points

Action	1	2	3	4	5	6	7	8	9	10	11	12	13	14	15	16	Possible Cause	
Replace plummet or plummet strainer		X							X	X				X			Fuel hose plummet clogged	
Replace fuel hose									X	X				X			Fuel hose cracked or leaking	
Fill tank with correct fuel mixture										X				X			Fuel tank empty	
Clean or replace diaphragm and filters		X						X	X	X		X	X		X		Diaphragm pump defective	Fuel System Possible Cause
Clean or replace filter element									X				X				Air filter clogged	
See owner's manual		X						X	X	X		X	X		X		Incorrect setting of diaphragm pump	
See owner's manual for correct fuel mixture												X					Too little oil in fuel mixture	
Push choke control all way in								X				X					Too much choke	
Clean the valve		X						X	X	X							Fuel tank check valve clogged	
Replace gaskets and tighten loose joints											X						Gasoline leaking	
Turn back needles or blow out jets		X									X						Fuel jets closed or clogged	
Clean engine cooling fins and fan screen											X						Cylinder cooling ineffective	
Have the engine professionally decarbonized											X						Excessive carbon deposits on piston and cylinder	Engine Possible Cause
Replace piston rings									X								Worn piston rings	
Remove clutch and clean						X											Clutch shoes jammed	
Clean and lubricate clutch bearing						X											Needle bearing jammed on crankshaft	
Replace clutch shoes							X										Worn clutch shoes	
Replace clutch spring						X	X										Damaged clutch spring	
Replace seals							X										Worn or damaged crankshaft seals	
Fill oil tank with correct grade of oil					X												Empty oil tank	
Clean vent hole, pump, and oil strainer			X		X												Impurities in oil tank vent hole or oil strainer	
Reset oil pump setscrew			X	X	X												Oil pump feeding set incorrectly	Lube System Possible Cause
Replace gaskets and tighten loose joints		X	X		X												Defective gaskets or loose joints	
Clean oil hole	X		X		X												Sawdust in bar oil hole	
Replace O-rings		X	X		X												Damaged O-rings	
Clean before mounting	X																Sawdust between bar, inner guard, and engine	

FUEL SYSTEM TROUBLESHOOTING

You have determined that it is likely that you have a problem in your fuel system. Eliminate these possibilities in this approximate order.

Engine Will Not Start

Probable Causes	Remedies
Fuel tank empty. Water in fuel or fuel stale.	Fill fuel tank. Empty fuel tank, dry fuel lines, refill tank.
Fuel filter clogged or water in fuel filter.	Replace fuel filter.
Air filter dirty or wet.	Clean or replace air filter.
Engine flooded.	If caused by overchoking, close choke and open throttle. Attempt to start. If that fails, remove spark plug. Pull starter rope several times. Allow air or sunlight to reach cylinder. Replace plug. If it still floods, carburetor is likely problem.
Fuel cap vent clogged.	Clean or replace fuel cap.
Fuel line clogged or plugged.	Blow out or replace fuel line.
Carburetor mixture adjustments incorrect.	Readjust carburetor.
Fuel pump diaphragm damaged.	Replace fuel pump diaphragm.
Fuel pump clogged.	Clean carburetor and integral fuel pump.
Carburetor needles, jets, gaskets, or diaphragms defective or leaking.	Clean and rebuild carburetor.

Engine Starts but Runs Poorly at All Speeds

Probable Causes	Remedies
Incorrect fuel mixture.	Empty fuel tank and refill with fresh, precisely measured fuel mixture. Clean and gap plug.
Carbon building in exhaust ports.	Scrape clean with wood or plastic scraper.
Fuel stored incorrectly, left in fuel tank. Water in fuel filter as a result.	Empty fuel tank and refill with fresh fuel. Replace fuel filter.
Carburetor incorrectly adjusted.	Adjust carburetor.
Fuel tank vent plugged.	Clean vent.
Excessive piston-ring or cylinder wear.	Replace.

Engine Won't Run at Full Speed

Probable Causes	Remedies
Dirty air filter.	Replace air filter.
Fuel cap vent partially clogged.	Clean fuel cap.

Fuel filter clogged—some water in fuel filter.	Replace fuel filter.
Carburetor incorrectly adjusted.	Adjust carburetor.
Carburetor loose.	Tighten carburetor.
Choke sticking.	Adjust or replace choke linkage.
Carburetor diaphragms defective.	Replace carburetor diaphragm.
Carburetor valve dirty.	Clean and rebuild carburetor.
Fuel tank vent plugged.	Clean vent.
Pin holes in fuel line.	Replace.

Engine Overheats

Probable Causes	Remedies
Dirty air filter.	Clean or replace air filter.
Carburetor incorrectly adjusted (too lean).	Adjust carburetor.
Carburetor loose.	Tighten carburetor.
Carburetor base gasket leaking air.	Replace carburetor gasket.
Carburetor worn or defective.	Clean and rebuild carburetor.
Too little oil in fuel.	Use correct mixture.
Timing incorrectly adjusted (advanced).	Reset timing.

IGNITION SYSTEM TROUBLESHOOTING

You have determined that it's likely you have a problem in the ignition system. Eliminate these possibilities in their approximate order.

Engine Does Not Turn Over

Probable Causes	Remedies
Defective starter.	Repair or replace starter.
Engine seized.	Rebuild engine or junk saw.
Loose screws behind flywheel or caught between flywheel and coil lamination.	Replace or retighten screws.

Engine Will Not Start

Probable Causes	Remedies
Switch OFF.	Turn switch ON.
No fuel in tank.	Fill tank with correct mixture.
Switch broken or shorted.	Replace switch.

Spark plug fouled or set at incorrect gap.	Replace spark plug.
Spark plug cable loose or broken.	Tighten or replace cable.
High-tension wire shorting inside saw housing.	Replace high-tension wire.
Ground connection loose.	Tighten ground connection.
Breaker points loose.	Tighten and regap points.
Condenser bad.	Replace condenser.
Points bent, burned, dirty, oily, or incorrectly set.	Replace or regap points.
Timing wrong.	Set ignition timing.
Fuel pick-up plugged or split.	Replace fuel filter or line.
Armature air gap too wide.	Reset armature air gap.
Internal ignition wiring worn.	Replace ignition wiring.
Magneto bad.	Replace magneto (coil).

Engine Starts but Runs Poorly at All Speeds

Probable Causes	Remedies
Spark plug worn or wrong size.	Replace spark plug.
Timing wrong.	Set ignition timing.
Damaged magneto coil windings.	Replace magneto.
Coil assembly has loose internal connection.	Replace coil.
Condenser has poor internal connection and opens with heat or vibration.	Replace condenser.

MECHANICAL TROUBLESHOOTING

You have checked your fuel and ignition system without locating the problem. You believe that the problem is mechanical. Eliminate these possibilities in this approximate order.

Engine Will Not Start

Possible Causes	Remedies
Crankcase nuts and bolts are loose.	Tighten crankcase nuts and bolts.
Defective crankcase seals or O-ring.	Replace seals and O-ring.
Defective reed valve.	Replace reed valve.
Flywheel key sheared.	Replace flywheel key.
Piston rings worn or seized.	Rebuild engine.

Engine Starts But Runs Poorly At All Speeds

Possible Causes	Remedies
Muffler dirty or clogged.	Clean or replace muffler.
Exhaust ports clogged with carbon.	Clean exhaust ports.
Crankcase seals leaking.	Replace crankcase seals.
Defective cylinder gasket.	Replace cylinder gasket.
Worn piston rings.	Rebuild engine.
Piston damaged.	Replace piston.
Air leak at carburetor gasket.	Replace carburetor gasket.
Defective crankcase O-ring.	Replace crankcase O-ring.
Cracked casting.	If casting cannot be welded, junk it.

Engine Won't Run Full Speed

Possible Causes	Remedies
Throttle linkage bent.	Replace throttle linkage.
Muffler clogged.	Clean muffler.
Exhaust ports clogged.	Clean exhaust ports.
Reed valves leaking.	Replace reed valves.
Worn piston rings.	Rebuild engine.

Engine Overheats

Possible Causes	Remedies
Cylinder fins or exhaust system or sawdust cover dirty or clogged.	Clean entire saw. Most common cause of overheating.
Flywheel cover loose, parts of engine shrouds loose or missing.	Tighten all nuts, bolts, and screws.
Flywheel vanes broken.	Replace flywheel.
Lean carburetor mixture.	Use correct mixture.
Timing advanced.	Reset timing.
Cooling air intake plugged.	Clear cooling air intake.

EXAMPLE OF TROUBLESHOOTING PROCEDURE: IGNITION SYSTEM

Is spark plug terminal properly connected with spark plug?

YES

Unscrew spark plug. Is spark plug in good condition?

YES

NO

NO

Press spark plug terminal firmly onto spark plug; if necessary install new spring connector.

Clean spark plug and readjust spark gap. Does a strong spark bridge the electrode gap when checking the ignition?

NO

Frayed or worn insulation of high tension or ground lead? Faulty ignition switch?

YES

NO

Replace faulty lead or switch.

Insert screwdriver into spark plug terminal instead of spark plug and hold it about 1/4 inch from ground. Does a spark jump this gap?

NO

YES

Install new spark plug.

Does flywheel look to be in proper condition?

YES

NO

Replace flywheel. Spark test positive?

NO

Check lead terminals at breaker points and repair if necessary.
Check breaker points, replace burned contact points and adjust ignition timing. Does engine run now?

Check condenser. Is it in good condition?

NO

NO

Replace condenser.

YES

Check magneto edge gap. Is it correct according to owner's manual?

YES

NO

Check high-tension wire and replace if necessary. Does a spark jump now?

Readjust magneto edge gap. Does engine run now?

NO

NO

Check armature and replace if necessary. Does engine run when spark test is positive?

NO

Ignition system in satisfactory condition. Check fuel and carburetion system to find the cause of trouble.

IF IT WON'T START

Troubleshooting is a process of discovering what's wrong. If your chain saw doesn't start, follow this chart first.

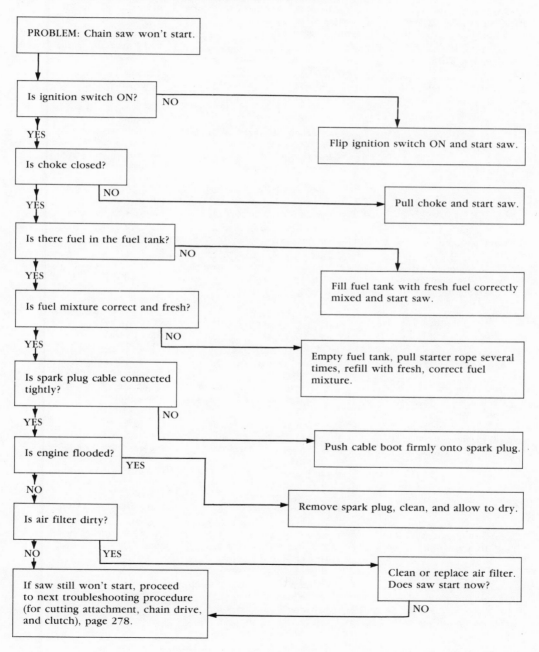

PROBLEM: Chain saw won't start.

Is ignition switch ON? — NO → Flip ignition switch ON and start saw.

YES

Is choke closed? — NO → Pull choke and start saw.

YES

Is there fuel in the fuel tank? — NO → Fill fuel tank with fresh fuel correctly mixed and start saw.

YES

Is fuel mixture correct and fresh? — NO → Empty fuel tank, pull starter rope several times, refill with fresh, correct fuel mixture.

YES

Is spark plug cable connected tightly? — NO → Push cable boot firmly onto spark plug.

YES

Is engine flooded? — YES → Remove spark plug, clean, and allow to dry.

NO

Is air filter dirty? — YES → Clean or replace air filter. Does saw start now? — NO →

NO

If saw still won't start, proceed to next troubleshooting procedure (for cutting attachment, chain drive, and clutch), page 278.

TROUBLESHOOTING: CUTTING ATTACHMENT, CHAIN DRIVE, AND CLUTCH

Trouble	Probable Causes	Remedies
Chain will not stay in adjustment, loses tension, is either too tight or too loose. (Bar and sprocket are in good condition.)	Chain adjustment screw bent or stripped or chain adjustment nut sheared.	Replace chain adjustment mechanism.
Bar wobbles, will not cut straight.	Guide bar bolts or nuts stripped.	Rethread or replace bolts, replace nuts.
Just doesn't cut right, fails to cut, cuts poorly or only with force.	1. Chain dull. 2. Improperly sharpened. 3. Chain on backward. 4. Air filter dirty. 5. Incorrect chain tension. 6. Worn or damaged bar. 7. Carbon blocking exhaust ports. 8. Carburetor adjustment incorrect.	1. Sharpen chain. 2. See Chapter 8, owner's manual, and Saw Chain Troubleshooting Guide. 3. Reverse chain. 4. Clean or replace air filter. 5. Adjust chain tension. 6. Repair, regroove, or replace bar. 7. Clean entire saw and exhaust ports. 8. Adjust carburetor.
Extreme or rapid chain wear. Chain dulls quickly.	Worn sprocket.	Replace sprocket.
1. Chain doesn't rotate properly, slips at high speeds, clutch slips. 2. Chain does not rotate.	1. Clutch linings and/or sprocket dirty or oily. 2. Clutch shoe linings worn. NOTE: EXTREMELY TIGHT CHAIN MAY CAUSE ANY OF THESE PROBLEMS.	1. Wash clutch and sprocket in clean gasoline. Dry clutch shoes and roughen linings with emery cloth. 2. Replace clutch shoes. AVOID CUTTING AT LESS THAN FULL SPEED. DOUBLE-CHECK TENSION OFTEN.
1. Saw chain rotates at idle. 2. Saw chain rotates at idle accompanied by extraneous or loud noises.	1. Engine idle speed too high. 2. Clutch springs stretched or dead. Spring hooks damaged. 3. Sprocket bearings damaged.	1. Readjust carburetor idle speed adjustment screw. 2. Replace all clutch springs and hooks. 3. Replace sprocket bearings.
No oil reaching saw chain.	1. Oil tank empty. 2. Guide bar oil inlet holes clogged. 3. Oil pick-up clogged. 4. Oil pick-up hose damaged.	1. Fill chain oil tank. 2. Clean guide bar oil holes. 3. Wash oil pick-up in gasoline, blow dry with compressed air. 4. Install new pick-up hose line.
Chain saw loses chain oil, oil leaks from saw body.	1. Gasket between oil pump and crankcase defective. 2. Gasket between handle shroud and crankcase defective.	Install new gaskets, clean oil pump.
1. Chain lubrication does not function. 2. Oil pump not operating.	1. Drive pins of cover plate broken or pump is loose. 2. Oil pick-up clogged or oil feed holes plugged. Oil vent clogged.	1. Install new pump cover plate, tighten pump. 2. Clean.

INDEX

Note: Text references appear in Roman type.
Illustrations are denoted in italics.